Course 1

21st Century Assessments

connectED.mcgraw-hill.com

Send all inquiries to:
McGraw-Hill Education
8787 Orion Place
Columbus, OH 43240

ISBN: 978-0-02-143948-5
MHID: 0-02-143948-6

Printed in the United States of America.

5 6 7 8 9 LHS 22 21 20 19 18 17

21st Century Assessments

Contents

Teacher's Guide to

21st Century Assessment Preparation

Whether it's the print ***21st Century Assessments*** or online **ConnectED**, *Glencoe Math* meets all of your assessment preparation needs.

How to Use this Book

21st Century Assessments includes the core assessment preparation materials needed to prepare students for upcoming online state assessments. Additional assessment preparation can be found in the interactive Student Edition or online **ConnectED**. See page vi for details.

Assessment Item Types

- Familiarize students with commonly-seen item types on online assessments.
- Each type comes with a description of the online experience, helpful hints, and a problem for students to try on their own.

Countdown

- Prepare students in the 20 weeks leading up to the state assessment.
- Each week consists of a two-page countdown that contains five problems, addressing multiple CCSS domains.
- **Ideas for Use** Assign each weekly countdown as in-class work, homework, a practice assessment, or a weekly quiz. Assign one problem per day or assign the five problems all at once.

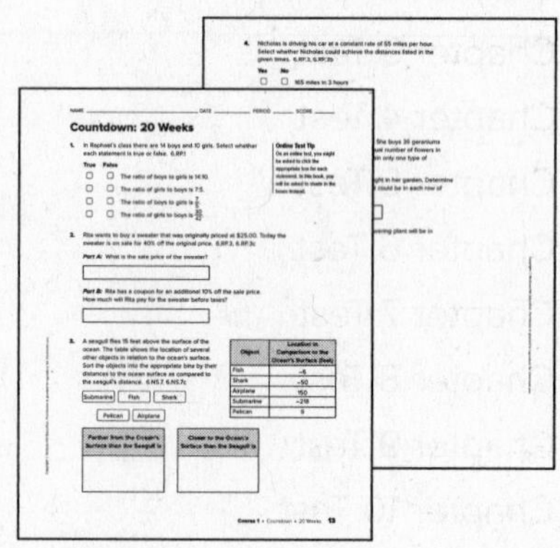

Chapter Tests

- Each six-page test contains 20 problems that assess all of the CCSS presented in the chapter.
- All problems mirror the item types found on online assessments, including several multi-part problems.
- **Ideas for Use** Assign as in-class work, homework, a practice assessment, a diagnostic assessment before beginning the chapter, or a summative assessment upon completion of the chapter.

Performance Tasks, by Chapter

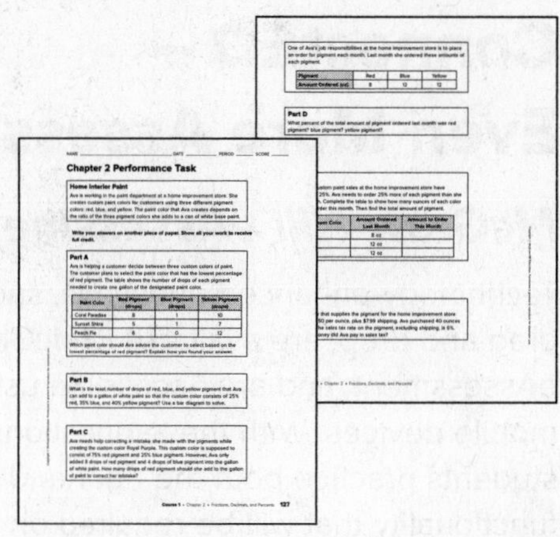

- Each two-page performance task measures students' abilities to integrate knowledge and skills across multiple standards, which help prepare them for college and future careers. Each rubric comes with samples of student work for correct or partially-correct responses.
- **Ideas for Use** Assign as in-class work, homework, a practice assessment, or as part of the summative assessment upon completion of the chapter.

Benchmark Tests

Four benchmark tests are available in this book. All problems on each test mirror the item types found on online assessments, including several multi-part problems. Each benchmark test includes a performance task.

- The ***first*** benchmark test is an eight-page assessment that addresses the CCSS from Chapters 1–4.
- The ***second*** benchmark test is similar in format to the first benchmark test, but addresses the CCSS from Chapters 5–8.
- The ***third*** and ***fourth*** benchmark tests are each twelve-page assessments that address the CCSS from the entire year, Chapters 1–12.
- **Ideas for Use** Assign each benchmark test as a diagnostic assessment prior to instruction or as a summative assessment. Assign the third and fourth benchmark tests as end-of-course assessments, using each one as a different version, or assign one as a diagnostic assessment prior to starting the school year. To score the performance tasks, refer to the rubrics located in the **Answers** section.

Go Online to Find More!

Charts for additional question analysis are available online for each countdown, chapter test, and benchmark test question in this book. These charts provide DOK levels, CCSS standards and mathematical practices correlations, and more.

Student scoring rubrics are available online for each chapter and benchmark performance task in this book. These student rubrics include a description of tasks students should perform correctly aligned with the task's maximum number of points.

- **Ideas for Use** Use the Student Scoring Rubric as a guide for student expectations, a student self-evaluation tool, as well as a final teacher evaluation tool.

ConnectED – Even More Assessment Preparation!

McGraw-Hill eAssessment

Technology-enhanced questions, such as drag and drop, are available in McGraw-Hill's eAssessment, and are accessible using mobile devices. With these questions, your students practice both the rigor and functionality that will be required on an online assessment.

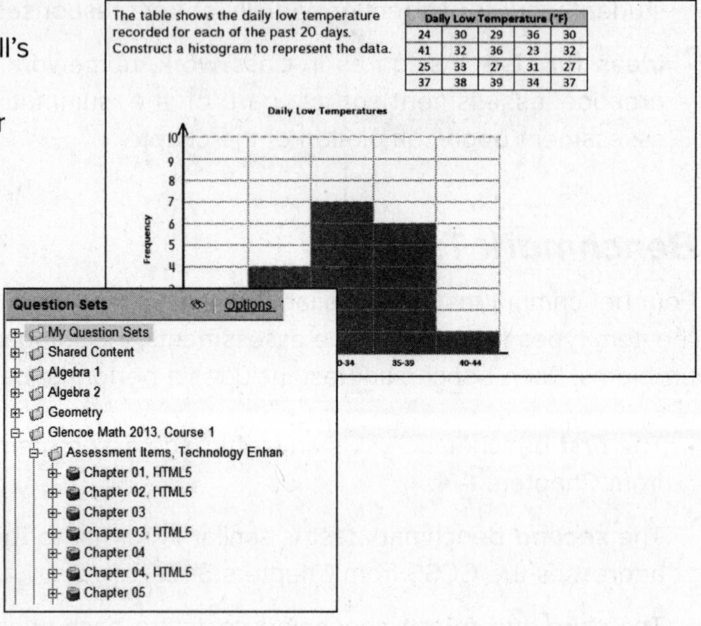

- Go to McGraw-Hill eAssessment.
- Expand your course folder.
- Expand the **Assessment Items, Technology Enhanced** folder.
- Drag selected chapter question sets into the test generator. HTML5 question sets are accessible using mobile devices.

Even More Performance Tasks!

Find additional performance tasks online. These tasks are also located in the interactive Student Edition, at the end of each chapter. Detailed rubrics are located in the Teacher Edition and online.

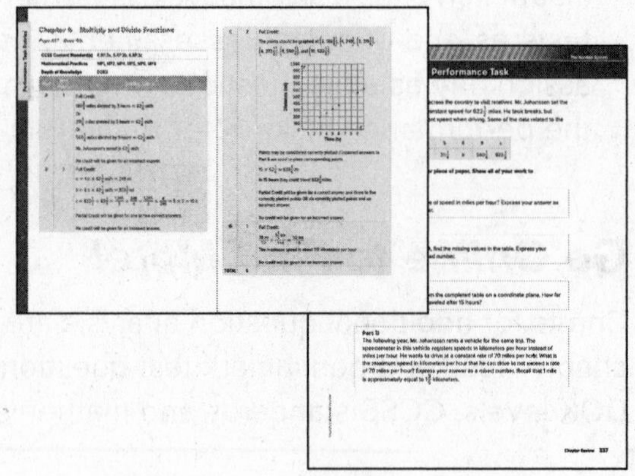

Assessment Item Types

You will encounter selected-response, constructed response, and technology-enhanced item types when taking an online assessment. Use these next several pages to become familiar with these item types. With each type, there is one for you to try on your own.

Selected-Response Items

You will be asked to select one or more given responses for a set of options.

Multiple True/False or Multiple Yes/No

The quotient $\frac{a}{b} \div \frac{c}{d}$ is found. Select whether each statement is true or false. 6.NS.1

True	False	
☐	■	The quotient is always greater than 1.
☐	■	The quotient is equal to $\frac{db}{ca}$.
■	☐	To find the quotient, multiply $\frac{a}{b} \times \frac{d}{c}$.
■	☐	$\frac{a}{b} \div \frac{c}{d} = \frac{ad}{cb}$ because $\frac{c}{d} \times \frac{ad}{cb} = \frac{a}{b}$.

ONLINE EXPERIENCE Click the appropriate box for each statement.

HELPFUL HINT There are usually several statements, as opposed to one true-false statement. *All* of the statements must be selected correctly.

Try On Your Own!

The graph shows the rate at which L'Shaundra reads a novel. She continues to read at this rate until she finishes a 174-page novel. Select the appropriate box to indicate whether the answer to each question is yes or no. 6.EE.9

Yes	No	
☐	☐	Will L'Shaundra finish reading the novel in 1 hour 27 minutes?
☐	☐	Does the equation $p = 0.5m$ represent the relationship between the number of pages p and the number of minutes m?
☐	☐	Will L'Shaundra have read 88 pages after 44 minutes?
☐	☐	Are all three points (14, 28), (26, 52), and (56, 122) found on the graph of the line?

Another example of a selected-response item is shown below.

Multiple Correct Answers

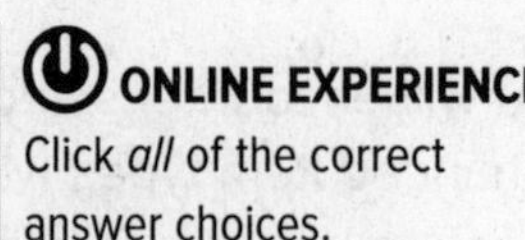

ONLINE EXPERIENCE Click *all* of the correct answer choices.

HELPFUL HINT Read *each* answer choice carefully. There is often more than one correct answer, as opposed to a single correct answer for a traditional multiple-choice problem.

A representative sample of students from Jones Middle School is surveyed as to how many servings of vegetables they eat each day. The dot plot shows the responses. 6.SP.5, 6.SP.5a, 6.SP.5c

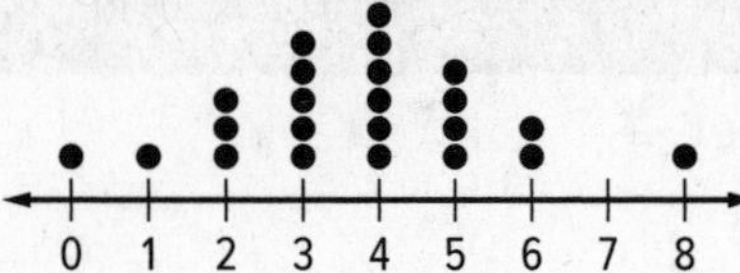

Select all of the statements that are valid based on the survey results.

- ■ There were 23 students surveyed.
- ■ Fewer than one fourth of the students failed to meet the goal of at least 3 servings per day.
- ☐ The mean number of servings is 4.1.
- ■ The interquartile range is 6 less than the range.
- ☐ Due to the outlier, the median is the measure that best represents the data.

Try On Your Own!

Miguel plans to build a wooden crate to store pool toys. He first draws a net as his blueprint. He wants the crate to be 6 feet by 4 feet by 3 feet when it is finished. Select all of the statements that are true. 6.G.4

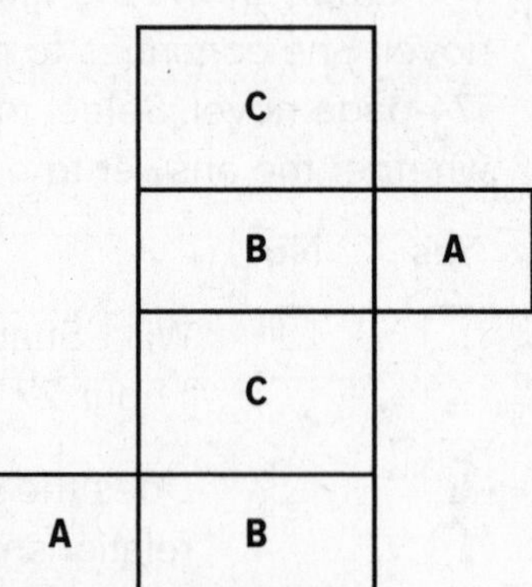

- ☐ The crate represented by the blueprint will not have a lid.
- ☐ The volume of the crate is greater than 100 ft^3.
- ☐ Miguel will need 108 ft^2 of wood to make the crate.
- ☐ A can of paint covers 75 ft^2. Miguel will need 3 cans to paint the inside and outside of the box.
- ☐ The surface area of the crate is represented by the expression 2[(6)(4) + (6)(3) + (4)(3)].

Constructed-Response Items

You will be asked to generate a response, using letters, numbers, and mathematical symbols.

Type Entry

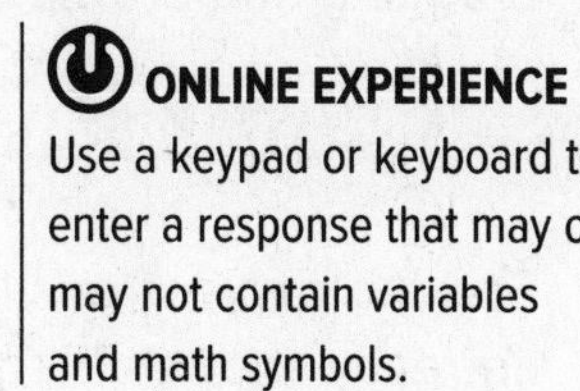
ONLINE EXPERIENCE
Use a keypad or keyboard to enter a response that may or may not contain variables and math symbols.

One leg of a right isosceles triangle is 12 centimeters long. Another right triangle has twice the area of the first isosceles triangle. What is the height of the second right triangle? 6.G.1

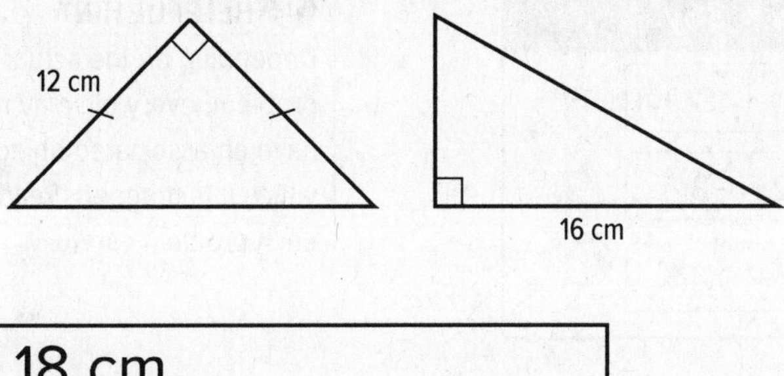
12 cm
16 cm

18 cm

Try On Your Own!

Ms. Hernandez is collecting chicken eggs from students who raise chickens. She wants to collect 5 dozen eggs to sell at the Farmer's Market. The table shows the number of eggs she has collected so far. Let x represent the number of eggs left to collect. Write an equation in the form of $x + p = q$ that represents how many more eggs Ms. Hernandez needs to collect. 6.EE.7

Child	Eggs Collected
José	8
Kendrick	Twice as many as José
Caro	Three fewer than Kendrick

Technology-Enhanced Items

Many of the items on online tests are technology-enhanced items. In these items you will be asked to use computer-based technology, such as dragging and drawing objects, to solve the problem presented.

Bin Sort

Sort the expressions listed at the bottom into the category that correctly shows an equivalent expression. 6.EE.3

ONLINE EXPERIENCE
Sort objects by dragging them into their appropriate bins.

HELPFUL HINT
Depending on the actual problem, every bin may not have an associated object to which it is dragged. Read each problem carefully.

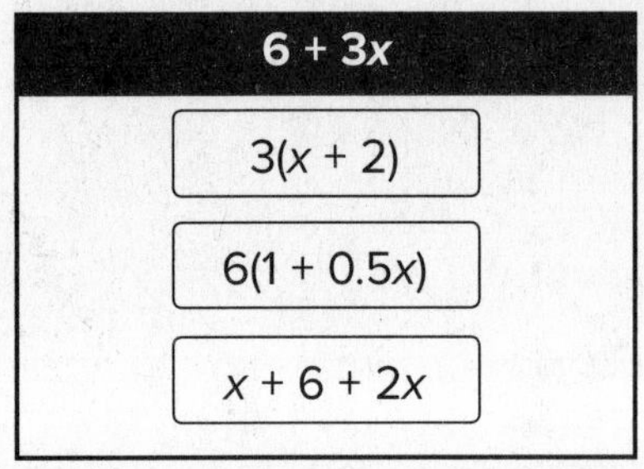

$24x + 36y$

- $2(12x) + 18(2y)$
- $12(2x + 3y)$
- $(6x + 9y)4$

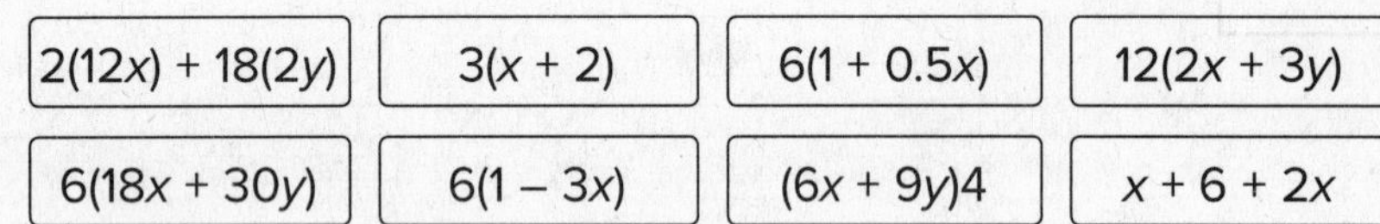

2(12x) + 18(2y)
3(x + 2)
6(1 + 0.5x)
12(2x + 3y)
6(18x + 30y)
6(1 – 3x)
(6x + 9y)4
x + 6 + 2x

Try On Your Own!

Destiny wants to conduct a survey, and she wants to be sure that she asks a statistical question. Sort the questions into the category that correctly describes whether or not the question is a statistical question. 6.SP.A.1

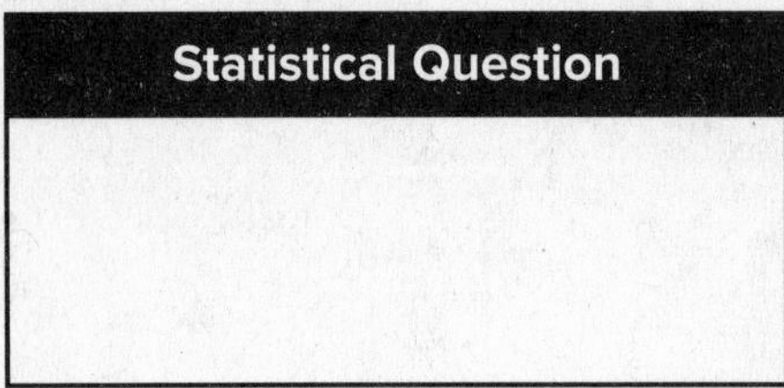

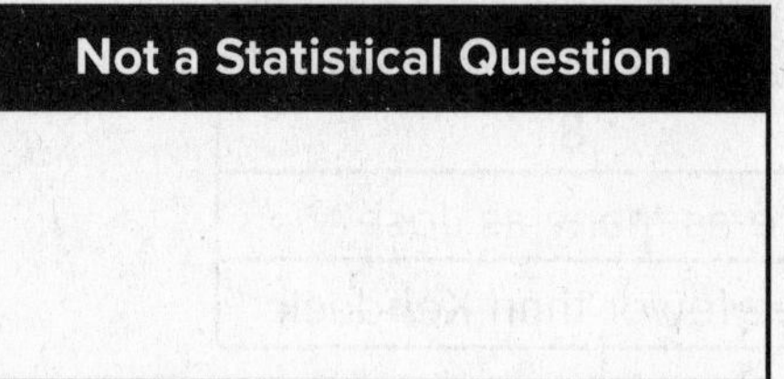

Question 1	What is the favorite card game of each person in our class?
Question 2	When is the birthday of the oldest student in your math class?
Question 3	How many boys are on the A-Team?
Question 4	How tall are the girls at your school?
Question 5	How many annual concerts are held in each U.S. state capital?

Another example of a technology-enhanced item is shown below.

Drag and Drop

Allison claims that different powers can be equivalent. Drag digits into the boxes to create an expression that supports Allison's claim. 6.EE.1

0	1	2	3	4
5	6	7	8	9

A sample answer is shown.

$$2^6 = \boxed{8}^2 = \boxed{4}^{\boxed{3}}$$

ONLINE EXPERIENCE
Drag objects to their appropriate locations, not necessarily in bins. In this book, write or draw the object in its appropriate location as opposed to dragging it.

HELPFUL HINT
Depending on the actual problem, not all of the objects are dragged to complete the problem correctly. Read each problem carefully.

Try On Your Own!

A *fortnight* is a unit of time that is commonly used in Great Britain. Six fortnights is the same as 84 days. Drag the correct numbers to complete the table to show how the number of fortnights and the number of days are related. 6.RP.1, 6.RP.3, 6.RP.3a

14	12	168	78	504	11	210	93
24	28	180	420	360	16	6	13

Fortnights	Days
1	
	84
	154
15	

Some problems on an online assessment will require you to complete multiple parts. One or more parts may be technology-enhanced. An example is below.

Construct Statistical Graphs

The table shows the average amount 20 teens collected per hour at a fundraiser. Coleman predicted that most teens collected $6 or more per hour. 6.SP.4

ONLINE EXPERIENCE
Click to shade sections of the graph. If you make a mistake, click to deselect a section that you selected.

Average Amount Collected per Hour			
$5.00	$3.50	$3.20	$4.25
$7.50	$4.00	$9.10	$7.75
$6.50	$5.00	$5.25	$6.15
$8.00	$7.75	$6.60	$5.50
$2.50	$3.50	$4.85	$7.40

Part A: Complete a histogram to represent the data.

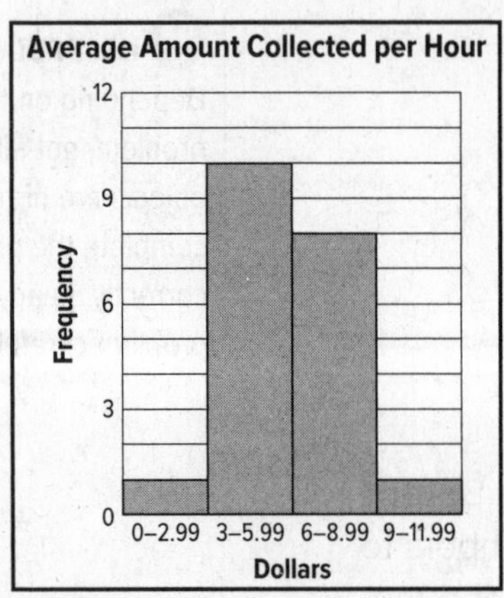

Part B: Is Coleman's prediction valid? Select yes or no.

Yes No

Try On Your Own!

The table shows the average number of texts sent per day by students in Scarlett's class. Scarlett predicted that more people sent 80 to 99 texts than 0 to 19 texts per day. 6.SP.4

Number of Texts per Day			
52	34	68	21
66	52	87	99
45	78	77	49
51	69	81	56
75	64	95	88
27	39	56	19

Part A: Complete a histogram to represent the data.

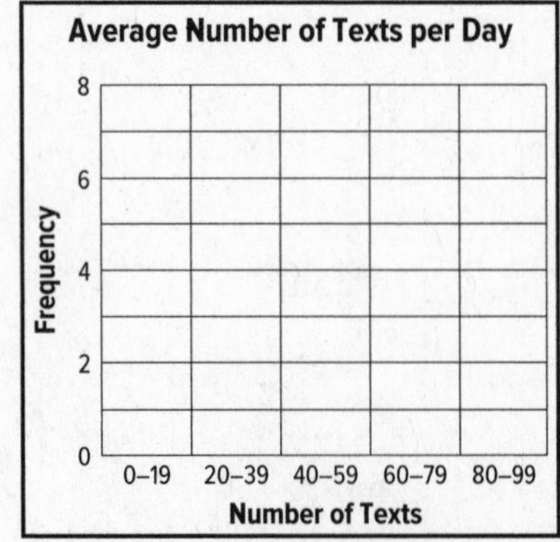

Part B: Is Scarlett's prediction valid? Select yes or no.

Yes No

Another example of a technology-enhanced item is shown below.

Coordinate Plane

Jake works half an hour each day and makes $3 per day babysitting. Graph the ordered pairs that show how much money Jake has after working 1, 2, and 3 days. 6.NS.8, 6.EE.9

ONLINE EXPERIENCE
Click the buttons **Add Point** and **Connect Line** to plot points and draw lines on a coordinate plane.

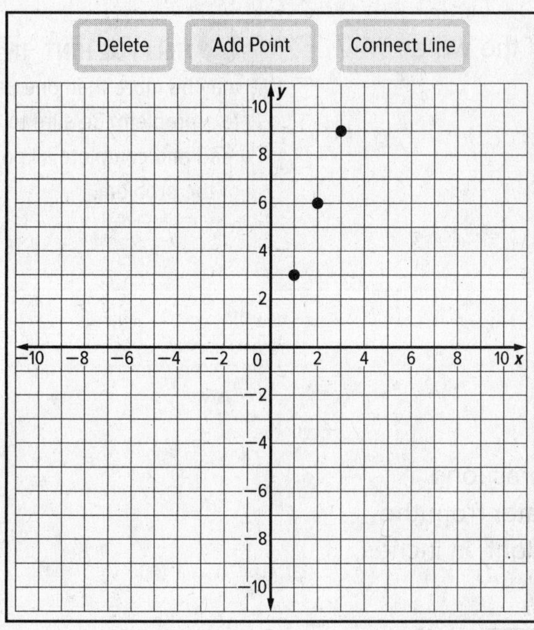

Try On Your Own!

Karl starts to graph a rectangle by plotting two vertices. Graph the other two vertices and the sides to complete one possible rectangle. 6.NS.8, 6.G.3

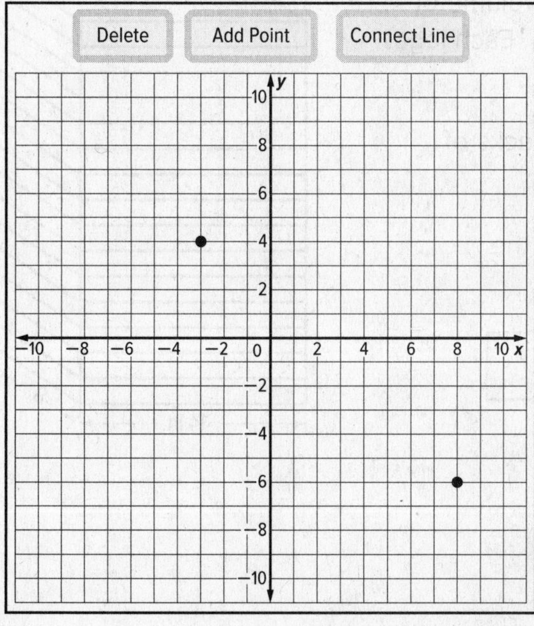

Another example of a multipart technology-enhanced item is shown below.

Volume of Solids

The base of an aquarium measures 24 inches by 10 inches. There is currently 3,840 cubic inches of water in the aquarium. 6.G.2

Part A: Shade the aquarium to show the height of the water.

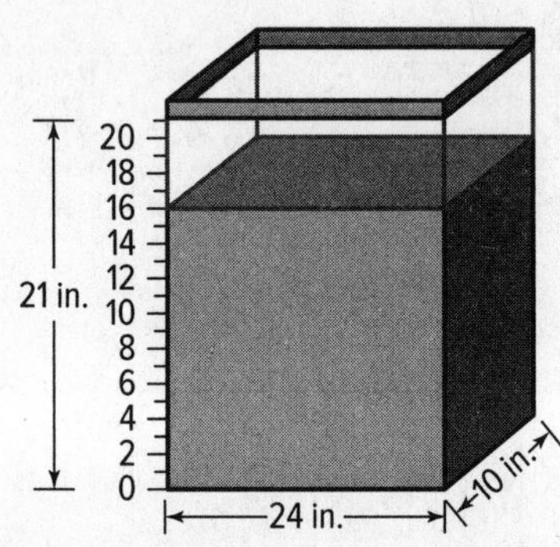

Part B: Another aquarium has a base that is twice as long and twice as wide as the aquarium shown. The water from the first aquarium is poured into it. To what vertical height, in inches, does the water reach?

4

ONLINE EXPERIENCE Click to shade sections of a solid. If you make a mistake, click to deselect the sections you selected.

HELPFUL HINT There may be more than one part to a problem. Be sure to read and complete all parts of the problem.

Try On Your Own!

Georgia stacks 14 packs of 8.5-inch by 11-inch paper. Each pack is 2 inches thick. Then she stacks the same volume of legal-sized paper, which is 8.5 inches by 14 inches. Each legal pack is also 2 inches thick. 6.G.2

Part A: Shade the prism to show the number of packs of 8.5-inch by 14-inch paper she stacked.

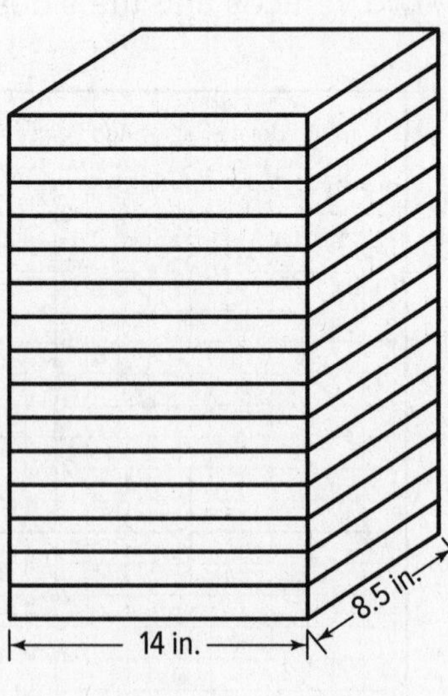

Part B: What is the combined volume of paper in the two stacks?

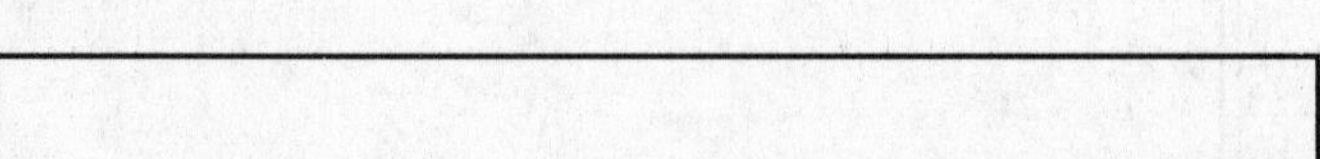

Performance Tasks

These tasks measure your ability to integrate knowledge and skills across multiple topics, which helps prepare you for college and future careers. An example of a performance task is shown below, with guidance about how to complete it.

Movie Time 6.RP.3, 6.NS.3, 6.NS.8, 6.EE.2, 6.EE.2a, 6.EE.2c, 6.EE.5, 6.EE.6, 6.EE.7, 6.EE.9

The local movie theater offers some summer packages.

Package A is $8 per movie.
Package B is $25 per month and $5 per movie.
Package C is $50 per month for unlimited movies.

This performance task has 5 parts, Parts A–E. Read each part and follow the guiding instructions for how to complete it.

Part A

Grayson wants to evaluate each package. Let x be the number of movies he plans to see. Write an expression to represent the cost of each package. Identify whether each expression is numeric or algebraic. Explain your answer.

Write an expression for the cost of Package A.

Write an expression for the cost of Package B.

Write an expression for the cost of Package C.

Identify each expression as numeric or algebraic. Explain your answer.

Part B

Grayson thinks that he will probably see 6 movies each month. Which package should he choose? Justify your answer.

Calculate how much Grayson will spend with each package. Show your work.

Grayson sees 6 movies each month. He would spend $☐ with Package A, $☐ with Package B, and $☐ with Package C.

How do the costs compare? Which package should Grayson choose? Justify your answer.

Part C

Grayson chooses Package A. He spends $72 at the movies one month. How many movies did he see? Write and solve an equation to find the answer. Would either of the other packages have been a better choice for this number of movies? Explain your answer.

Write and solve an equation to find the number of movies Grayson saw. Show your work.

Would either of the other packages have been a better choice? Explain your answer.

Part D

Grayson wants to know how many movies he would need to see each month so that the cost of Package B would equal the cost of Package C. Complete the table for each package, and then graph each function on the coordinate plane. For what number of movies is the cost the same? How does the graph show this number?

Complete each table to show the number of movies or cost in each package.

Package B	
Number of Movies	**Cost ($)**
2	
8	
	85

Package C	
Number of Movies	**Cost ($)**
4	
9	
	50

Graph the function for each movie package on the coordinate plane. Be sure to label the functions.

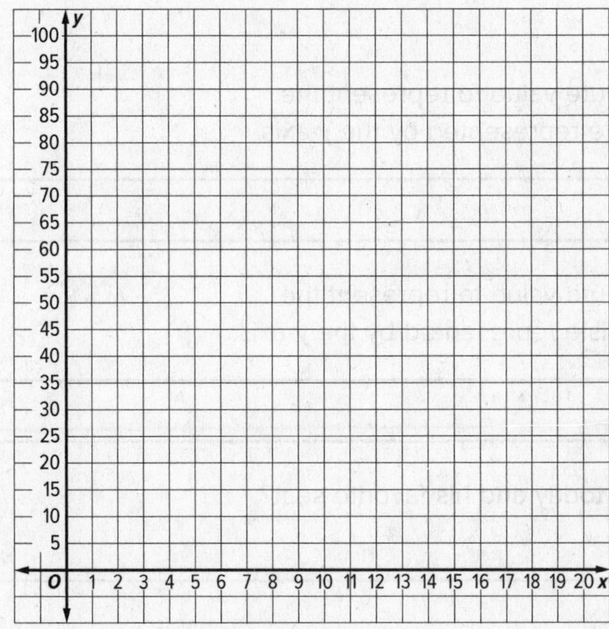

For what number of movies will the cost be the same?
How does the graph show this number?

Part E

Grayson maps the theater on a coordinate plane, plotting each seat at a gridline intersection and using the axes to represent aisles. He plots his favorite seat as well as where he and his friend had to sit today. How far is Grayson's seat today from his favorite seat? How far is he sitting from his friend today? Use absolute value expressions to justify your answers.

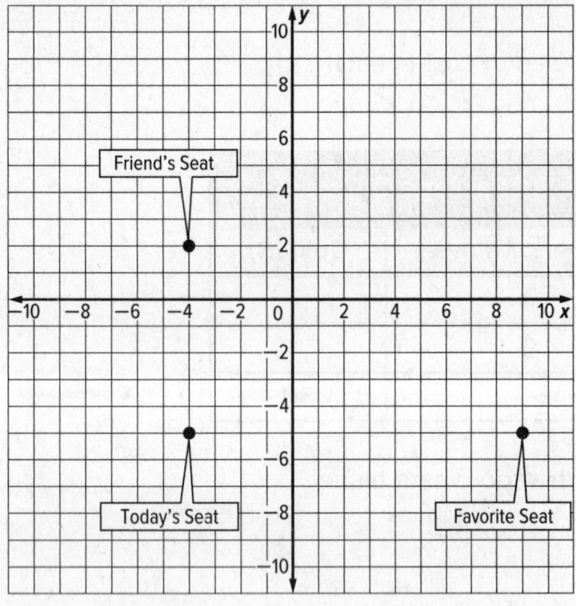

HELPFUL HINT Use the graph to double-check your answers.

Write and evaluate an expression using absolute value to represent the distance from Grayson's seat today to the aisle represented by the *y*-axis.

Write and evaluate an expression using absolute value to represent the distance from Grayson's favorite seat to the aisle represented by the *y*-axis.

What is the distance between Grayson's seat today and his favorite seat? Explain how you determined this distance.

What is the distance between Grayson's seat today and his friend's seat? Explain how you determined this distance.

NAME ______________________ DATE ____________ PERIOD ________ SCORE ________

Countdown: 20 Weeks

Online Test Tip

On an online test, you might be asked to click the appropriate box for each statement. In this book, you will be asked to shade in the boxes instead.

1. In Raphael's class there are 14 boys and 10 girls. Select whether each statement is true or false. 6.RP.1

True	False	
☐	☐	The ratio of boys to girls is 14:10.
☐	☐	The ratio of girls to boys is 7:5.
☐	☐	The ratio of boys to girls is $\frac{7}{5}$.
☐	☐	The ratio of girls to boys is $\frac{30}{42}$.

2. Rita wants to buy a sweater that was originally priced at $25.00. Today the sweater is on sale for 40% off the original price. 6.RP.3, 6.RP.3c

Part A: What is the sale price of the sweater?

Part B: Rita has a coupon for an additional 10% off the sale price. How much will Rita pay for the sweater before taxes?

3. A seagull flies 15 feet above the surface of the ocean. The table shows the location of several other objects in relation to the ocean's surface. Sort the objects into the appropriate bins by their distances to the ocean surface as compared to the seagull's distance. 6.NS.7, 6.NS.7c

Object	Location in Comparison to the Ocean's Surface (feet)
Fish	−6
Shark	−50
Airplane	150
Submarine	−218
Pelican	9

Submarine | Fish | Shark

Pelican | Airplane

Farther from the Ocean's Surface than the Seagull is	Closer to the Ocean's Surface than the Seagull is

4. Nicholas is driving his car at a constant rate of 55 miles per hour. Select whether Nicholas could achieve the distances listed in the given times. 6.RP.3, 6.RP.3b

Yes	No	
☐	☐	165 miles in 3 hours
☐	☐	240 miles in 4 hours
☐	☐	330 miles in 6 hours
☐	☐	504 miles in 9 hours

5. Yolanda buys two types of flowering plants. She buys 36 geraniums and 63 marigolds. She wants to plant an equal number of flowers in each row of her garden. Each row will contain only one type of flowering plant. 6.NS.4

Part A: Yolanda uses all the plants she bought in her garden. Determine the greatest number of flowering plants that could be in each row of the garden.

☐

Part B: How many rows of each type of flowering plant will be in Yolanda's garden?

☐ rows of geraniums

☐ rows of marigolds

NAME ______________________ DATE __________ PERIOD ________ SCORE ________

Countdown: 19 Weeks

1. The distance between point (2, 2) and point (8, 2) is 6 units on a coordinate plane. Select all of the pairs of points that are 6 units apart. 6.NS.8

- ☐ (1, 7) and (1, 1)
- ☐ (3, 3) and (–5, 3)
- ☐ (–3, 4) and (–3, –2)
- ☐ (0, 0) and (–2, –4)
- ☐ (–1, 5) and (5, 5)
- ☐ (–8, 3) and (–2, 3)

2. During back-to-school week, all school supplies are tax-free. Rajiv took advantage of this sale and bought a ruler for \$0.79, three pens for \$1.49 each, and two notebooks for \$2.25 each. 6.NS.3

Part A: What is the total cost for Rajiv's purchases?

Part B: Rajiv paid using a \$10 bill. How much change did he receive?

3. A football field is 120 yards long. Sort the lengths into the appropriate bins by comparing them to the length of a football field. 6.RP.3

4 miles	400 feet	4,000 inches
1,760 inches	$\frac{1}{10}$ mile	120 feet

Longer than a Football Field	Shorter than a Football Field

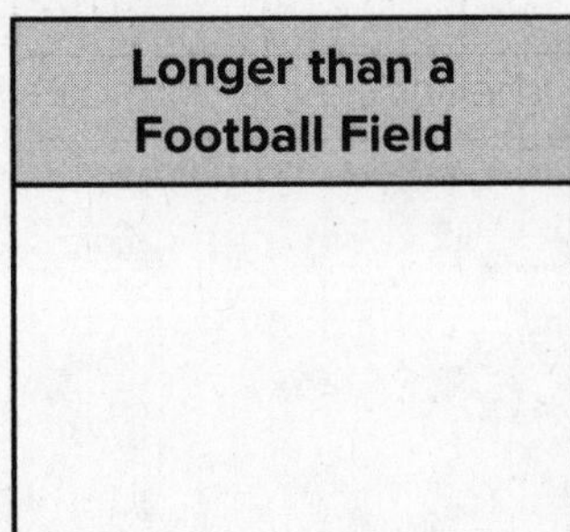

Online Test Tip
On an online test, you might be asked to drag the lengths to a bin. In this book, you will be asked to write each length in the space provided.

4. Kelly keeps track of her test scores as shown in the table.

Test	Number of Items	Number Correct
1	50	35
2	40	27
3	60	48
4	100	75

Complete the table by ordering Kelly's test scores from least to greatest percent scored. 6.RP.3, 6.RP.3c

	Test	Test Score (%)
Least		
Greatest		

5. Makayla wants to buy a carton of juice. She could buy a 48-ounce container for $2.88 or a 64-ounce container for $3.52. 6.RP.2

Part A: What is the cost per ounce of the juice in the 48-ounce container?

Part B: What is the cost per ounce of the juice in the 64-ounce container?

Part C: Which container is the better buy? Justify your response.

Online Test Tip

On an online test, you might be asked to use a keypad with math symbols to enter your answers. In this book, you will be asked to write your answers in the spaces provided.

NAME _______________ DATE _______ PERIOD _______ SCORE _______

Countdown: 18 Weeks

1. A recipe for fruit salad calls for 2 strawberries for every 3 pieces of melon. 6.RP.3, 6.RP.3a

Part A: Complete the ratio table.

Number of Strawberries	2	4		8
Number of Melon Pieces	3		9	

Part B: Graph the data on the coordinate plane.

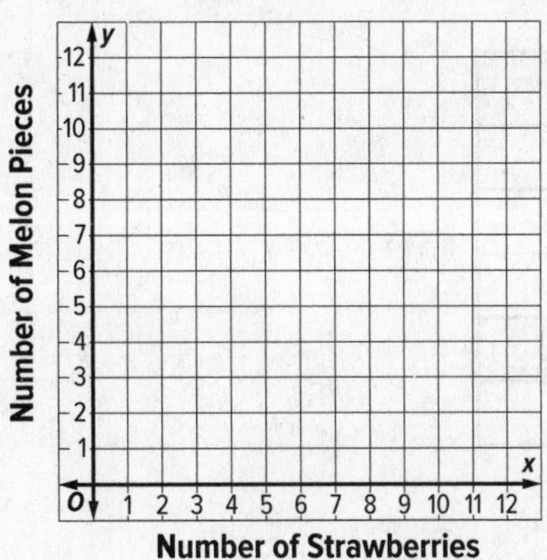

Online Test Tip

On an online test, you might be asked to click the button to plot the points. In this book, you will be asked to draw the points on the graph.

2. A building blueprint has a scale of 2 inches equal to 25 feet. On the blueprint, the 10-story building has a height of 12 inches. What is the actual height of 1 story? 6.RP.3, 6.RP.3b

3. Ronald picked many oranges from his trees. He squeezed out 256 fluid ounces of juice. How many half-gallon containers of juice was he able to fill? 6.RP.3, 6.RP.3d

4. The table shows the temperatures at noon for the past five days.

Day	Temperature (°F)
Monday	–4
Tuesday	2
Wednesday	0
Thursday	–6
Friday	3

Complete the table to order the temperatures from least to greatest.
6.NS.7, 6.NS.7b

	Day	Temperature (°F)
Least		
Greatest		

5. Select whether each expression is equivalent to the sum 45 + 63.
6.NS.4

Yes	No	
☐	☐	15(3 + 4)
☐	☐	9(5 + 7)
☐	☐	7(7 + 9)
☐	☐	3(21 + 15)

NAME ______________________ DATE ____________ PERIOD ________ SCORE ________

Countdown: 17 Weeks

1. Li wants to buy a jacket that is originally priced at $65.00. Today the store is advertising the jacket for 40% off the original price. 6.RP.3, 6.RP.3c

Online Test Tip
On an online test, you might be asked to use a keypad with math symbols to enter dollar amounts. In this book, you will be asked to write the amount in the space provided.

Part A: What is the sale price of the jacket?

[ ]

Part B: Li has a coupon for an additional 10% off the sale price. What is the price of the jacket after the coupon?

[ ]

2. Students' bicycles are parked in the bicycle rack. There are 8 red, 10 blue, 3 black, and 4 other colors. Select whether each statement is true or false. 6.RP.1

True	False	
☐	☐	The ratio of red to blue bicycles is 4:5.
☐	☐	The ratio of black to red bicycles is 8:3.
☐	☐	The ratio of blue bicycles to all other colors is 2:3.
☐	☐	The ratio of black to the total number of bicycles is 3:25.

3. Kim needs to place 32 mystery books and 56 biography books on library shelves. She is to place the maximum number of books on each shelf so that all the shelves have the same number of books. Each shelf will contain only one type of book. 6.NS.4

Part A: Determine the number of books to be placed on each shelf.

[ ]

Part B: How many shelves will Kim use for each type of book?

[ ]

4. The table shows the elevations of several objects compared to sea level.

Object	Elevation (ft)
Scuba diver	–75
Light in a lighthouse	137
Shark	–48
Fish	–6
Top of weather buoy	10
Submarine	–182

Complete the table to order the objects from farthest away to closest to sea level. 6.NS.7, 6.NS.7b

	Object	Elevation (ft)
Farthest		
Closest		

5. A carpenter has a board $18\frac{1}{2}$ feet long. He needs to cut as many $1\frac{3}{4}$-feet-long pieces as possible. How many pieces can the carpenter cut? Explain how you found your answer. 6.NS.1

NAME ______________________ DATE __________ PERIOD ________ SCORE ________

Countdown: 16 Weeks

1. A theater received $8,917 in ticket sales for one performance of a play. Tickets for preferred seats cost $45 each and regular seats cost $34 each. All of the theater's 75 preferred seats were sold out that evening. How many tickets were sold? 6.NS.2

Online Test Tip

On an online test, you might be asked to use a keypad with math symbols to enter the number. In this book, you will be asked to write the number in the space provided.

2. The table shows the elevations of five objects as compared to sea level. 6.NS.7, 6.NS.7b

Object	Elevation (ft)
Duck	21
Swimmer	–1
Fish	–50
Goose	3
Submarine	–125

Complete the table to order the objects from closest to sea level to farthest from sea level.

	Object	Elevation (ft)	Distance from sea level (ft)
Closest			
Farthest			

3. The length of a garden is $51\frac{1}{3}$ feet. One section of fencing is $3\frac{2}{3}$ feet long. 6.NS.1

Part A: How many sections of fencing are needed along the length of the garden?

Part B: For each piece of fencing, 4 stakes are used to secure it in place. The stakes are equally spaced along the fencing piece, with one stake at each end. How far apart are the stakes on one piece of fencing?

4. Rosina finds a pair of shorts on the sale rack for $12.50. This price reflects a discount of 60%. What is the original price of the shorts? What is the amount of the discount? 6.RP.3, 6.RP.3c

5.00	7.50	12.50	17.50
18.75	20	20.83	31.25

Original price of shorts: $ ☐

Amount of discount: $ ☐

5. The ratio of boys to all students in a class is 2:5. Select whether each statement is true or false. 6.RP.3, 6.RP.3b

True	False	
☐	☐	There could be 4 boys and 10 girls in the class.
☐	☐	There could be 8 boys and 12 girls in the class.
☐	☐	There could be 10 boys among the 25 students in the class.
☐	☐	There could be 20 boys among the 30 students in the class.
☐	☐	There could be 9 girls among the 15 students in the class.

NAME ________________ DATE ________ PERIOD ______ SCORE ______

Countdown: 15 Weeks

1. Select whether each statement shows an example of the Distributive Property. 6.EE.3

Yes	No	
☐	☐	$4(2x + 5) = 8x + 5$
☐	☐	$7(3x + 2) = 10x + 9$
☐	☐	$15x + 25 = 5(3x + 5)$
☐	☐	$6x + 300 = 6(x + 50)$

Online Test Tip

On an online test, you might be asked to click the appropriate box for each statement. In this book, you will be asked to shade in the boxes instead.

2. Praedup uses the inequality $r + 2 \geq 25$ to represent his rock and shell collection, where r is the number of rocks in his collection. Select all of the values that could be the number of rocks in Praedup's collection. 6.EE.5

☐ 15

☐ 25

☐ 5

☐ –50

☐ 82

☐ 23

☐ 22

3. Nancy is running on a trail that is 5.3 miles long. After 20 minutes, she has run 1.45 miles. 6.EE.7

Part A: Write an addition equation to find how much farther Nancy has to run to complete the trail.

Part B: Solve the equation to find the number of miles Nancy has to run to get to the end of the trail.

4. A survey asked a group of students to name their favorite school subject. The results are shown in the table.

Favorite Subject	Portion of Student Responses
Math	0.4
History	$\frac{3}{25}$
Reading	28%
Science	$\frac{1}{5}$

Complete the table to order the school subjects from least to greatest percent of students who chose that subject as their favorite. 6.RP.3

	Favorite Subject	Percent of Students
Least		
Greatest		

5. Point (3, –4) is plotted on a coordinate plane. Select whether each statement is true or false about point (3, –4). 6.NS.6, 6.NS.6b

True	False	
☐	☐	It is located in Quadrant IV.
☐	☐	It is a reflection of point (–3, –4) over the *x*-axis.
☐	☐	It has the same location as point (–4, 3).
☐	☐	It is a reflection of point (3, 4) over the *y*-axis.
☐	☐	It is a reflection of the point (–3, 4) over the *x*-axis and then over the *y*-axis.

NAME ______________________ DATE __________ PERIOD ________ SCORE ________

Countdown: 14 Weeks

1. For the school bake sale, members of the cheerleading squad bake the number of muffins shown in the table. 6.EE.1

Name	Number of Muffins
Robert	4^3
Alicia	4×3
Joe	3^4
Melanie	8^2

Part A: Circle the names of the squad members who bake the same number of muffins.

Robert Alicia Joe Melanie

Part B: Another squad member, Miki, also bakes the same number of muffins as the members you circled in Part A. Miki represents the number as a power of 2. What must be the value of Miki's exponent? Justify your answer.

2. A company manufactures small, solid, plastic cubes. They use the expression s^3, where s is the length of a side, to find the volume of plastic needed to make a cube. Luis claims that the volume of plastic needed to make a cube with side length 8 millimeters is 24 cubic millimeters. Do you agree with Luis's claim? Explain your reasoning. 6.EE.2, 6.EE.2c

3. Soto designs and makes personal flags. The fabric he purchases is measured in feet. However, Soto needs to know the number of inches for each fabric because the dimensions of his flags are in inches. 6.RP.3, 6.RP.3d

Fabric Color	Length (ft)	Length (in.)
Blue	3	
Red		60
Yellow	$2\frac{1}{2}$	
Green	12	
Purple		240

Part A: Complete the table.

Part B: Write an expression that Soto could use to convert $16\frac{3}{4}$ feet of white fabric to inches. Then find the number of inches, and show your work.

4. Justin bought a hat for $36 and two admission tickets to a baseball game. Let *t* represent the cost of an admission ticket. Select whether each statement is true or false. 6.EE.2, 6.EE.2a, 6.EE.2c

True	False	
☐	☐	The expression $2(t + 36)$ represents the total amount Justin spent.
☐	☐	When each admission ticket costs $5.50, Justin will spend $47 in all.
☐	☐	The expression $2t + 36$ represents the total amount Justin spent.
☐	☐	When each admission ticket costs $9.50, Justin will spend $91 in all.

5. The table shows the distance of five divers from the surface of the water.

Diver	Distance from Water Surface (m)
A	–450
B	15
C	–230
D	–99
E	–100

Select all of the divers whose distance from the surface is less than Diver E's distance. 6.NS.7, 6.NS.7c

☐ Diver A

☐ Diver B

☐ Diver C

☐ Diver D

Online Test Tip

On an online test, you might be asked to click all of the correct answer choices. In this book, you will be asked to shade a box next to each correct answer choice.

NAME ______________________ DATE ____________ PERIOD ________ SCORE ________

Countdown: 13 Weeks

1. Write the appropriate number in each box to find the product. 6.NS.4

$7 \times 28 = 7(20 + \square) = 140 + \square = \square$

7	8	9	14	28
56	169	196	728	1,456

2. Jessica wants to buy the items shown in the table for her aquarium. She has $40 to spend. She has a coupon for 20% off her total purchase. Determine the most items she can buy if she does not want to buy more than one of any item. Justify your answer. (Ignore sales tax.) 6.RP.3, 6.RP.3c

Item	Cost ($)
Artificial plant pack	13
Aquarium gravel	10
Coral bubbler	25
Driftwood	7
Eiffel Tower ornament	8

3. Cheryl sends the same number of e-mails each week as shown in the table. Let *w* represent the number of weeks that Cheryl sends e-mails. Let *n* represent the total number of e-mails sent. 6.EE.9

Week (*w*)	Total Number of E-mails (*n*)
1	7
2	14
3	21
4	28

Part A: Select whether each statement is true or false.

True **False**

☐ ☐ The equation $w = 7 + n$ represents the relationship between the number of weeks and the total number of e-mails.

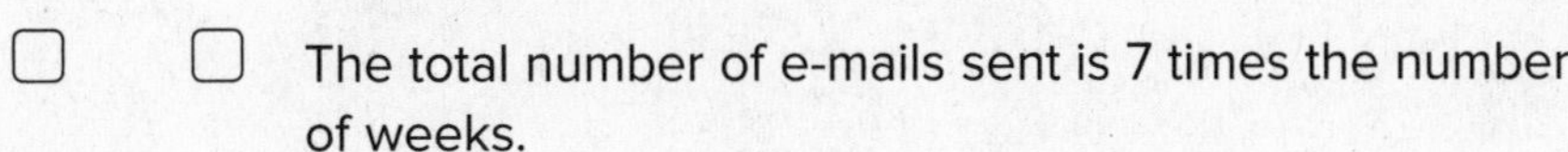

☐ ☐ The total number of e-mails sent is 7 times the number of weeks.

☐ ☐ The number of e-mails Cheryl sends depends on the number of weeks.

Part B: Cheryl claims that based on the relationship shown in the table, in week 6 she will send over 40 e-mails. Do you agree with Cheryl's claim? Provide evidence to support your answer.

4. Juanita purchased amusement park tickets for herself and her brothers. The cost of each ticket was x dollars. Juanita bought 3 tickets on Tuesday and 1 ticket on Wednesday. She paid $8 for herself and her brothers to ride the bus to the park. The expression $4x + 8$ represents the amount of money Juanita spent. Select all of the expressions that are equivalent to $4x + 8$. 6.EE.3, 6.EE.4

- ☐ $3x + 9$
- ☐ $4(x + 2)$
- ☐ $2(x + 4)$
- ☐ $2(2x + 4)$
- ☐ $8 + 4x$
- ☐ $12x$
- ☐ $\frac{1}{2}(8x + 16)$

5. Write the appropriate term in each box to create an expression equivalent to $7x + 2x + 6y$. 6.EE.3

$3x$	$9x$	$15x$	$3y$
2	3	$2y$	$6y$

$7x + 2x + 6y = \square(\square + \square)$

Online Test Tip

On an online test, you might be asked to drag the expressions into the spaces provided. In this book, you will be asked to write in the spaces.

NAME ______________________ DATE ____________ PERIOD ________ SCORE ________

Countdown: 12 Weeks

1. Members of a book club named their favorite genre of book. Circle the ratios that compare the number of members who did *not* choose mystery to the total number of responses. 6.RP.1

Genre	Number of Responses
Science Fiction	7
Mystery	8
History	6
Biographies	3

$\frac{1}{3}$ 1 to 8   2:3   2:1

$\frac{2}{3}$ 8:24   16 to 24   3 to 2

2. Irfan is transferring the drawing of figure *ABCD* to a coordinate plane. He plots point *A* at (–2, –1), and point *B* at (1, 3) on a coordinate plane. Graph the ordered pairs that show points *C* and *D*, and then connect the points to form Irfan's figure. 6.NS.8

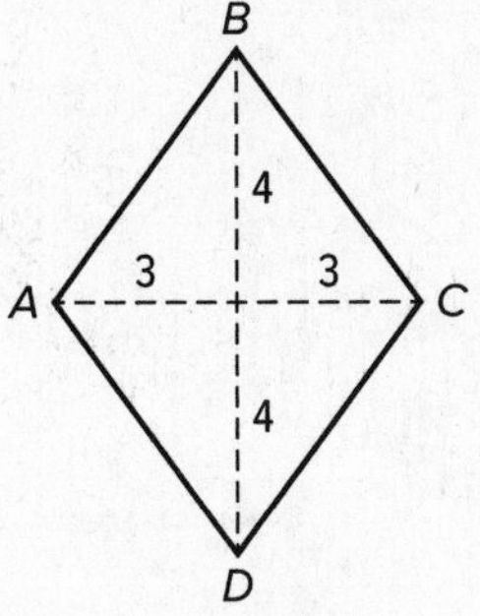

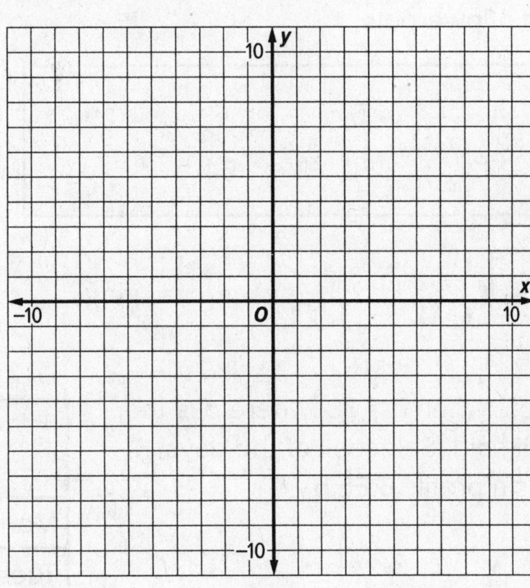

Online Test Tip

On an online test, you might be asked to click buttons to plot points and graph line segments. In this book, you will be asked to draw the points and lines.

3. Kwasi reads 30 minutes before school. He reads x more minutes after school. Write an equation to represent the total number of minutes y Kwasi reads. 6.EE.9

4. Latoya has a 25-pound bag of potting soil. She puts 3 pounds of potting soil in each of f flowerpots. The amount of potting soil that remains can be represented by the expression $25 - 3f$. 6.EE.2, 6.EE.2c

Part A: Latoya puts soil in 7 flowerpots. How much potting soil remains?

 pounds

Part B: Latoya realizes that she actually has two 25-pound bags of potting soil. Write the appropriate numbers and symbols in the spaces to represent the number of pounds of potting soil remaining after Latoya puts 3 pounds in each of f flowerpots.

2	3	4	5	6	+
25	27	28	50	54	–

f

5. A fruit stand makes a profit when $p > 38$, where p is the number of pounds of fruit sold. Select all of the days that the fruit stand makes a profit. 6.EE.5

- ☐ Monday
- ☐ Tuesday
- ☐ Wednesday
- ☐ Thursday
- ☐ Friday
- ☐ Saturday

Day	Amount of Fruit Sold (lb)
Monday	32
Tuesday	45
Wednesday	39
Thursday	44
Friday	38
Saturday	56

NAME ______________________ DATE __________ PERIOD ________ SCORE ________

Countdown: 11 Weeks

1. Using the numbers, write two powers that have the same value. 6.EE.1

2	3	6	8

$\square^{\square} = \square^{\square}$

2. A rectangle has an area of $(24x + 30)$ square units. Select all of the dimensions that are possible for this rectangle. 6.EE.3

$24x + 30$

- ☐ width 6 units; length $(4x + 5)$ units
- ☐ width 4 units; length $(6x + 7)$ units
- ☐ width 3 units; length $(21x + 27)$ units
- ☐ width 8 units; length $(3x + 4)$ units
- ☐ width 2 units; length $(15 + 12x)$ units

3. In the last basketball game, Elena scored 2 more than one fourth of her team's total points. 6.EE.2, 6.EE.2a, 6.EE.6

Part A: Let n represent the number of points Elena's team scored. Write an expression for the number of points Elena scored.

Part B: The team scored 40 points. How many points did Elena score?

Online Test Tip

On an online test, you might be asked to use a keypad with math symbols to enter your expression. In this book, you will be asked to write your response in the space provided.

4. Joan runs at a constant rate for 2 hours. She takes 45 minutes to run 6 miles. De'Quan also runs at a constant rate. He runs $11\frac{1}{4}$ miles in 1 hour 15 minutes. 6.RP.3, 6.RP.3a, 6.RP.3d

Part A: Complete the table for Joan's running times and distances.

Joan's Running				
Distance (mi)	6	2		
Time (min)	45		30	75

Part B: Does Joan or De'Quan run more miles in 75 minutes? Justify your response.

5. The diagram shows the amount of fabric that Christine needs to make 1 tablecloth, including the fabric that will hang over the sides. The fabric costs $1.50 per square foot. Christine plans to make 1 tablecloth for each of the 4 seasons of the year. What is the total cost of the fabric that Christine needs for the tablecloths? 6.NS.3

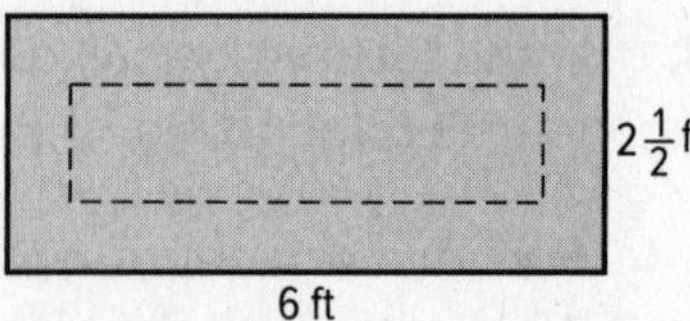

NAME ______________________ DATE ____________ PERIOD ________ SCORE ________

Countdown: 10 Weeks

1. Steve surveyed the students in his class to find out their favorite sport. The table shows the results of the survey. What percent of Steve's classmates did *not* select soccer as their favorite sport? 6.RP.3, 6.RP.3c

Favorite Sport	
Sport	**Number of Students**
Basketball	8
Football	7
Soccer	12
Other	13

2. Two-fifths of the girls in a school signed up to play softball. An equal number of girls signed up to play pitcher, infield, and outfield. What fraction of girls in the school signed up to play outfield? 6.NS.1

3. Select all of the equations for which the solution is 20. 6.EE.5

- ☐ $n - 4 = 24$
- ☐ $10n = 200$
- ☐ $\frac{n}{5} = 4$
- ☐ $7 + n = 13$

Online Test Tip

On an online test, you might be asked to click all of the correct answer choices. In this book, you will be asked to shade a box next to each correct answer choice.

4. A hiker walks at an average rate of 2 miles per hour. 6.EE.7

Part A: Write a multiplication equation to find how long it will take for the hiker to walk 11 miles. Let *n* represent the number of hours.

Part B: Solve the equation for *n*. How many hours does the hiker walk?

5. Select whether each set of dimensions represents a triangle with an area of 24 square units. 6.G.1

Yes	No	
☐	☐	base = 8 units, height = 12 units
☐	☐	base = 6 units, height = 8 units
☐	☐	base = 4 units, height = 6 units
☐	☐	base = 3 units, height = 4 units
☐	☐	base = 16 units, height = 3 units

NAME ______________ DATE ________ PERIOD ______ SCORE ______

Countdown: 9 Weeks

1. Lina stocked fruit to sell at a market. The ratio of apples to oranges is 1:4. Lina stocked no more than 200 of each type of fruit. 6.RP.3, 6.RP.3a

Part A: Complete the table to determine how many apples and oranges Lina may have stocked. Choose appropriate numbers for the last two columns.

Apples		3			15		
Oranges	8		32	48			

Part B: How many apples would Lina stock if she has 104 oranges?

2. William has 42 red tulip bulbs and 56 yellow tulip bulbs. He plans to use all the bulbs to make potted gifts for his teachers. William claims he can make 7 pots of tulips with an equal total number of red and yellow tulips in each pot. Do you agree with William's claim? Justify your reasoning. 6.NS.4

3. Kimi has posted 3 × 3 × 3 × 3 puppy photos on a social network. 6.EE.1

Part A: Write the appropriate numbers in the boxes to represent 3 × 3 × 3 × 3 as a power.

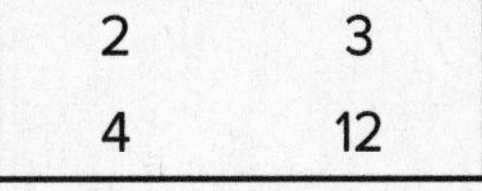

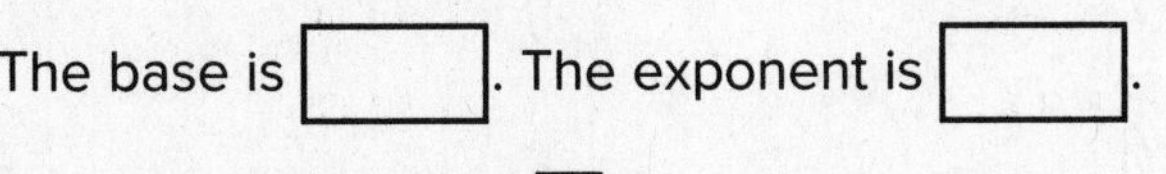

The power is ☐☐.

Online Test Tip
On an online test, you might be asked to drag the numbers into the appropriate box. In this book, you will be asked to write the numbers instead.

Part B: How many puppy photos did Kimi post on the social network?

4. The diagram shows the coordinates of the vertices of a right trapezoid when it is drawn on a coordinate plane. Select whether each statement is true or false. 6.G.3

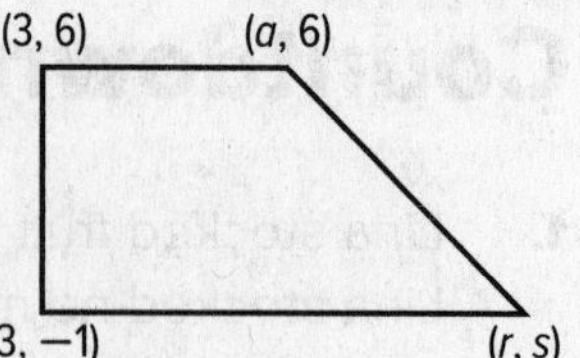

True	False	
☐	☐	The length of the longest horizontal side is $r - 3$.
☐	☐	The length of the vertical side is 5.
☐	☐	$a = 3$
☐	☐	$r > s$
☐	☐	The length of the shortest horizontal side is $a - 6$.

5. The box-and-whisker plot displays the weights of 24 pets. Select all of the values that are quartiles of the data. 6.SP.5, 6.SP.5c

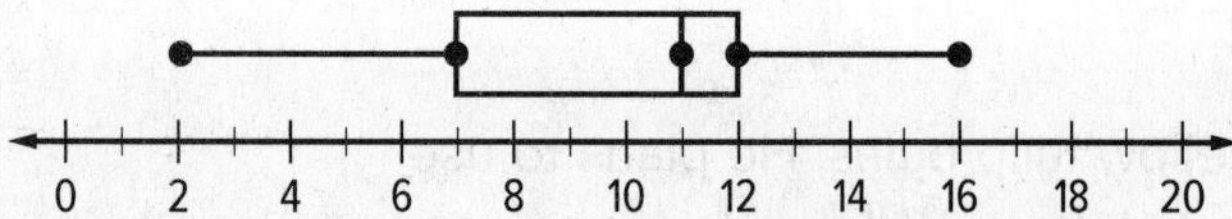

- ☐ 2
- ☐ 10
- ☐ 7
- ☐ 16
- ☐ 5
- ☐ 12
- ☐ 14
- ☐ 9
- ☐ 8

NAME ______________________ DATE __________ PERIOD ______ SCORE ______

Countdown: 8 Weeks

Online Test Tip
On an online test, you might be asked to click the appropriate box for each statement. In this book, you will be asked to shade in the boxes instead.

1. Benjamin needs to gather data about astronauts and space travel to write a report. Select whether each question can be classified as a statistical question. 6.SP.1

Yes	No	
☐	☐	How many astronauts have walked on the moon?
☐	☐	How many days did the missions stay on the moon?
☐	☐	How many times did Neil Armstrong travel into space?
☐	☐	How old were the astronauts when they traveled into space?

2. The raised vegetable garden in Susan's yard is in the shape of a rectangular prism with a volume of 48 cubic feet and a height of $\frac{3}{4}$ foot. 6.G.2

Part A: The base of the garden is not a square and the width is greater than 2 feet. What could be the length and width of the raised garden? Explain.

Part B: The base of the garden is a square. What is the width and length of the raised garden?

3. Rey fenced off triangular areas *A* and *B* in his yard for his two pets. Rey claims that the combined area of these two triangles is equal to the area of triangle *C*. Is Rey's claim correct? Justify your answer. 6.G.1

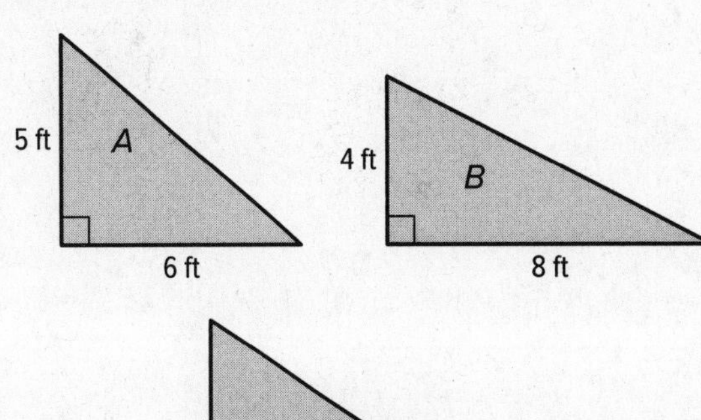

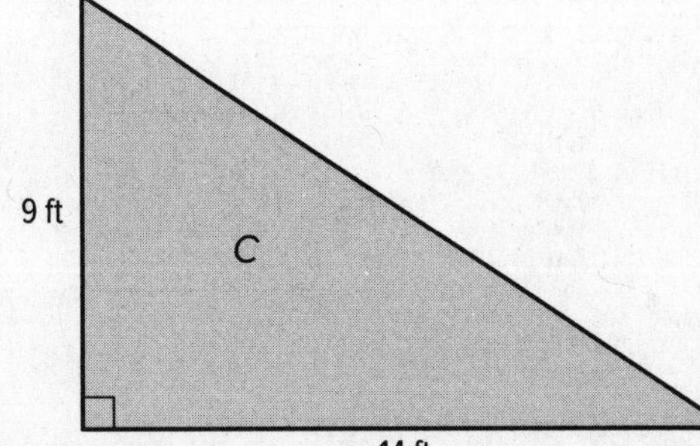

4. The table shows the average amount of money the boys and girls in Zina's class spent on their science fair projects. Zina spent at most $2 more than the average amount spent by the girls in her class. 6.EE.6

Average Amount Spent on Project	
Male	$15
Female	$16

Part A: Let z represent the amount of money Zina spent. Write the appropriate numbers and operations in the boxes to create an inequality of the situation.

+	−	×	÷	1
2	14	15	16	31

z ☐ ☐ ≤ ☐

Part B: What is the greatest amount that Zina could have spent?

☐

5. Select all of the products of 2.74 × 7.5. 6.NS.3

- ☐ 20.05
- ☐ 205.50
- ☐ 20.50
- ☐ 20.55
- ☐ 20,550
- ☐ 205.5
- ☐ 20.550
- ☐ 205.05

NAME ______________________ DATE ____________ PERIOD ________ SCORE ________

Countdown: 7 Weeks

1. Monique has five weeks to save at least $80 for a ski trip. Let n represent the amount she has to save each week. 6.EE.8

Part A: Write and solve an inequality to find the amount of money Monique needs to save each week.

Part B: Interpret the solution in the context of the problem.

2. Winifred has a college pennant on her wall. The pennant covers 54 square inches of wall space. Select all the possible values for x and y. 6.G.1

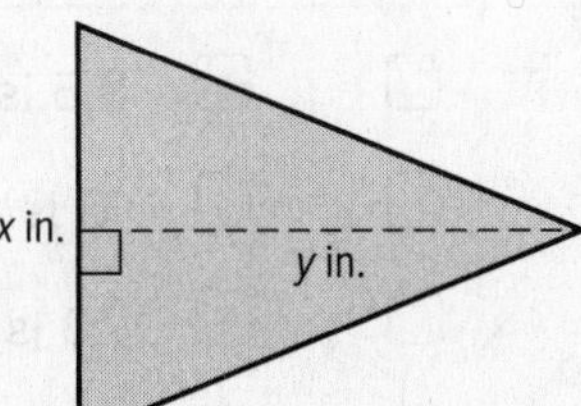

- ☐ $x = 6, y = 9$
- ☐ $x = 4, y = 13.5$
- ☐ $x = 6, y = 18$
- ☐ $x = 9, y = 12$

3. The diagram shows the dimensions of a school playground. What is the area of the playground? 6.G.1

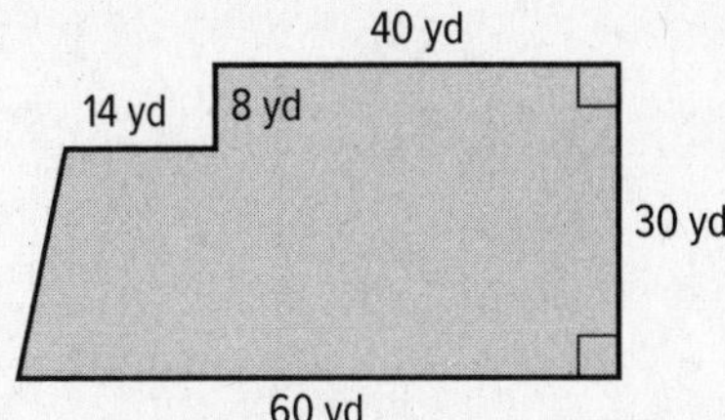

4. In the last six basketball games, Russell averaged 20 points per game. The lists show the number of points per game for 4 other players. Select whether each set of numbers has the same average as Russell. 6.SP.3

Yes	No	
☐	☐	20, 20, 20, 20, 20, 23
☐	☐	15, 16, 17, 18, 19, 35
☐	☐	16, 17, 20, 20, 21, 22
☐	☐	15, 17, 19, 21, 22, 26

5. The list shows Moira's quiz scores: 6, 4, 10, 7, 10, 8, 9, 6. Select whether each statement is true or false in representing the quiz scores. 6.SP.3

True	False	
☐	☐	6 is a mode of the quiz scores.
☐	☐	8.5 is the median quiz score.
☐	☐	10 is a mode of the quiz scores.
☐	☐	7.5 is the median quiz score.
☐	☐	4 is the range of the quiz scores.

Online Test Tip

On an online test, you might be asked to click the appropriate box for each statement. In this book, you will be asked to shade in the boxes.

NAME ______________________ DATE __________ PERIOD ______ SCORE ______

Countdown: 6 Weeks

1. The ratio of the areas of two parallelograms is 4:9. The perimeter of the smaller parallelogram is 20 units. What is the perimeter of the larger parallelogram? 6.G.1

2. The box plot shows some student test scores. 6.SP.4

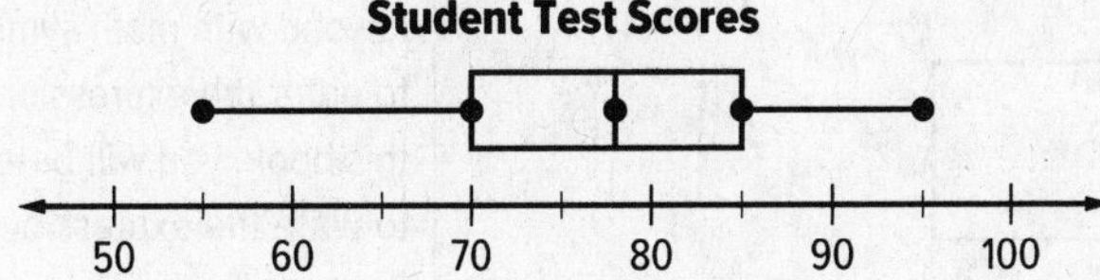

Select whether each statement is true or false in representing the student test scores.

True	False	
☐	☐	Half of the test scores are between 70 and 85.
☐	☐	The lowest test score is 60.
☐	☐	The mean of the test scores is 78.
☐	☐	The median test score is 78.
☐	☐	The mode of the test scores is 85.
☐	☐	More than 25% of the test scores are between 55 and 70.

3. The diagram shows the dimensions of a gift box that Andrea needs to wrap. What is the least amount of wrapping paper needed to completely cover the box? 6.G.4

1.8 in.

6 in.

10 in.

4. A rectangular bathtub is $5\frac{1}{2}$ feet long, $1\frac{1}{2}$ feet wide, and 3 feet high. Daniel fills the tub to a depth of 2 feet. What is the volume of the water in the tub? 6.G.2

Online Test Tip

On an online test, you might be asked to use a keypad with math symbols to enter the expression. In this book, you will be asked to write the expression in the space provided.

5. At a fabrication plant, 9 of the employees each earn $10,000 per quarter and 1 employee earns $70,000 per quarter. 6.SP.5, 6.SP.5c

Part A: Find the median and mean salary per quarter.

Part B: The industry employee average salary for fabrication plants is $13,000 per quarter. Mr. Gomez is trying to recruit people to work for the plant. How might he advertise the position using the mean salary?

Part C: Evaluate the advertisement in Part B. Do you agree with the claim made in the advertisement? Explain.

NAME ______________________ DATE __________ PERIOD ________ SCORE ________

Countdown: 5 Weeks

1. The figure shows a trapezoid with a height of 4 units. The area of the trapezoid is 20 square units. Select all of the dimensions for a and b that would represent the trapezoid. 6.G.1

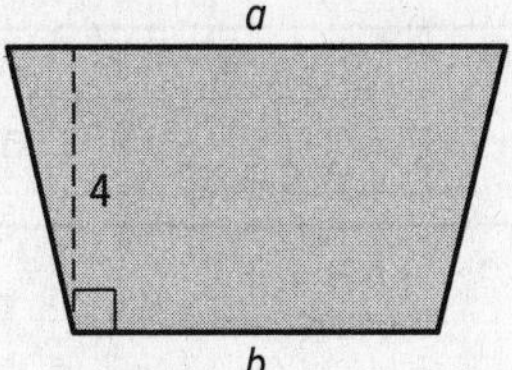

- ☐ a = 3 units, b = 2 units
- ☐ a = 6 units, b = 4 units
- ☐ a = 12 units, b = 8 units
- ☐ a = 7.5 units, b = 2.5 units
- ☐ a = 4 units, b = 1 units
- ☐ a = 23 units, b = 17 units

2. A homeowner has two rectangular structures in her backyard. The dimensions of the hot tub are 6 feet by 8 feet. The dimensions of the fire pit are 7 feet by 9 feet. The length of the square backyard is 20 feet. What area of the yard is not covered by the hot tub and the fire pit? 6.G.1

3. The diagram shows the dimensions of a wooden toy chest. One can of wood stain covers 12 square feet. How many cans are needed to stain all 6 outside surfaces of the toy chest? 6.G.4

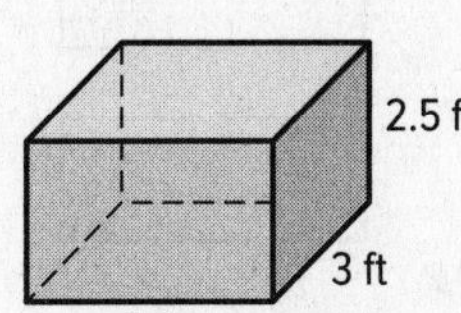

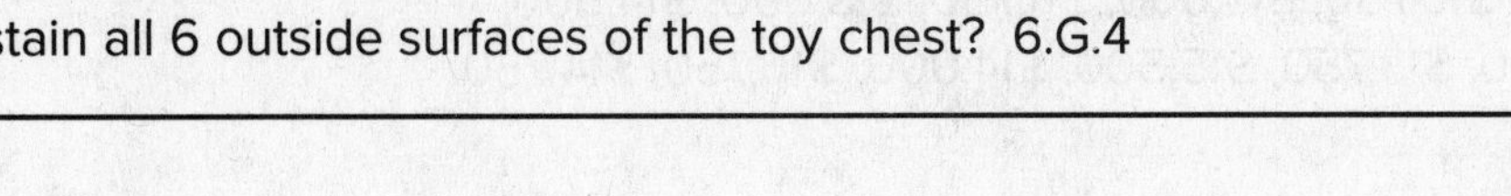

4. The list shows Jim's recent golf scores. 6.SP.5, 6.SP.5c

72, 78, 81, 77, 92, 80, 78, 84, 75

Part A: What is the range of the scores?

Part B: What is the interquartile range? Justify your answer.

5. Ryne is collecting some data about his favorite minor league baseball team. He finds information about the players' salaries, years of experience, and favorite uniform numbers. Write the measure that best represents each set of data. 6.SP.5, 6.SP.5c

Online Test Tip
On an online test, you might be asked to drag the words into the space provided. In this book, you will be asked to write the words instead.

mode median mean

Favorite uniform number: 7, 14, 11, 22, 3, 1, 99, 30, 27, 12, 19

Years of experience: 3, 1, 6, 3, 2, 3, 3, 3, 1, 4, 3

Salary: $10,750, $13,500, $11,750, $13,000, $14,500, $12,000, $13,750, $15,500, $14,000, $15,750, $14,750

NAME ________________ DATE ________ PERIOD ______ SCORE ______

Countdown: 4 Weeks

1. The original dimensions of a rectangular garden that Emma designs is 10 feet long and 6 feet wide. She now plans to double the area of the garden by changing one or both of the dimensions. She wants the area of the garden to be 120 square feet, but neither the length nor the width can be greater than 25 feet. 6.G.1

Part A: Complete the table to find the measures in Emma's options.

	Length (ft)	Width (ft)	Area (ft²)	Perimeter (ft)
Original Design	10	6	60	
Option 1	10		120	
Option 2	15		120	
Option 3	20		120	
Option 4	5		120	

Part B: Emma has 50 feet of garden fencing. Which option will let Emma surround the garden completely with the greatest amount of fencing?

Part C: For Option 5, Emma multiplies the width in her original plan by $\frac{1}{2}$. Does this option meet the requirements for her garden? Explain.

2. The diagram shows a placemat made with white fabric and gray fabric. Select whether each statement is true or false in representing the diagram. 6.G.1

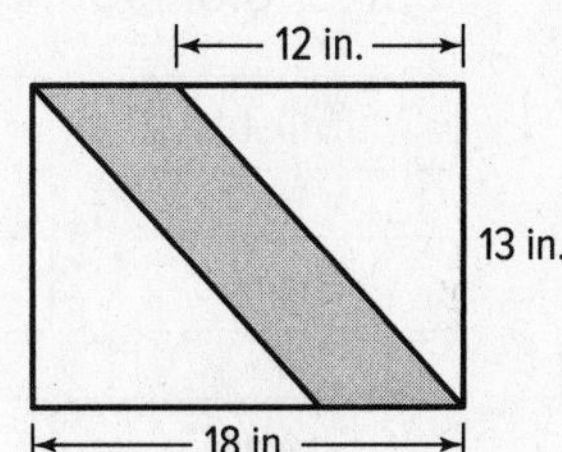

True	**False**	
☐	☐	The length of the placemat is 12 in.
☐	☐	The area of the gray fabric is 78 in^2.
☐	☐	The area of the placemat is 2,808 in^2.
☐	☐	The area of the white fabric is 156 in^2.

Online Test Tip
On an online test, you might be asked to click the appropriate box for each statement. In this book, you will be asked to shade in the boxes instead.

3. A trapezoid has an area of 33.6 square centimeters and a height of 4 centimeters. 6.G.1

Part A: What is the sum of the base lengths of the trapezoid?

[ ]

Part B: The length of one of the bases of the trapezoid is three times the length of the other base. What are the lengths of the bases?

[ ]

4. The table shows the number of miles Jayden cycled each week for 5 weeks. Write the appropriate numbers to find the mean number of miles Jayden cycled per week. 6.SP.3

Week	Number of Miles
1	16
2	19
3	20
4	18
5	22

1	2	3	4	5	6	16
17	18	19	20	21	22	38

$$\frac{\square + \square + \square + \square + \square}{\square} = \square$$

Mean: [ ] miles

5. Six students kept track of the numbers of hours they spent on their science projects each week. Sort the names of the students into the appropriate bins based on a comparison of the median and mode of his or her data set. 6.SP.3, 6.SP.5, 6.SP.5c

Student	Number of Hours Spent on Science Project
Julieta	4, 6, 4, 5, 4, 5
Kayla	5, 5, 5, 5, 5, 5
Fina	3, 6, 3, 4, 2, 3
Miguel	4, 1, 5, 5, 3, 2
Shane	4, 6, 2, 2, 6, 2
William	3, 1, 6, 4, 4, 5

Julieta | Kayla

Fina | Miguel

Shane | William

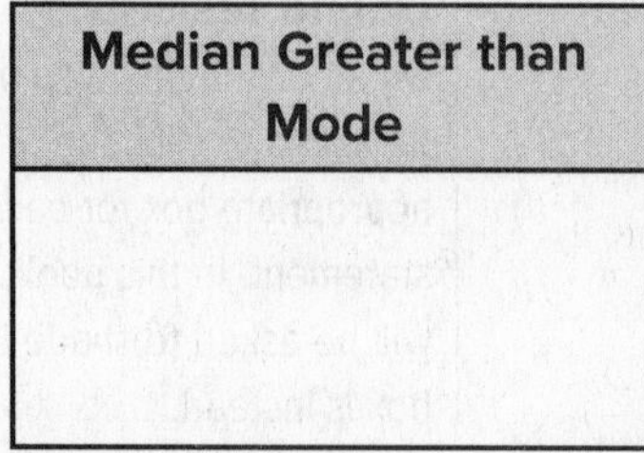

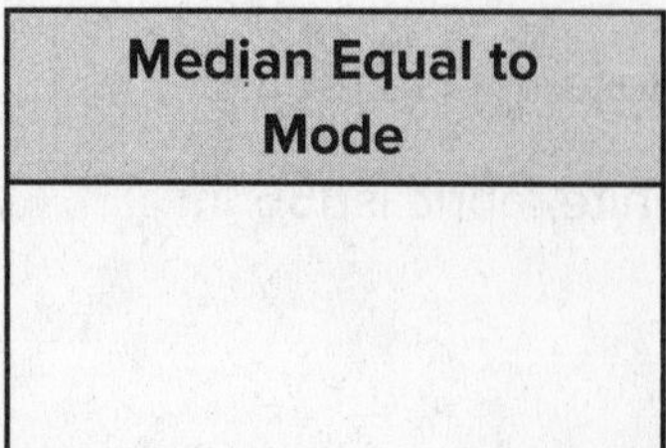

Median Less Than Mode

NAME ______________________ DATE __________ PERIOD ______ SCORE ______

Countdown: 3 Weeks

1. Figure *RSTV* has vertices located at *R*(3, 2), *S*(7, 2), *T*(7, 8), and *V*(3, 8). 6.G.3, 6.NS.8

Part A: Graph the figure *RSTV* on the coordinate plane.

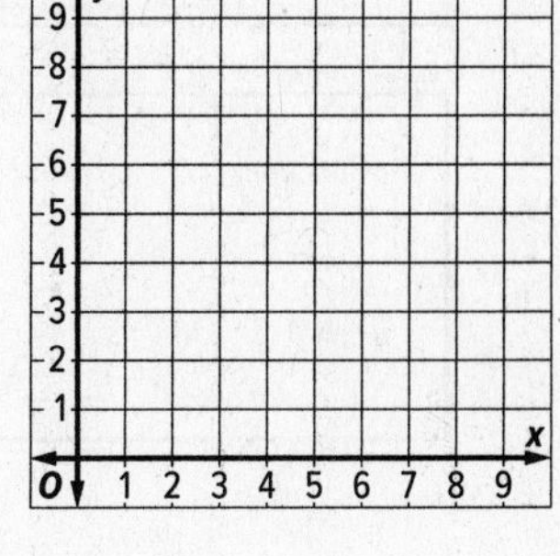

Part B: Select whether each statement is true or false about figure *RSTV*.

True	False	
☐	☐	Figure *RSTV* is a rectangle.
☐	☐	The length of $\overline{TV}$ is 4 units.
☐	☐	The length of $\overline{TV}$ is greater than the length of $\overline{TS}$.
☐	☐	The expression 2 × 4 + 6 represents the perimeter of figure *RSTV*.
☐	☐	The area of figure *RSTV* is 24 square units.

2. The diagram shows the dimensions of an outdoor patio. Select all of the expressions that represent the area of the patio in square feet. 6.G.1

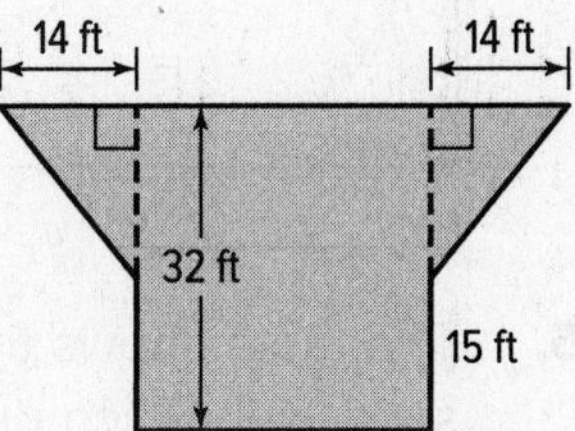

☐ (14 × 17) + (30 × 32)

☐ 119 + 960

☐ 14 + 32 + 14 + 15 + 30

☐ $(2 \times \frac{1}{2} \times 14 \times 17) + (32 \times 30)$

☐ 960 + 119 + 119

☐ $(30 \times 15) + \left(\frac{1}{2}\right)(17)(30 + 58)$

3. The table shows Mateo's scores on some math quizzes. Compare and contrast the measures of variation for both weeks. 6.SP.5, 6.SP.5c

Month	Mateo's Math Quiz Scores
March	75, 70, 80, 90, 85, 75, 80, 90
April	85, 80, 72, 80, 90, 80, 85, 95

4. The list shows the number of hours Rachael volunteered at six events: 15, 18, 5, 20, 17, and 21. Identify the outlier in the data set. Then describe how the outlier affects the mean. 6.SP.5, 6.SP.5c

outlier: ☐ hours

5. The table shows the ages of the members of a swim club. Paco draws a histogram and uses it to conclude that 12 members are over the age of 39. 6.SP.4, 6.SP.5a

Ages of Swim Club Members									
11	18	25	32	39	47	57	59	40	35
41	26	28	15	20	38	42	12	12	20
18	45	19	41	21	50	28	16	35	24
20	40	14	18	31	19	58	17	27	30

Part A: Complete the histogram to represent the data.

Ages of Swim Club Members

Frequency: 0, 2, 4, 6, 8, 10, 12, 14

Age: 11–17, 18–24, 25–31, 32–38, 39–45, 46–52, 53–59

Online Test Tip

On an online test, you might be asked to click in the graph to shade the appropriate sections. In this book, you will be asked to draw the shading in the graph.

Part B: Is Paco's statement valid? Explain your reasoning.

NAME ______________ DATE __________ PERIOD ________ SCORE ________

Countdown: 2 Weeks

1. The diagram shows the dimensions of two boxes of macaroni. 6.G.2

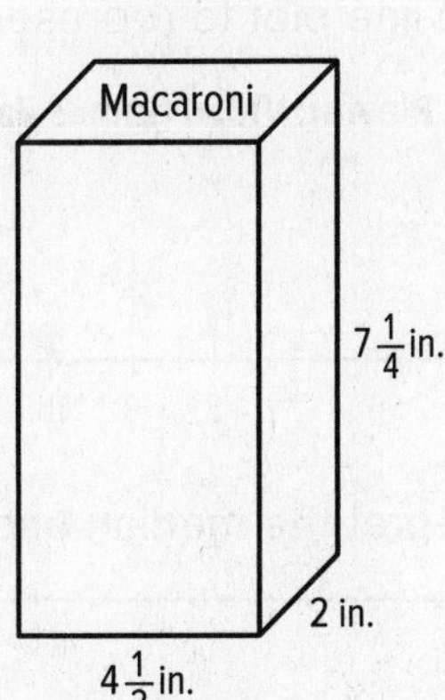

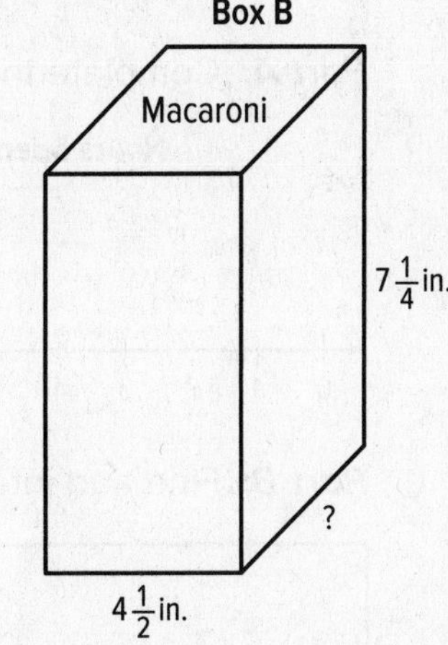

Part A: Find the volume of Box A.

Part B: The volume of Box B is $97\frac{7}{8}$ cubic inches greater than the volume of Box A. Explain a method you could use to find the width of Box B. Then find the width of Box B.

2. A rectangular prism has a length of 6.2 centimeters, a width of 2.4 centimeters, and a height of 3 centimeters. Select all of the expressions that are equivalent to the surface area, in square centimeters, of the rectangular prism. 6.G.4

- ☐ (6.2)(2.4)(3)
- ☐ 2(6.2) + 2(3) + 2(2.4)
- ☐ 37.2 + 29.76 + 14.4
- ☐ 2(6.2)(3) + 2(6.2)(2.4) + 2(3)(2.4)
- ☐ 2(18.6 + 14.88 + 7.2)

Online Test Tip

On an online test, you might be asked to click all of the correct answer choices. In this book, you will be asked to shade a box next to each correct answer choice.

3. Sofia asked a group of middle school students how many hours a week they spend playing video games. The table shows the results of her survey. 6.SP.4, 6.SP.5, 6.SP.5c

Hours Spent Playing Video Games Each Week					
10	8	6	7	3	12
15	6	2	6	9	11
12	6	13	9	1	7
5	8	2	10	6	9

Part A: Complete the line plot to represent the data.

Part B: Find and interpret the median and mode of the data.

4. The histogram shows the number of minutes students spend on chores each day. Select whether each statement is true or false. 6.SP.5, 6.SP.5a, 6.SP.5c

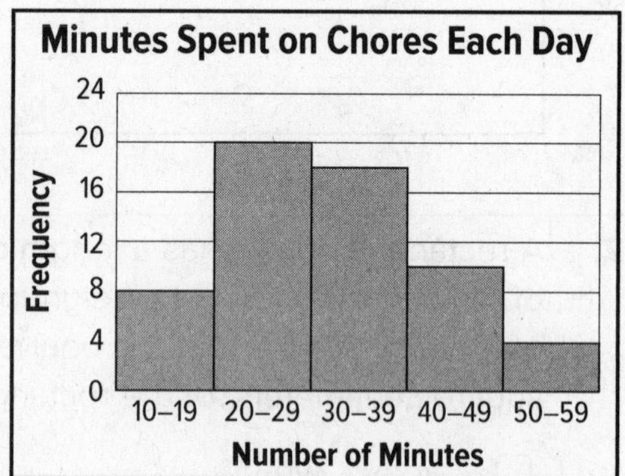

True	False	
☐	☐	The data represent the responses of 60 students.
☐	☐	The interval 30–39 represents the greatest number of students.
☐	☐	More students spend at most 39 minutes on chores than spend more than 39 minutes on them.
☐	☐	The greatest amount of time a student spends on chores could be 59 minutes.

5. The box-and-whisker plot shows the hours spent on a project by students in an art class. Find the median and the measures of variability. Then describe the data. 6.SP.4, 6.SP.5, 6.SP.5c

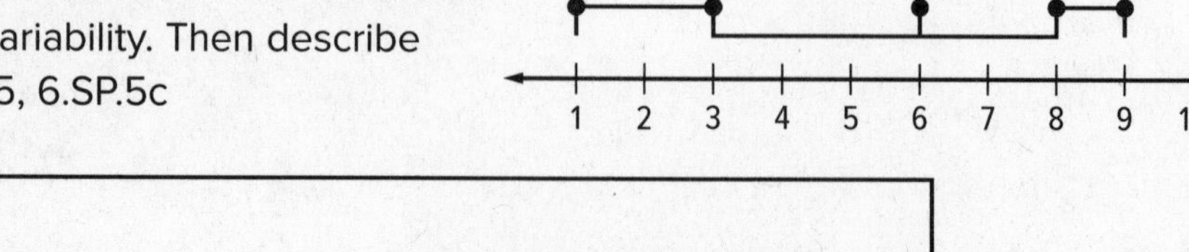

NAME ________________ DATE ________ PERIOD ______ SCORE ______

Countdown: 1 Week

1. Evan fills the prism shown with $148\frac{1}{2}$ cubic inches of sand. Shade the height of the sand in the prism. 6.G.2

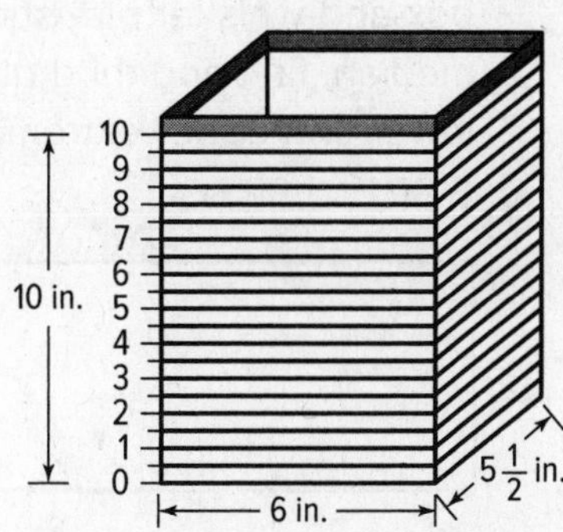

2. The table shows the scores Maliah earned on her first five history tests. 6.SP.5, 6.SP.5b, 6.SP.5c

History Test Scores				
80	75	90	75	95

Part A: Sort the score she earned on her sixth test into the appropriate bin based on the measure of center for 6 test scores.

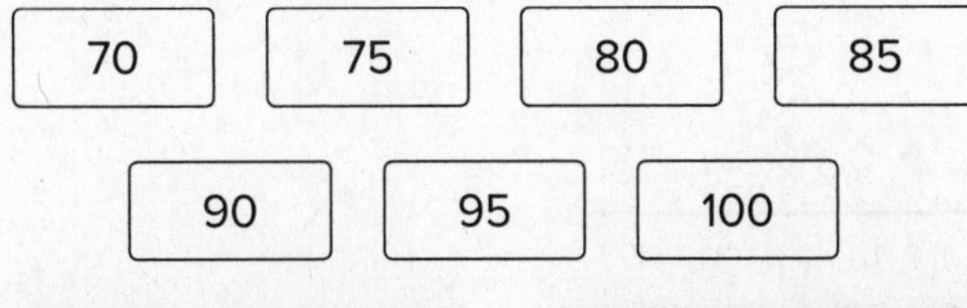

Mean is 85.	Median is 82.5.	Mode is 90.

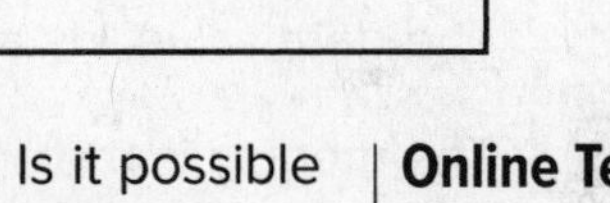

Part B: The range of scores on the sixth test is 0–100. Is it possible for Maliah to get a test score that will change her mean score to 90? Explain your reasoning.

Online Test Tip

On an online test, you might be asked to use a keypad with math symbols to enter the answer. In this book, you will be asked to write the answer in the space provided.

3. Write a set of data that contains ten values and can be represented by the box-and-whisker plot shown. State the median, first and third quartiles, and lower and upper extremes. 6.SP.4, 6.SP.5, 6.SP.5c

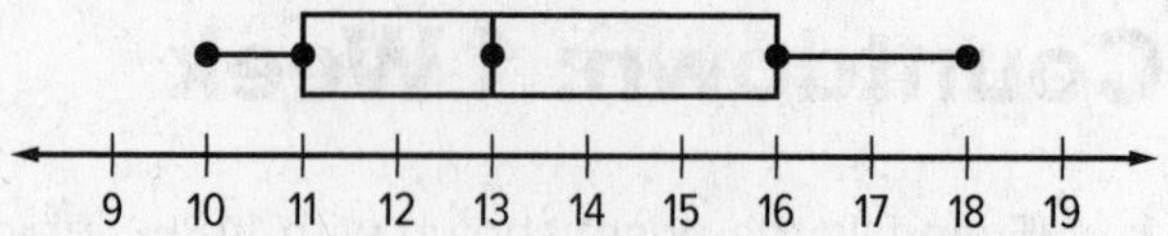

4. The line plot represents the number of concert tickets sold by band members. Susan gave several interpretations of the data. Select whether each of her statements is true or false in interpreting the data. 6.SP.2, 6.SP.5, 6.SP.5d

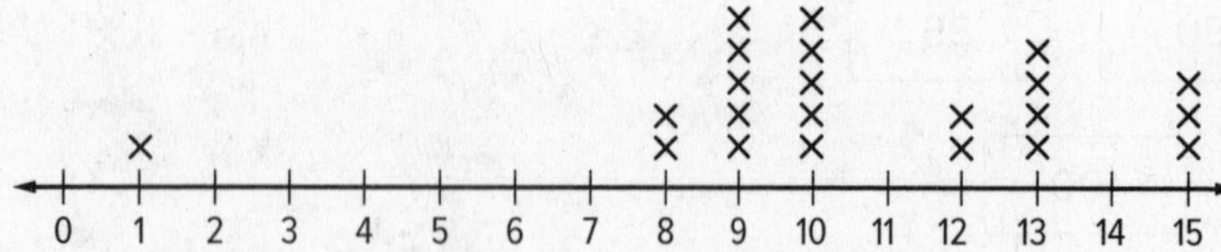

True	False	
☐	☐	The shape of the data is symmetric.
☐	☐	The data value 1 is an outlier.
☐	☐	The median is the appropriate measure to use to describe the center.
☐	☐	The spread of the data around the center is about 2.3 tickets, which is the mean absolute deviation.

5. The high temperatures over the past six days were 82°, 78°, 70°, 72°, 71°, and 67°. Find the measure of center that best describes the data. Explain why you think it is the best measure for this data. 6.SP.5, 6.SP.5c, 6.SP.5d

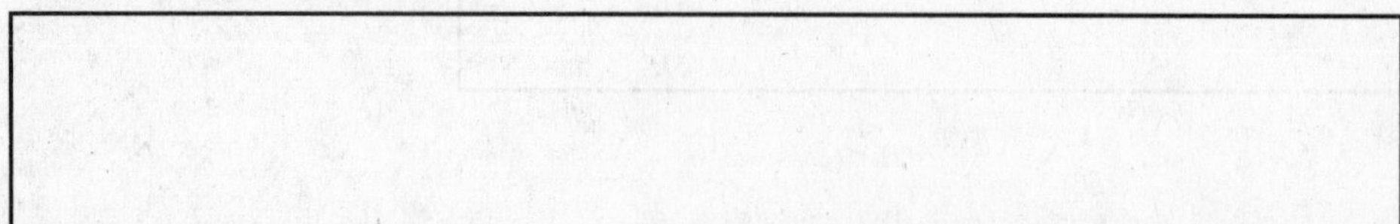

NAME ______________________ DATE ____________ PERIOD ________ SCORE ________

Chapter 1 Test

1. Miriam buys 24 petunia plants and 40 azalea plants. She wants to plant an equal number of flowers in each row of her garden. Each row will contain only one type of flowering plant. 6.NS.4

Part A: Determine the greatest number of plants that could be in each row of the garden.

[ ]

Part B: Miriam plants the greatest number of flowering plants possible in each row. How many rows of each type of flower will be in Miriam's garden?

[ ]

2. For a family picnic, Akeela wants to buy the same number of bratwurst and buns. The bratwurst come in packages of 6, and the buns are sold in packages of 8. 6.NS.4

Part A: What is the least number of bratwurst and buns that Akeela could buy?

[ ]

Part B: How many packages of each should Akeela buy to have the least number of total packages?

[ ]

3. Billy has both baseball and football card collections. He arranges his cards in equal rows. Using his current card collection, Billy is able to make rows of 9 cards, with each row containing only one type of card. Select all the ways that Billy can have each type of card in his collection. 6.NS.4

- ☐ 27 baseball cards and 45 football cards
- ☐ 18 baseball cards and 24 football cards
- ☐ 36 baseball cards and 72 football cards
- ☐ 15 baseball cards and 63 football cards
- ☐ 27 baseball cards and 81 football cards

4. Thulani goes to the library every 7 days. He goes to the market every 4 days. Today, August 1, Thulani goes to both the library and the market. How many more times will he go to both places on the same day for the remainder of the year? 6.NS.4

5. Alicia took a poll to determine her classmates' favorite pets. She wrote the results on the board: Dog, 8; Cat, 5; Bird, 2; and Fish, 3. Select whether each statement is true or false. 6.RP.1

True	False	
☐	☐	The ratio of birds to dogs is 4:1.
☐	☐	The ratio of fish to cats is 3 to 5.
☐	☐	The ratio of dogs to the other pets is 4:5.
☐	☐	The ratio of birds to the total number of pets is 9 to 1.

6. Jillian has 3 pencils and 4 pens. Select all of the ways to write the ratio of pens to pencils. 6.RP.1

- ☐ 4 + 3
- ☐ 4 to 3
- ☐ $\frac{4}{3}$
- ☐ 3:4
- ☐ 4:3
- ☐ 4 – 3

7. George surveyed his friends about recent driving trips their families took for vacation. Write the appropriate unit rate for each distance traveled. 6.RP.2

$\frac{1 \text{ hour}}{50 \text{ miles}}$	$\frac{144 \text{ miles}}{3 \text{ hours}}$	$\frac{45 \text{ miles}}{1 \text{ hour}}$
$\frac{48 \text{ miles}}{1 \text{ hour}}$	$\frac{1 \text{ hour}}{45 \text{ miles}}$	$\frac{100 \text{ miles}}{2 \text{ hours}}$
$\frac{90 \text{ miles}}{2 \text{ hours}}$	$\frac{50 \text{ miles}}{1 \text{ hour}}$	$\frac{1 \text{ hour}}{48 \text{ miles}}$

200 miles in 4 hours

270 miles in 6 hours

1,440 miles in 30 hours

8. The table shows the cost of the fruit that Nadine bought at the market. 6.RP.2

Fruit	Amount (lb)	Cost ($)
Lemons	2	0.84
Oranges	5	2.25
Bananas	3	1.17

Part A: Complete the table to order the unit prices of the fruit from least to greatest.

	Fruit	Unit Price ($ per lb)
Least		
Greatest		

Part B: How much more do 10 pounds of oranges cost than 10 pounds of bananas? Justify your response.

9. A recipe calls for 3 eggs for every batch. Write the appropriate numbers in the table to show the eggs needed for different batches. 6.RP.3, 6.RP.3a, 6.RP.3b

$\frac{2}{3}$	1	$\frac{4}{3}$	3
4	6	7	12
15	36	63	135

Batches	2	4		12	
Number of Eggs			21		45

10. Victoria reads at a constant rate of 10 pages in 16 minutes. 6.RP.3, 6.RP.3a

Part A: Use Victoria's reading rate to complete the table.

Number of Pages		25	35	
Time (min)	8			64

Part B: How many minutes will Victoria take to read 100 pages?

11. Antoine and Angela both like to walk for exercise. Today they are walking together. Antoine walks every 3 days, and Angela walks every 5 days. Circle all the days on which they will walk together again. 6.NS.4

8 days 12 days 15 days 25 days 45 days

12. Ciara takes 6 minutes to make 1 bracelet. 6.RP.3, 6.RP.3a, 6.RP.3b

Part A: Use Ciara's rate to complete the ratio table.

Number of Bracelets	1	2		5
Time (min)	6		18	

Part B: Write the values in the table as ordered pairs (bracelets, minutes).

Part C: Graph the ordered pairs on the coordinate plane.

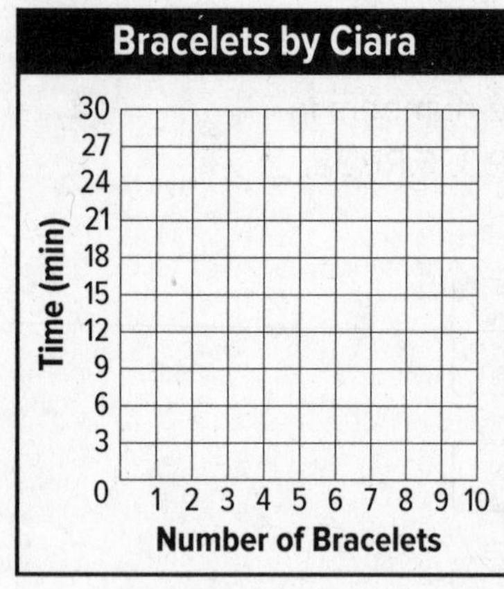

13. The graph shows the distance Melvyn can ride his bike for different periods of time. He rides his bike at a constant rate of speed. On Tuesday, Melvyn rode his bike for one hour. How many miles did he travel? Explain how you solved the problem. 6.RP.3, 6.RP.3b

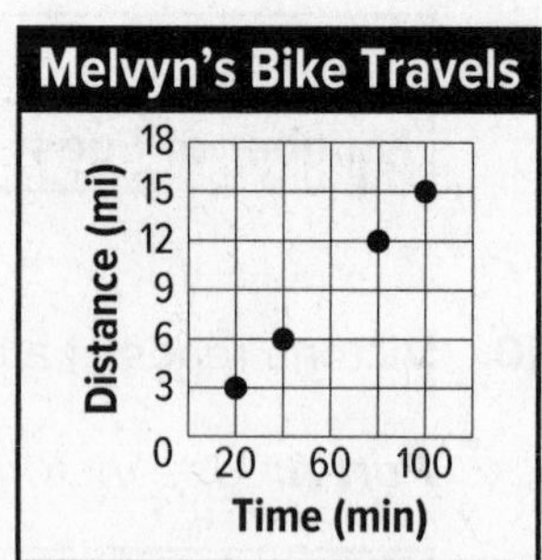

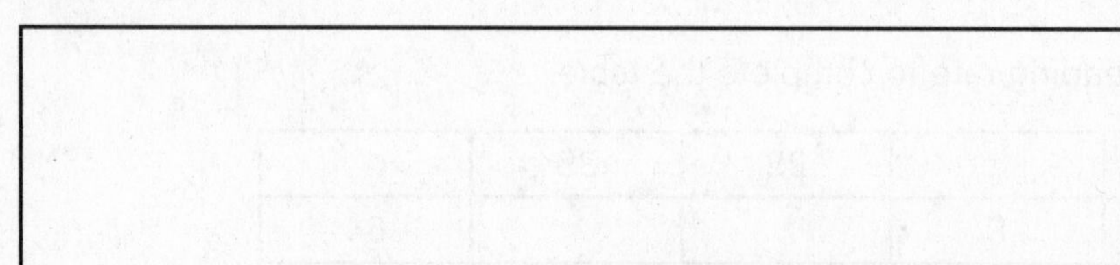

14. Rosario paid $2.50 for 3 pounds of apples. Select all of the rates that are equivalent to the rate Rosario paid. 6.RP.3, 6.RP.3b

- ☐ $0.80 for 1 pound
- ☐ $4.50 for 5 pounds
- ☐ $7.50 for 9 pounds
- ☐ $9.60 for 11 pounds
- ☐ $10.00 for 12 pounds

15. On a map, 2 inches represents 75 miles of actual distance. 6.RP.3

Part A: Two towns are 6 inches apart on the map. How many miles apart are the two towns?

Part B: Two cities are 600 miles apart. How many inches apart on the map are the two cities?

16. A 6-ounce drink costs $2.16, and a 10-ounce drink costs $3.25. Which drink is the better buy? Justify your answer. 6.RP.3

17. Jen wrote the ratio $\frac{2}{3}$. Select whether each action will result in an equivalent ratio. 6.RP.3, 6.RP.3a

Yes	No	
☐	☐	Multiply the numerator by 3 and the denominator by 2.
☐	☐	Multiply the numerator by 2 and the denominator by 3.
☐	☐	Add 6 to the numerator, and add 6 to the denominator.
☐	☐	Multiply the numerator by 7 and the denominator by 7.

18. Sally earns $37.00 for 4 hours of babysitting. At this rate, how much more would she earn for 9 hours of babysitting? 6.RP.3

19. The table shows the rate at which four people walk. 6.RP.3, 6.RP.3a, 6.RP.3b

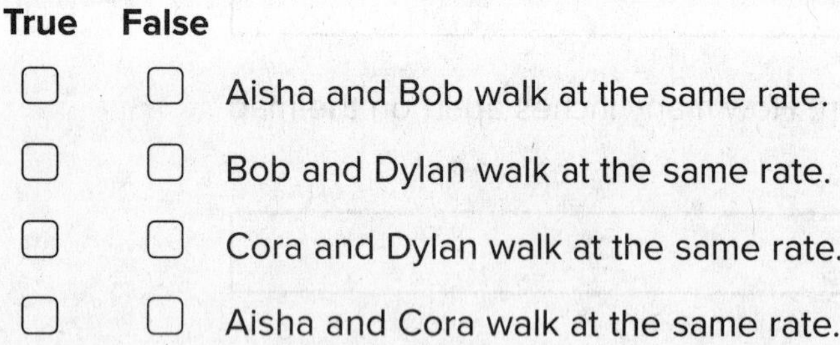

Person	Distance (mi)	Time (h)
Aisha	5.0	2.0
Bob	7.5	5.0
Cora	9.0	3.6
Dylan	3.75	2.5

Part A: Select whether each statement is true or false.

True	False	
☐	☐	Aisha and Bob walk at the same rate.
☐	☐	Bob and Dylan walk at the same rate.
☐	☐	Cora and Dylan walk at the same rate.
☐	☐	Aisha and Cora walk at the same rate.

Part B: Emilio walks 19.2 miles in 6.0 hours. Fala walks 10.5 miles in 3.0 hours. Compare the unit rates of the 6 people. Graph the walking rates in miles per hour on the number line. Label each point with the first initial of the person's name.

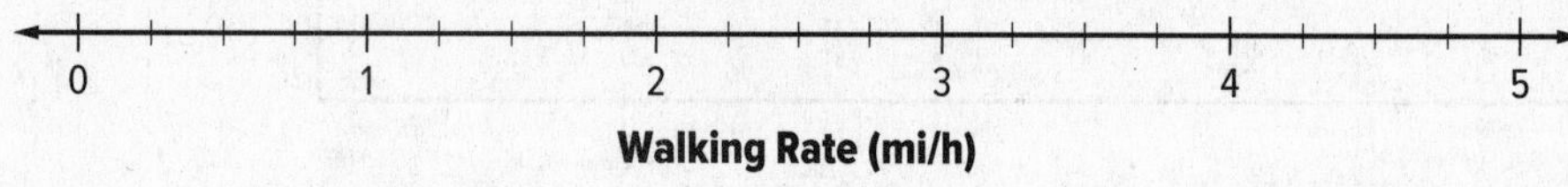

20. A manufacturer of rubber balls estimates that 3 out of every 500 balls produced are defective. The manufacturer produces 100,000 balls each week. Predict the number of rubber balls that are not defective each week. 6.RP.3

NAME ______________________ DATE __________ PERIOD ________ SCORE ________

Chapter 2 Test

1. After 20 minutes Juan had completed 14 questions, which is 0.7 of his assignment. What percent of the assignment had Juan *not* completed? 6.RP.3

2. Sort the decimals into the appropriate bins by how they compare to 100%. 6.RP.3

0.01	0.953	1.32	2.002
0.86	1	12.5	1.015

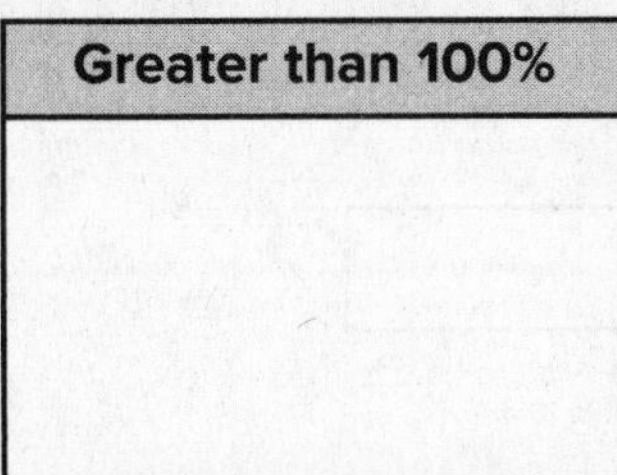

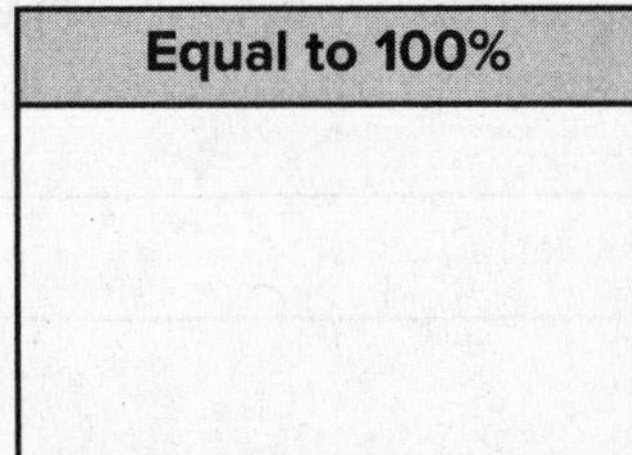

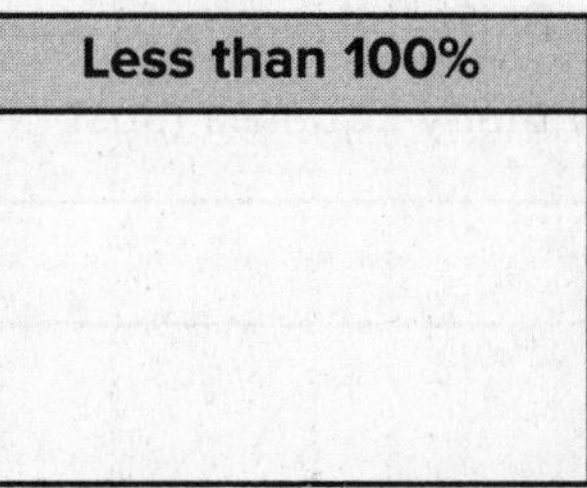

3. Stephanie surveyed the students in her class to find out their favorite color. Her results are in the table. What percent of Stephanie's classmates did *not* choose blue as their favorite color? 6.RP.3

Stephanie's Results

Color	Number
Red	6
Blue	9
Other	10

4. A principal states that 50% of the students in the school are girls. The fractions of girls in several classrooms at the school are listed. Select whether 50% could be used as an estimate to represent each fraction. 6.RP.3

Yes	No	
☐	☐	$\frac{4}{9}$
☐	☐	$\frac{1}{8}$
☐	☐	$\frac{7}{12}$
☐	☐	$\frac{5}{6}$
☐	☐	$\frac{9}{20}$

5. Ralph made the pattern shown on the grid. 6.RP.3

Part A: Select all of the expressions that represent the portion of the model that Ralph shaded.

- ☐ 64%
- ☐ 0.36
- ☐ 0.25
- ☐ $\frac{9}{25}$
- ☐ 36%
- ☐ $\frac{1}{2}$

Part B: Ralph wants to show $\frac{13}{20}$ on another grid of the same size. How many squares must he shade?

6. Sort the fractions into the appropriate bins by their decimal equivalents. 6.RP.3

$\frac{36}{48}$	$\frac{15}{24}$	$\frac{75}{120}$
$\frac{65}{130}$	$\frac{10}{16}$	$\frac{18}{24}$

Equal to 0.5	**Equal to 0.625**	**Equal to 0.75**

7. Regina scored 84% on a test. She answered 63 items correctly. How many items did Regina answer incorrectly? 6.RP.3, 6.RP.3c

8. The Wilson family had a celebration dinner at a local restaurant. The cost of the dinner was $80.00. 6.RP.3, 6.RP.3c

Part A: The Wilsons plan to leave an 18% tip for the server. How much money would the tip be?

Part B: The sales tax rate is 7.5%. How much money do the Wilsons have to pay for the sales tax on the dinner?

Part C: What is the total amount that the Wilsons pay?

9. A student conducted a survey of sixth-grade students to determine the number of movies they watch each month. Complete the table to order the responses from least to greatest percent of students. 6.RP.3

Movies Watched per Month				
Number of Movies	0–4	5–6	7–8	9+
Portion of Student Responses	27%	0.2	$\frac{1}{4}$	$\frac{7}{25}$

	Number of Movies Watched	**Percent of Students**
Least		
Greatest		

10. Parminder estimated that between 25% and 50% of students walk to school. Circle each fraction that could represent the percent of students who walk to school. 6.RP.3

$\frac{3}{10}$ $\frac{2}{5}$ $\frac{2}{3}$ $\frac{3}{8}$ $\frac{2}{9}$ $\frac{7}{20}$ $\frac{6}{11}$

11. Josie made a pattern using red and blue tiles. Three fourths of the tiles were blue. Select all of the ways Josie could write the fraction of blue tiles as a decimal. 6.RP.3

- ☐ Divide 4 by 3.
- ☐ Divide 3 by 4.
- ☐ Divide 1 by 4.
- ☐ Multiply the numerator by 10. Then use place value.
- ☐ Multiply the numerator and the denominator by 25. Then use place value.
- ☐ Multiply the denominator by 2.5. Then use place value.
- ☐ Multiply the numerator and denominator by $3\frac{1}{3}$. Then use place value.

12. To celebrate the 6th anniversary of a store opening, the manager has a sale of "$6.00 off every item in the store." What percent of the different prices would equal $6 off? Write a number so that each statement represents a $6.00 discount. 6.RP.3, 6.RP.3c

120	16	30	50	60	6	24	10	15

10% off of $☐

☐% off of $40

20% off of $☐

25% off of $☐

☐% off of $12

13. Carmen has $100 to spend. Sales tax in her city is 10%. Which 3 different items can Carmen buy to spend as much of her $100 as possible? Explain your answer. 6.RP.3, 6.RP.3c

Item	Price ($)
Jeans	25.00
Belt	23.50
Shoes	35.00
Skirt	30.00
Purse	31.00

14. A light bulb manufacturer estimates that $\frac{1}{4}$% of light bulbs produced will be defective. The manufacturer produces 200,000 light bulbs in one month. About how many bulbs can they expect to be defective? 6.RP.3, 6.RP.3c

15. Marie scored a 75% on her last test. Select all of the statements that could be true. 6.RP.3, 6.RP.3c

- ☐ Marie answered 1 item incorrectly out of 4 items.
- ☐ Marie answered 40 items correctly out of 50 items.
- ☐ Marie answered 15 items incorrectly out of 60 items.
- ☐ Marie answered 18 items incorrectly out of 24 items.
- ☐ Marie answered 42 items correctly out of 56 items.

16. An electronics store buys a television at a wholesale price of $120. The store then sells the television to its customers for $300. What percent of the wholesale price is the selling price? 6.RP.3, 6.RP.3c

17. At basketball practice, Derrick tossed a basketball from the free-throw line to the basket 80 times. Of his 80 attempts, he made 66 baskets. 6.RP.3, 6.RP.3c

Part A: What percent of throws did Derrick make?

Part B: At practice the next day, Derrick made 54 baskets out of 70 attempts. Describe how Derrick's overall percentage for the two days compares to his percentage for the previous day. Justify your answer.

18. Mr. Allen estimated that 50 people at a basketball game were cheering for the visiting team. Select all of the statements that could represent this estimate. 6.RP.3, 6.RP.3c

- ☐ 24% of 195 people
- ☐ 18% of 487 people
- ☐ 62% of 148 people
- ☐ 67% of 77 people
- ☐ 11% of 512 people

19. Fifteen hundredths of the students in the sixth grade wore a blue shirt yesterday. Sort the expressions into the bin that describes whether or not the expression represents the numeral. 6.RP.3

0.015	15%
0.15	1,500
$\frac{100}{15}$	$\frac{15}{100}$
1.5	0.15%

Represents fifteen hundredths	Does not represent fifteen hundredths

20. Alphonse did enough sit-ups to rank in the 99th percentile for boys his age. This means that less than 1% of all the boys did more sit-ups than Alphonse. Select whether each decimal could represent the fraction of boys who did more sit-ups than Alphonse. 6.RP.3

Yes	No	
☐	☐	0.01
☐	☐	0.002
☐	☐	0.95
☐	☐	0.04
☐	☐	0.103
☐	☐	0.0056

NAME _______________ DATE _______ PERIOD _____ SCORE _____

Chapter 3 Test

1. Roberta buys a sweater and a scarf. The sweater costs $24.79 and the scarf costs $8.89. 6.NS.3

Part A: What is the total cost of the two items?

[ ]

Part B: Roberta has a $50 gift card. How much is left on the card after she pays for the two items?

[ ]

2. Greg found $0.72 on the floorboard of his car. Select all of the expressions that are equivalent to 0.72. 6.NS.3

- ☐ 0.2 – 0.92
- ☐ 0.82 – 0.01
- ☐ 0.9 – 0.18
- ☐ 0.3 + 0.42
- ☐ 0.7 + 0.2
- ☐ 0.05 + 0.67

3. LaToya's mother uses 5.84 pounds of apples to make applesauce. She got them from a bag of apples that weighs 16.3 pounds. How many pounds of apples are left in the bag? 6.NS.3

[ ]

4. A runner estimated that he ran about 12 miles. Select all of the rates and times that the runner could have run. 6.NS.3

- ☐ 3.3 miles per hour for 3.8 hours
- ☐ 6.1 miles per hour for 1.9 hours
- ☐ 5.8 miles per hour for 2.3 hours
- ☐ 6.75 miles per hour for 3.4 hours

5. A bus travels about 400 miles between cities. Select whether the rates and times could represent the estimated distance the bus traveled. 6.NS.3

Yes	No	
☐	☐	53.2 miles per hour for 7.74 hours
☐	☐	39.8 miles per hour for 10.15 hours
☐	☐	47.6 miles per hour for 9.8 hours
☐	☐	76.3 miles per hour for 5.24 hours

6. The table shows the cost of several items, including tax. Suzanne needs to buy school supplies. She has $5.25 to spend. Select all of the items that Suzanne can buy. 6.NS.3

Item	Cost ($)
Pencil	0.75
Notebook	1.50
Marker	1.05
Pen	1.55

- ☐ 3 notebooks
- ☐ 4 pens
- ☐ 4 markers
- ☐ 6 pencils
- ☐ 3 markers and 2 pens
- ☐ 2 notebooks and 3 pencils

7. Katrina runs 4.23 miles each day. How many miles does she run in 2 weeks? 6.NS.3

8. Kami bought some material to make a blanket in the shape of a rectangle. The material costs $12.00 per square yard. How much did Kami pay for the material? 6.NS.3

1.35 yd

2 yd

9. Write the appropriate number of decimal places in each sum, difference, product, or quotient. Do not count a zero in the final decimal place. 6.NS.3

0	1	2
3	4	5

12.59 – 6.09 ☐ decimal places

0.75 × 0.9 ☐ decimal places

15.25 ÷ 0.25 ☐ decimal places

18 + 3.4 + 22.15 ☐ decimal places

1.945 × 3.8 ☐ decimal places

10. Manuel was examining the product of 48 × 0.73. He realized that he could create other multiplication problems that have the same product. Select whether each expression has the same product as 48 × 0.73. 6.NS.3

Yes	No	
☐	☐	43 × 0.78
☐	☐	4.8 × 7.3
☐	☐	0.48 × 73
☐	☐	7.8 × 4.3
☐	☐	480 × 0.073

11. Zach walks at a rate of 2.83 miles per hour. Nora walks at a rate of 2.18 miles per hour. How many miles farther will Zach have walked after they each walk for 1.5 hours? 6.NS.3

☐

12. A football stadium holds 55,296 people. The seating is divided into 36 sections. 6.NS.2

Part A: There is an equal number of seats in each section. How many seats are in each section?

☐

Part B: The seats in each section are in 32 rows. There is an equal number of seats in each row. How many seats are in each row?

☐

13. A principal paid $5.74 for one school shirt that displays the school mascot. 6.NS.3

Part A: Select all of the numbers of shirts that he could have purchased at that price.

- ☐ 12 shirts for $68.88
- ☐ 84 shirts for $493.64
- ☐ 125 shirts for $717.50
- ☐ 392 shirts for $2,284.52

Part B: During the first month on sale, the school store sold 186 shirts for $6.50 each. How much profit did the school make on these shirts?

14. Sort each number of miles and number of hours traveled into the appropriate bin to identify the rate in miles per hour. 6.NS.2

718 miles in 5.95 hours	45.8 miles in 4 hours	2,865 miles in 24.8 hours

419.72 miles in 80.6 hours	935.47 miles in 22.75 hours

Less Than 10 Miles per Hour	Between 10 and 99 Miles per Hour	Greater Than 100 Miles per Hour

15. Althea wants to save $286.15 in a year to buy a new bicycle. She estimates that she needs to save $4.50 each week to reach her goal. Is Althea's estimate reasonable? Justify your answer. 6.NS.2

16. A garden is 22.5 feet wide and 58.1 feet long. 6.NS.3

Part A: About how many square feet is the garden? Write the appropriate numbers to estimate the area.

1	2	3	4	5
6	7	8	9	0

☐☐
× ☐☐
☐☐☐☐

Part B: A 3.8-pound bag of fertilizer covers 1,000 square feet. Each bag costs $9.95. How many bags are needed to cover the garden? About how much will it cost to buy the bags of fertilizer?

Bags: ☐

Cost estimate: ☐

Part C: Were your estimates in Parts A and B reasonable? Explain. Use the actual square footage and cost of the bags in your explanation.

Area: ☐

Cost: ☐

17. A manufacturer makes paper clips that are shipped in boxes of 100. One day 4,725 paper clips were made and were packaged in 47 boxes with 25 clips left over. Select all of the division problems that have the same quotient of 47 R 25. 6.NS.2

- ☐ 1,811 ÷ 38
- ☐ 4,069 ÷ 86
- ☐ 5,052 ÷ 107
- ☐ 18,308 ÷ 389

18. The table shows the workout results of four joggers. 6.NS.3

Jogger	Distance (mi)	Time (h)
Wesley	7.7	3.50
Xavier	3.5	1.25
Yvette	4.224	1.76
Zubin	5.175	2.25

Complete the table to order the joggers from the slowest to fastest rate.

	Jogger	Rate (mph)
Slowest		
Fastest		

19. Joshua was experimenting with the division problem 0.72 ÷ 0.8 and noticed that he could create other division problems with the same quotient. Select all of the division problems that have the same quotient. 6.NS.3

- ☐ 72 ÷ 8
- ☐ 7.2 ÷ 8
- ☐ 0.072 ÷ 0.008
- ☐ 72 ÷ 80

20. The two rectangles have the same area. What is the perimeter of rectangle A? 6.NS.3

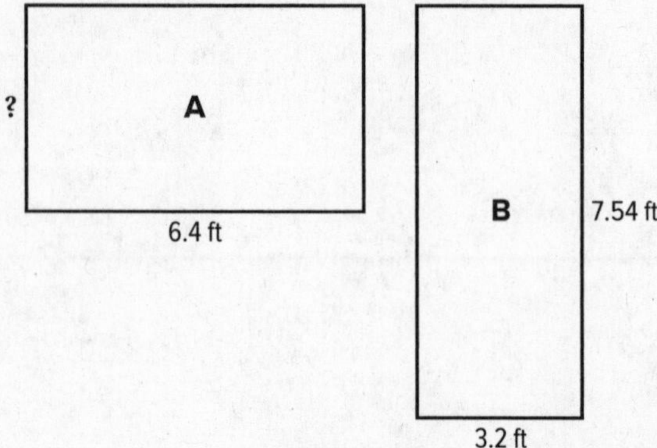

NAME ________________ DATE ________ PERIOD ______ SCORE ______

Chapter 4 Test

1. Henry is designing a rectangular flower garden and says the area is about 36 square feet. Select whether each set of dimensions could be the approximate dimensions of Henry's garden. 6.NS.1

Yes	No	
☐	☐	$3\frac{3}{4}$ feet wide by $8\frac{7}{8}$ feet long
☐	☐	$5\frac{5}{6}$ feet wide by $6\frac{1}{5}$ feet long
☐	☐	$2\frac{7}{8}$ feet wide by $7\frac{4}{5}$ feet long
☐	☐	$10\frac{2}{5}$ feet wide by $3\frac{4}{7}$ feet long

2. A farmer harvested 35 acres of corn and 20 acres of beans. Animals ate $\frac{1}{8}$ of the corn he originally planted. How many acres of corn did the farmer plant? 6.NS.1

3. Sort the fractions into the appropriate bins by their estimates. 6.NS.1

$\frac{5}{9}$ $\frac{1}{8}$ $\frac{2}{5}$ $\frac{3}{19}$ $\frac{3}{7}$

$\frac{7}{8}$ $\frac{6}{14}$ $\frac{9}{11}$ $\frac{2}{13}$ $\frac{10}{12}$

Estimate of 0	Estimate of $\frac{1}{2}$	Estimate of 1

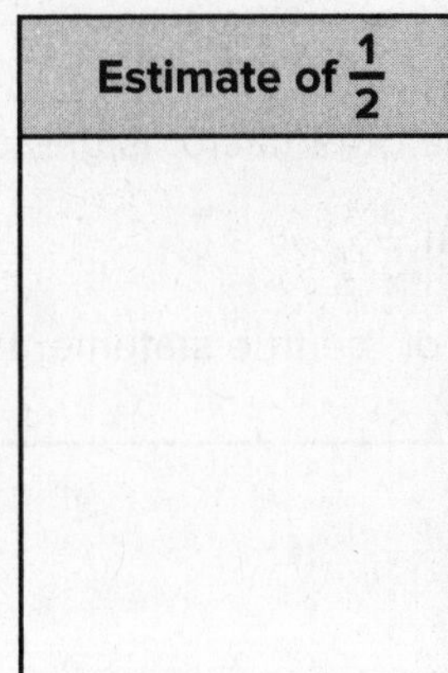

4. Of all the sixth grade students in the school, 40 students wear glasses. Select whether each expression could represent the number of sixth grade students who wear glasses. 6.NS.1

Yes	No	
☐	☐	$\frac{1}{3}$ of 60 students
☐	☐	$\frac{2}{5}$ of 100 students
☐	☐	$\frac{3}{5}$ of 50 students
☐	☐	$\frac{8}{9}$ of 45 students

5. Write a word problem in which you divide two fractions, two mixed numbers, or a mixed number and a fraction. Solve your word problem and show how you found the answer. 6.NS.1

Problem:

Solution:

6. The answer to a multiplication problem is $\frac{3}{5}$. 6.NS.1

Part A: Select whether each statement is true or false.

True	False	
☐	☐	Both factors are less than $\frac{3}{5}$.
☐	☐	One factor is less than $\frac{3}{5}$; the other factor is greater than $\frac{3}{5}$.
☐	☐	Both factors are greater than $\frac{3}{5}$.

Part B: Write an example to support one of the true statements.

7. On a grid, $\frac{2}{3}$ of the squares are shaded with a color. One fourth of all the squares on the grid are shaded blue. What fraction of the shaded squares are blue squares? 6.NS.1

8. Write the appropriate number for each product or quotient. 6.NS.1

$\frac{1}{6}$	$\frac{6}{25}$
$\frac{8}{75}$	$4\frac{1}{6}$
6	$9\frac{3}{8}$

$1\frac{1}{4} \div 7\frac{1}{2} =$ ☐

$\frac{2}{3} \div 6\frac{1}{4} =$ ☐

$\frac{4}{5} \div \frac{2}{15} =$ ☐

$1\frac{1}{4} \times 7\frac{1}{2} =$ ☐

$6\frac{1}{4} \times \frac{2}{3} =$ ☐

$1\frac{1}{2} \div 6\frac{1}{4} =$ ☐

$1\frac{1}{2} \div \frac{4}{25} =$ ☐

$\frac{4}{5} \times \frac{2}{15} =$ ☐

9. A survey asked 200 students to name their favorite fruit. The table shows the results of the survey. 6.NS.1

Fruit	Fraction of Students
Banana	$\frac{1}{8}$
Peach	$\frac{2}{5}$
Plum	$\frac{1}{10}$
Orange	$\frac{3}{8}$

Part A: How many students named a peach as their favorite fruit?

Part B: How many more students chose an orange rather than a plum? Justify your answer.

10. At an apple orchard, Margaret picked $19\frac{1}{2}$ pounds of apples. The cashier put the apples into 3 bags with the same weight. How many pounds of apples are in each bag? 6.NS.1

11. A bookcase has four identical, rectangular shelves. One shelf is shown. 6.NS.1

$2\frac{1}{2}$ in.

$8\frac{3}{4}$ in.

Part A: What is the total area of the four shelves?

Part B: How many books with spines that are $1\frac{1}{4}$ inches wide can fit on each shelf?

12. Two mixed numbers are divided. The quotient is $5\frac{1}{2}$. Select whether each statement is true or false. 6.NS.1

True	False	
☐	☐	Both the dividend and the divisor are less than $5\frac{1}{2}$.
☐	☐	The divisor is less than $5\frac{1}{2}$; the dividend is greater than $5\frac{1}{2}$.
☐	☐	Both the dividend and the divisor are greater than $5\frac{1}{2}$.
☐	☐	The dividend is less than $5\frac{1}{2}$; the divisor is greater than $5\frac{1}{2}$.

13. The length of a basketball court is 94 feet. 6.RP.3, 6.RP.3d

Part A: Sort the lengths into the appropriate bins by how each length compares to the length of a basketball court.

$\frac{1}{40}$ mi	30 yd	$\frac{1}{20}$ mi	1,128 in.	$102\frac{3}{5}$ ft

Less than 94 ft	Equal to 94 ft	Greater than 94 ft

Part B: What is the length of the basketball court in yards? Justify your answer.

14. A group orders 3 large veggie pizzas. Each slice represents $\frac{1}{8}$ of the entire pizza. The group eats $\frac{3}{4}$ of the pizza. How many slices of pizza are left? Justify your answer. 6.NS.1

15. Mrs. Benitez slices some oranges so that each wedge is $\frac{1}{4}$ of the orange. Then she cuts the same number of apples into pieces so that each piece is $\frac{1}{6}$ of the apple. Let n represent the number of each type of fruit. Select whether each statement is true or false. 6.NS.1

True	False	
☐	☐	There are $2n$ more pieces of apple than wedges of orange.
☐	☐	There are $n + 2$ more pieces of apple than wedges of orange.
☐	☐	There are $2n$ more wedges of orange than pieces of apple.
☐	☐	There are $n + 2$ more wedges of orange than pieces of apple.
☐	☐	The number of orange wedges can be represented by $n \div 4$.
☐	☐	The number of apple pieces can be represented by $n \div \frac{1}{6}$.

16. A tile pattern uses $\frac{1}{4}$ white tile, and the rest are colored tiles. Five colors are used equally. What fraction of the tile pattern is each color? 6.NS.1

17. A carpenter wants to cut a board $16\frac{1}{2}$ feet in length into $1\frac{7}{8}$ feet pieces. 6.NS.1

Part A: How many pieces can be cut from the board?

Part B: The carpenter cuts the leftover piece into four equal-length pieces. How long is each piece?

18. An adult elephant weighs 5,000 pounds. 6.RP.3, 6.RP.3d

Part A: Write the correct measurements in the boxes to show how to convert that weight to tons.

1 T	1 lb	1 oz	1 fl oz	16 oz	5,000 lb	8 fl oz
$2\frac{1}{2}$ T	$312\frac{1}{2}$ T	$\frac{2}{5}$ T	625 T	$\frac{2}{625}$ T	2,000 lb	1

Part B: A baby elephant weighs 260 pounds. How many ounces do the adult and baby elephants weigh together?

19. A brick of cheese is $\frac{3}{4}$ inch thick. A deli cuts the brick of cheese into slices that are $\frac{1}{10}$ inch thick. 6.NS.1

Part A: How many $\frac{1}{10}$-inch slices can be cut from the brick of cheese?

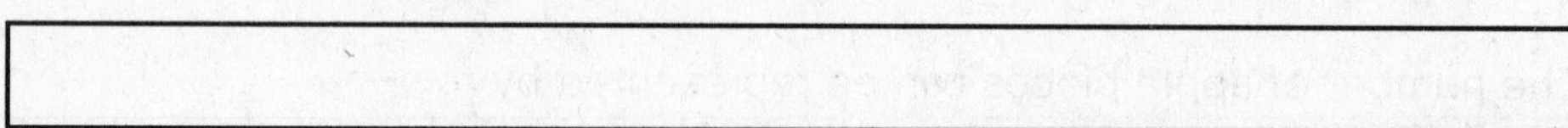

Part B: What is the thickness of the leftover piece of cheese?

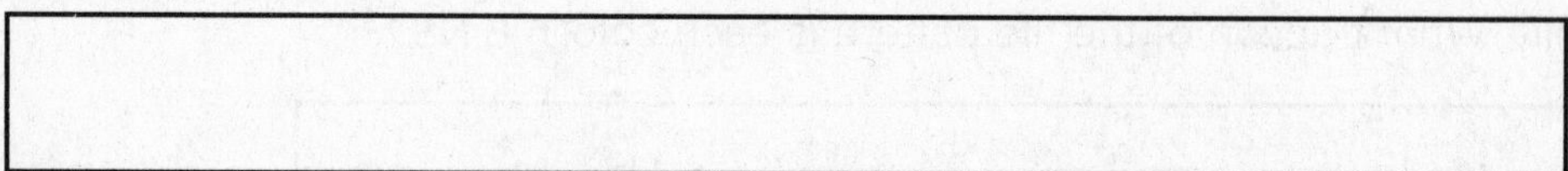

20. A bag of dog food weighs $31\frac{1}{4}$ pounds. After one week, $3\frac{1}{8}$ pounds of dog food was used. What fraction of the bag of dog food remains? 6.NS.1

NAME ______________________ DATE __________ PERIOD ______ SCORE ______

Chapter 5 Test

1. The eight values in the boxes show how much the price of one share of a stock has changed. Sort the amounts into the appropriate bins based on whether the stock is gaining value, losing value, or neither. 6.NS.5

\$3	\$25	–\$6	\$47
–\$20	–\$35	\$0	–\$1

Gaining Value	Losing Value	Neither

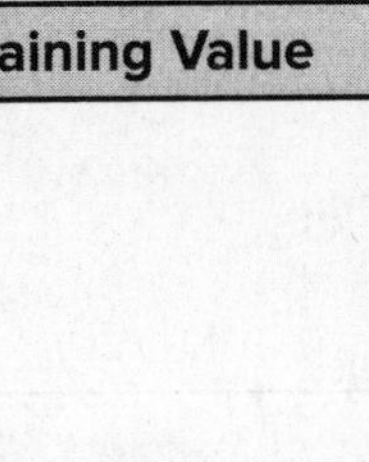

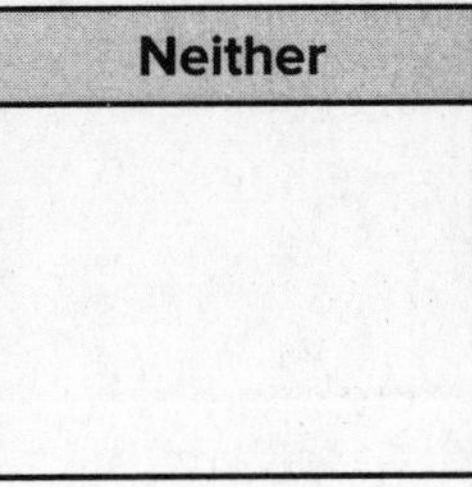

2. Write the point on the number line that represents the integer described by each statement. 6.NS.6, 6.NS.6a

A	B
C	D

A B C D

–5 –4 –3 –2 –1 0 1 2 3 4 5

Point ☐: the opposite of –3

Point ☐: the opposite of –2

Point ☐: the opposite of 3

Point ☐: the opposite of 2

3. Two points are graphed on a coordinate plane. Graph and label the four ordered pairs on the coordinate plane. 6.NS.6, 6.NS.6b

(–c, d)	(–e, –f)	(c, –d)	(–e, f)

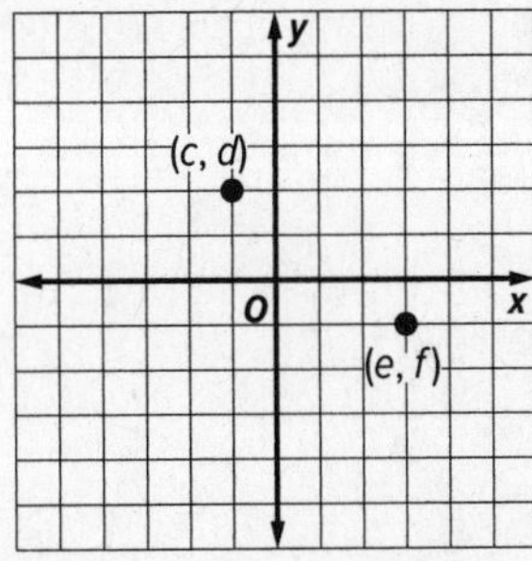

4. A paleontologist uncovered a bone in a hole that is 4.5 feet deep. A bird was in a tree at a height of 10.5 feet. A catfish lay at the bottom of a lake at a depth of 12.5 feet. 6.NS.6, 6.NS.6c

Part A: Graph the values given in the problem on the number line.

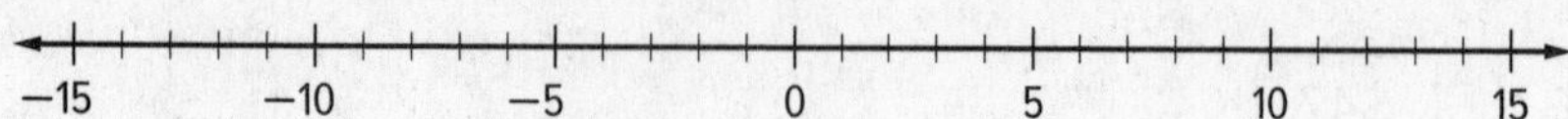

Part B: Nate claims that the catfish is closer to the surface of the water than either the bird or the bone is to ground level. Do you agree with his claim? Explain your reasoning.

5. The freezing point of water is 0°C. The table shows the temperature of a water sample that each student recorded during a science lab. 6.NS.7, 6.NS.7b

Student	Sample Temperature (°C)
Karen	−23.4
Claudia	37
Jamal	99.9
Mateo	−3.89

Part A: Write the temperatures in order from coldest to hottest.

Coldest **Hottest**

Part B: Mateo realizes he made an error in recording the temperature of his water sample. He should have recorded the temperature as −38.9°C. How does this new information change your answer to Part A?

6. Select whether each inequality about the coordinates of the points on the number line is true or false. 6.NS.6, 6.NS.6a, 6.NS.7, 6.NS.7a

A B C

−6 −5 −4 −3 −2 −1 0 1 2 3 4

True	False	
☐	☐	$A > B$
☐	☐	$C > B$
☐	☐	$C < A$
☐	☐	$A < 0$

7. Identify the phrase that *cannot* be described by the same absolute value expression as the other three. Explain your reasoning. 6.NS.7, 6.NS.7c

winning 6 marbles	owing \$3	6° below normal	account balance of –\$6

8. Lucia has a checking account. Her bank will not honor any check she writes that will make her account balance less than –\$20. Lucia wrote her landlord a check. When the check is cashed, her checking account will have a balance of –\$10. Explain whether or not the bank will honor the check Lucia wrote to her landlord. 6.NS.7, 6.NS.7d

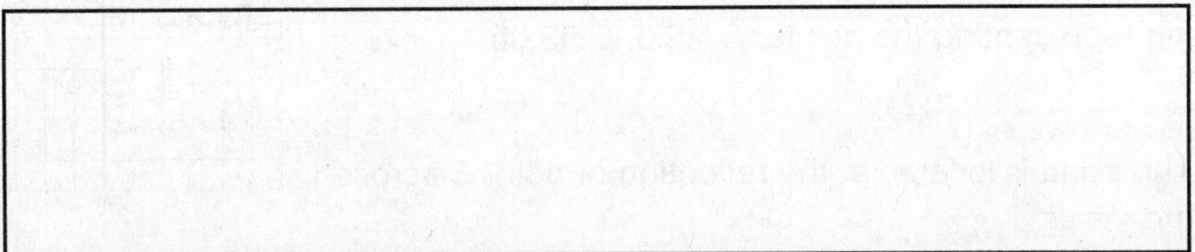

9. The coordinate plane represents a city, with (0, 0) as the city's center. Each unit on the city's coordinate plane represents 1 mile. The table shows the location of four city-owned buildings. 6.NS.8

Building	Location
A	(1, 0)
B	(–2, 3)
C	(–2, –4)
D	(3, –4)

Part A: On the coordinate plane, graph and label the ordered pairs that show the locations of Buildings *A*, *B*, *C*, and *D*.

Part B: Find the distance between buildings *C* and *D*: ☐ miles

10. Let *s* be an integer. Alonso claims that –*s* must always be less than 0. Iliana claims that –*s* is only sometimes less than 0. Whose statement is correct? Explain. Support your reasoning with an example. 6.NS.6, 6.NS.6a

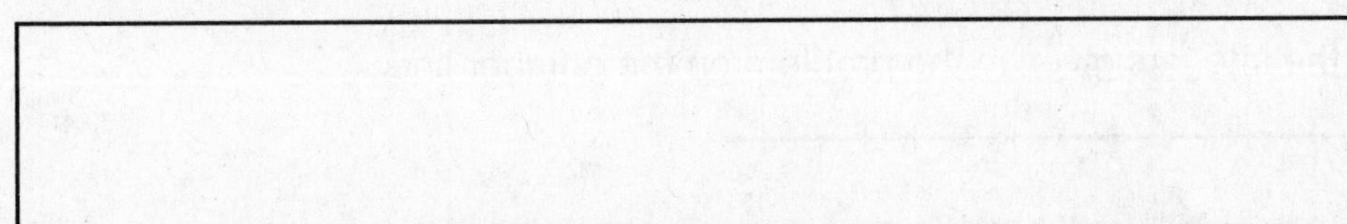

11. Omar divided a circular pizza into 8 equal sections. He gave his friend 3 sections. Explain why the amount he gave to his friend can be represented by a point plotted to the right of 0 on a number line. Then write the amount he gave to his friend as a decimal. 6.NS.6

12. Michael models the landscaping features in a yard on a coordinate plane. A patio is represented by figure *ABCD*. The pond is located at (4, –1). A bench is located at (–4, 3). A clock is located at (–1, –1). A water feature is located at (1, –3). Select whether each statement is true or false in representing the points. 6.NS.6, 6.NS.6b

True	False	
☐	☐	The pond is located at the reflection of point *C* across the *x*-axis.
☐	☐	A bench is located at the reflection of point *B* across the *y*-axis.
☐	☐	A clock is located at the reflection of point *D* across the *x*-axis.
☐	☐	A water feature is located at the reflection of point *A* across the *y*-axis.

13. Mrs. Ortiz measured the outside temperature at noon as –2°F. Later that day, she measured the temperature as –5°F. Write an inequality that correctly compares –2 and –5. Then explain the meaning of the inequality for the situation. 6.NS.7, 6.NS.7b

14. Katie owes Mathias $10 and Cabrini $5. Katie has $3 in her pocket. 6.NS.5

Part A: Explain the meaning of 0 in this situation.

Part B: Graph the integers given in the problem on the number line.

15. Afia's school is plotted at (–8, –3) on a coordinate plane. Her babysitter's house is located at (8, –3). What is the distance between Afia's school and her babysitter's house? Explain how you solved the problem. 6.NS.8

16. The table indicates Imamu's data usage over the last four months. Positive values indicate the amount of data that went over his data package plan, and negative values indicate the amount of data that was under the plan. Identify the month that Imamu used the least amount of data. Justify your response. 6.NS.7, 6.NS.7d

Month	Data (GB)
January	0.75
February	–2.25
March	1
April	–1.5

17. The average amount of time customers waited to get their food at a restaurant was 25 minutes. The table shows the difference between the average times and the actual times customers at four tables waited to get their food. Select whether each statement is true or false about the time spent waiting. 6.NS.7, 6.NS.7b

Table	Average Time – Actual Time Waiting (min)
A	$2\frac{1}{2}$
B	$-3\frac{1}{2}$
C	4.5
D	–5.75

True	False	
☐	☐	The time spent waiting at Table A is greater than the time spent waiting at Table B.
☐	☐	The time spent waiting at Table C is farther from 0 on a number line than the time spent waiting at Table D.
☐	☐	The time spent waiting at Table A is greater than the time spent waiting at Table C.
☐	☐	The customers at Table D spent the least time waiting.

18. The temperature in a freezer is set at –18°C. The temperature in a refrigerator is 21° warmer. Should the temperature of the refrigerator be represented by a positive integer or negative integer? Explain your reasoning. 6.NS.6, 6.NS.6a

19. Robert's house is represented by (0, 0) on the coordinate plane. A landscape planner suggested Robert plant trees at $\left(-3\frac{1}{2}, 4\right)$, $\left(2\frac{1}{2}, -2\frac{1}{2}\right)$, $\left(-4\frac{1}{2}, -4\right)$, and (3, 2). Did Robert correctly plot the location of the four trees? Justify your answer. 6.NS.6, 6.NS.6c

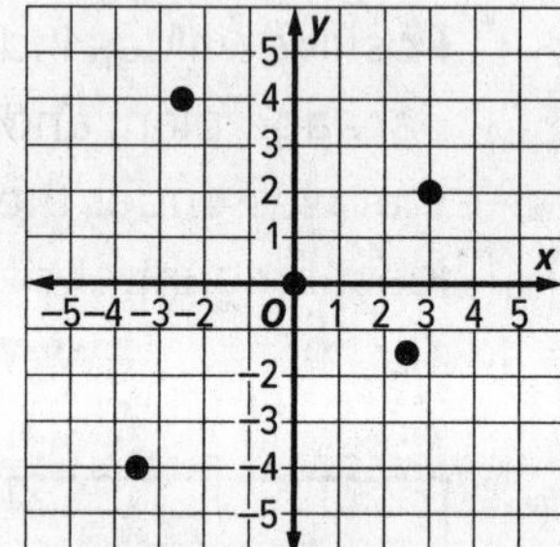

20. Consider this set of expressions. 6.NS.7, 6.NS.7c

|3| –|4| |–2| + |–3| |–5| – |4|

Part A: Simplify each expression.

A: |3| = ☐

B: –|4| = ☐

C: |–2| + |–3| = ☐

D: |–5| – |4| = ☐

Part B: Graph each value on the number line. Label the points.

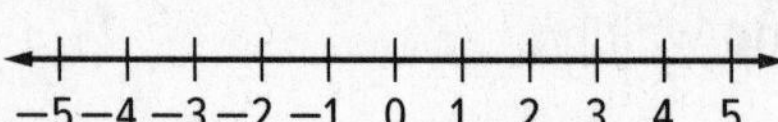

NAME _______________ DATE _______ PERIOD _______ SCORE _______

Chapter 6 Test

1. A teacher wrote the expression 4^5 on the board. Select all of the expressions that are equivalent to 4^5. 6.EE.1

- ☐ 4×5
- ☐ $4 + 4 + 4 + 4 + 4$
- ☐ $4 \times 4 \times 4 \times 4 \times 4$
- ☐ $5 \times 5 \times 5 \times 5$

2. A farmer has a square-shaped pen for his chickens. 6.EE.1

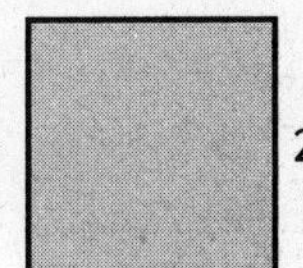

Part A: Write a power that represents the enclosed area. What is the area of the chicken pen?

Power: ☐

Square yards: ☐

Part B: The farmer needs to know the size of the chicken pen in square feet. Write a power that represents the enclosed area using feet, not yards. What is the area of the pen?

Power: ☐

Square feet: ☐

3. Using the numbers, write two powers that have the same value. 6.EE.1

2 | 3 | 4 | 9

Using each number only once: $\square^{\square} = \square^{\square}$

Using the numbers more than once: $\square^{\square} = \square^{\square}$

4. Select whether each expression simplifies to a value of 4. 6.EE.1

Yes	No	
☐	☐	$3 + 8 \div 2 \times 4$
☐	☐	$2 \times 5 - 4 + 1$
☐	☐	$12 \div (8 - 6 + 1)$
☐	☐	$9 \div 3 \times 3 + 3$

5. Hanako is curious to know how easy it is to write a power that has a value greater than 100. 6.EE.1

Part A: Sort the powers into their appropriate bins by how each compares to 100.

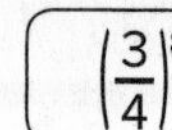

10^2 | 5^3 | 2^5 | $\left(\frac{3}{4}\right)^8$ | $(7.5)^4$ | $(9.93)^2$

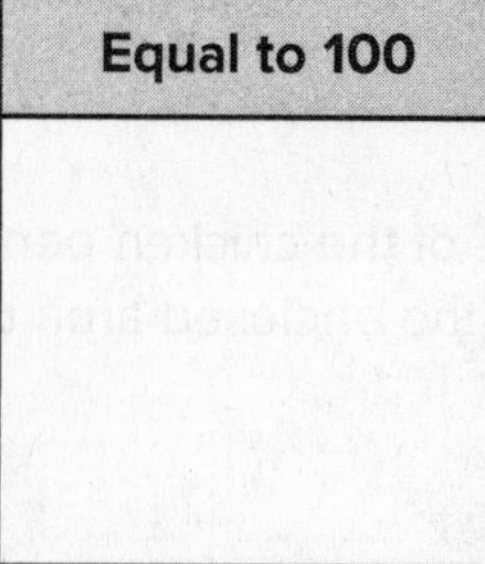
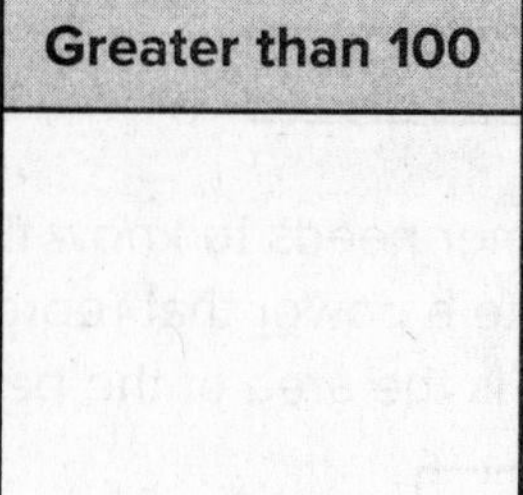

Less than 100	Equal to 100	Greater than 100

Part B: Between what two consecutive powers of 3 does 100 lie?

6. The expression $4(n + 8)$ represents the cost of 4 friends going to a ball game. Each person pays $\$n$ admission plus $8 for a team towel to wave. Select all the phrases that describe the expression $(n + 8)$. 6.EE.2, 6.EE.2b

- ☐ a product of two factors
- ☐ a constant
- ☐ a coefficient
- ☐ a factor
- ☐ like terms
- ☐ a sum of two terms
- ☐ a quotient

7. The width of a rectangle is x. The length is 5 times the width. 6.EE.2

Part A: Select all of the expressions that represent the length of the rectangle.

- ☐ $5x$
- ☐ $x + 5$
- ☐ $5 \cdot x$
- ☐ $5(x)$
- ☐ $\frac{5}{x}$

Part B: The width of the rectangle is 4 units. How many units is the perimeter?

8. The side lengths of a triangle are shown. Let x be 4 units. How many units is the perimeter of the triangle? Justify your answer. 6.EE.2, 6.EE.2c

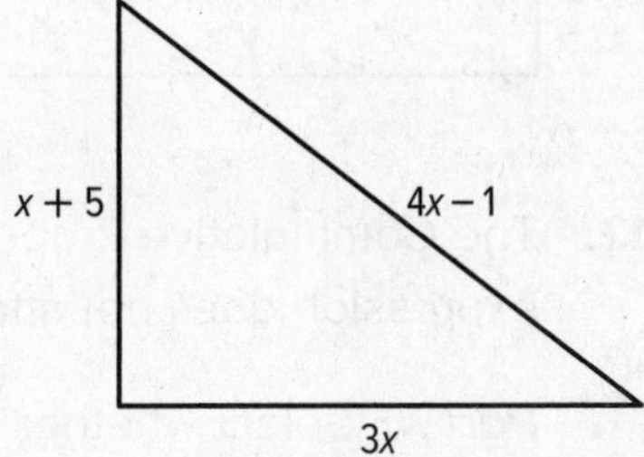

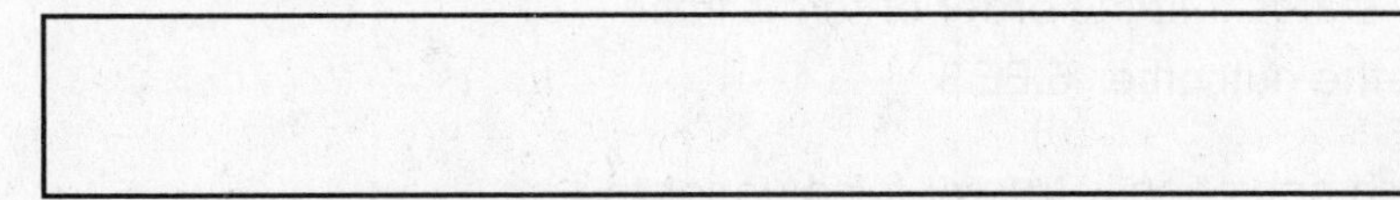

9. Juan has 3 more marbles than Ed. Let n represent the number of Ed's marbles. 6.EE.2, 6.EE.2c

Part A: Circle all of the expressions that represent the number of Juan's marbles.

$3n$	$3 - n$	$3 \div n$	$n + 3$
$3 + n$	$n \div 3$	$n - 3$	$3 \cdot n$

Part B: Ed has 11 marbles. How many marbles does Juan have?

10. A fitness club charges its members a one-time fee of $40 and a monthly rate of $25. Let *m* represent the number of months. Write an expression for the total amount paid after *m* months. Then find how much a customer will have paid after 5 months. 6.EE.2, 6.EE.2a, 6.EE.6

Expression: [ ]

Cost: [ ]

11. In the last basketball game, Kevin scored 2 less than a third of his team's points. 6.EE.2, 6.EE.2a, 6.EE.6

Part A: Let *n* represent the number of points Kevin's team scored. Write an expression for the number of points Kevin scored.

[ ]

Part B: Kevin scored 14 points. How many points did the team score?

[ ]

12. The Commutative Property states that the order of terms in an expression does not affect the outcome. 6.EE.3

Part A: Select whether each operation is true or false under the Commutative Property.

True	False	
☐	☐	addition
☐	☐	subtraction
☐	☐	multiplication
☐	☐	division

Part B: For a statement you marked as true in Part A, give an example that shows the Commutative Property applies.

[ ]

Part C: For a statement you marked as false in Part A, give an example that shows that the Commutative Property does not apply.

[ ]

13. Select all of the statements that are an example of an Identity Property. 6.EE.3

- ☐ $n - n = 0$
- ☐ $n + 0 = n$
- ☐ $n \cdot 1 = n$
- ☐ $n \div n = 1$

14. Antonio was trying to find 6×82 when his calculator stopped working. Show how he could use the Distributive Property to mentally find the product. 6.EE.3, 6.NS.4

15. The area of the rectangle is $42x + 14$. Select whether each set of dimensions could be the width and length of the rectangle. 6.EE.3, 6.NS.4

$42x + 14$

Yes	No	
☐	☐	width 7; length $6x + 2$
☐	☐	width 21; length $2x + 0.5$
☐	☐	width 2; length $7 + 21x$
☐	☐	width $3x + 1$; length 14
☐	☐	width 6; length $7x + 8$

16. The table shows the cost of some school supplies. Migina wants to buy 3 pencils, 4 pens, and 2 notebooks. 6.EE.1, 6.NS.3

Item	Cost
Pencils	$0.29
Pens	$1.45
Notebooks	$2.25

Part A: Write an expression to find the total cost of the items she wants to buy.

Part B: Migina has a $20 bill. Does she have enough money to buy the items she wants? Explain how you solved the problem.

17. A rectangular vegetable garden is $(x + 3)$ feet wide and $(2x + 7)$ feet long. 6.EE.3

Part A: Write an expression for the number of feet of fencing that is needed to completely enclose the garden. Justify your answer.

Part B: Let $x = 5$. How many feet of fencing are needed?

18. A square has a perimeter given by the expression $20x + 24y$. Write an expression for the length of one side of the square. 6.EE.3

19. Select all of the expressions that simplify to $11x + 10$. 6.EE.4

- ☐ $3(3x + 2) + 4 + 2x$
- ☐ $2(5x + 4) + x + 2$
- ☐ $3x + 2(3x + 5)$
- ☐ $x + 3(3x + 1) + x + 9$
- ☐ $3(x + 3) + x + 2(3x + 1)$

20. Select all of the expressions that have $3x + 2y$ as one of their factors. 6.EE.4

- ☐ $18x + 12y$
- ☐ $3x + 4y + 4x + 2y$
- ☐ $4x + y + 2x + 3y$
- ☐ $6x + 9y$

NAME ______________________ DATE __________ PERIOD ______ SCORE ______

Chapter 7 Test

1. Select all of the equations for which the solution is 4. 6.EE.5

- ☐ $5x = 20$
- ☐ $13 - n = 9$
- ☐ $22 \div n = 5.5$
- ☐ $x + 13 = 17$

2. Loviano bought an apple and an orange. He paid a total of $1.84. The apple cost $0.78. 6.EE.7

Part A: Let n represent the cost of the orange. Write an addition equation to find the cost of the orange.

Part B: Solve the equation. How much did Loviano pay for the orange?

3. The number line shows the distances between three towns: *A*, *B*, and *C*. 6.EE.7

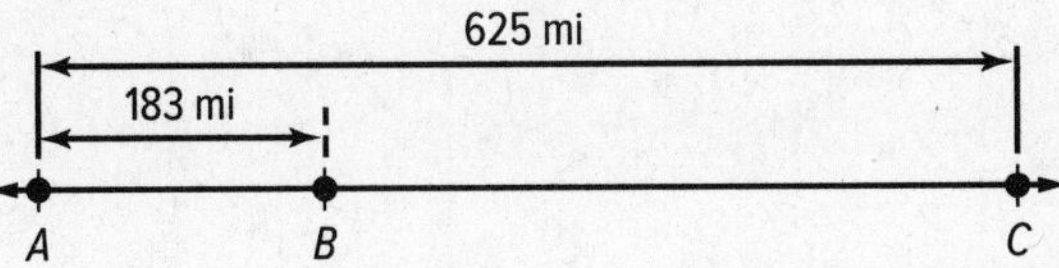

Part A: Write an addition equation to represent the number of miles n from Town B to Town C.

Part B: Solve the equation to find the number of miles from Town B to Town C.

4. The table shows the distances some landmarks are from the Nature Center. The eagle's nest is 1.6 kilometers farther from the Nature Center than the waterfall. Write and solve an addition equation to find how far the Nature Center is from the waterfall. 6.EE.7

Landmark	Distance to Nature Center (km)
Big rock	0.85
Waterfall	x
Eagle's nest	3.25

5. Joey and Armando live on the same street as a city park. The park is $\frac{9}{10}$ mile from Joey's home. Joey leaves home and walks to Armando's home. Then he and Armando walk $\frac{3}{5}$ mile to the park. Write and solve an equation to find how far Joey walked to get to Armando's home. 6.EE.7

6. Select whether each equation is an example of the Addition Property of Equality. 6.EE.7

Yes	No	
☐	☐	$x + 3 = 7$ $x + 3 - 3 = 7 - 3$
☐	☐	$x - 7 = 10$ $x - 7 + 7 = 10$
☐	☐	$x - 1.5 = 4.5$ $x - 1.5 + 1.5 = 4.5 + 1.5$
☐	☐	$x - \frac{2}{3} = \frac{4}{5}$ $x - \frac{2}{3} + \frac{2}{3} = \frac{4}{5} + \frac{4}{5}$

7. Peter is 12 years old. Peter is 5 years younger than his brother. 6.EE.7

Part A: Let n represent the age of Peter's brother. Write a subtraction equation to find the age of Peter's brother.

12	5	n	+
–	×	÷	=

Part B: Solve the equation to find the age of Peter's brother.

8. Martha bought a shirt for $12.64. 6.EE.7

Part A: The shirt was discounted $8.75. Write a subtraction equation to find the original cost of the shirt *n*.

Part B: Solve the equation to find the original price of the shirt.

9. Circle all of the equations that have the same solution as the equation $m - 10 = 6$. 6.EE.7

$6 = y + 10$	$48 = 3a$	$5 + n = 21$	$2x = 8$
$8 = \frac{x}{2}$	$18 = n - 2$	$\frac{a}{10} = 6$	$y - 6 = 10$

10. Kenji wants to know how many quarters equal $7.50. Select whether each equation represents the number of quarters *q* that equal $7.50. 6.EE.7

Yes	No	
☐	☐	$q + 0.25 = 7.50$
☐	☐	$0.25q = 7.50$
☐	☐	$\frac{q}{0.25} = 7.50$
☐	☐	$q - 0.25 = 7.50$

11. Select all of the equations that can be solved in one step by dividing each side by 8. 6.EE.7

☐ $\frac{n}{8} = 2$

☐ $4n = 8$

☐ $8n = 24$

☐ $24 = n - 8$

☐ $40 = 8n$

☐ $n + 8 = 16$

12. The equation $P = 4n$ relates the perimeter P of a square to the length of a side n. 6.EE.7, 6.RP.3

n

Part A: The side length of a square is 8.5 inches. What is the perimeter?

Part B: The perimeter of a square is 60 inches. What is the side length?

Part C: One side of a square measures 10 inches. What is the perimeter in feet?

13. Bethany solved the equation $3x = 12$. Her work is shown. Select whether each statement is true or false. 6.EE.7

$$3x = 12$$
$$3x - 3 = 12 - 3$$
$$x = 9$$

True	False	
☐	☐	Bethany solved the equation correctly.
☐	☐	Bethany should have divided each side by 3 instead of subtracting.
☐	☐	Bethany should have multiplied each side by 3 to get $x = 36$.
☐	☐	The solution should be $x = 4$.

14. Hakeem drives his car at a constant rate of 60 miles per hour. 6.RP.3, 6.EE.7

Part A: Hakeem travels 450 miles. Write a multiplication equation to find the number of hours n he drove.

Part B: Solve the equation to find how long Hakeem drives on his trip.

☐ hours

15. A teacher wrote the equation $\frac{x}{5} = 3$ on the board.

Part A: Write the numbers or letter to make each statement true. 6.EE.7

15	5	3
1	$\frac{1}{5}$	x

The variable is ☐.

The coefficient of x is ☐.

The quotient is ☐.

To solve, multiply each side of the equation by ☐.

Part B: Find the value of x that makes the equation true.

16. The quotient of a number n and 6 is 9. 6.EE.7

Part A: Write an equation to find the number.

Part B: Solve the equation to find the number n.

17. Selena solved $\frac{x}{7} = 14$ by dividing each side by 7. She found that $x = 2$. Describe and correct Selena's error. 6.EE.7

18. Write the appropriate numbers in the spaces to show the solution of each equation. 6.EE.5

2	3	4	6	8
9	12	16	18	20

$\frac{n}{2} = 6$ $\quad n = \square$

$12 - n = 4$ $\quad n = \square$

$2n = 18$ $\quad n = \square$

$n + 6 = 12$ $\quad n = \square$

19. Jingdan is trying to solve the equation $\frac{n}{5} = 12$. Select whether each statement is true or false. 6.EE.5

True	False	
☐	☐	The equation $5n = 12$ has the same solution as Jingdan's equation.
☐	☐	The equation $5 = \frac{n}{12}$ has the same solution as Jingdan's equation.
☐	☐	The equation $n - 12 = 48$ has the same solution as Jingdan's equation.
☐	☐	Jingdan was correct in adding 5 to each side to solve his equation.
☐	☐	Jingdan was correct in multiplying each side by 12 to solve his equation.
☐	☐	The solution to Jingdan's equation is 60.

20. Solve the equation $a = b - c$ for b. Select all of the expressions that are equivalent to b. 6.EE.7

- ☐ $a \times c$
- ☐ $a + c$
- ☐ $a - b$
- ☐ $a - c$
- ☐ $c + a$
- ☐ $c - a$

NAME ______________________ DATE __________ PERIOD ________ SCORE ________

Chapter 8 Test

1. Isabel plans to make apple pies. She buys a pack of pie pans for \$10 and some apples for \$2 per pound. 6.EE.2, 6.EE.2c

Part A: Complete the table to show Isabel's total cost for the various amounts of apples.

Apples (lb), x	$2x + 10$	Cost (\$), y
2	2(2) + 10	
4		
6		
8		

Part B: Isabel buys 15 pounds of apples. What is the total cost?

2. The expression $\frac{9}{5}C + 32$ can be used to determine the temperature in degrees Fahrenheit, given the temperature C in degrees Celsius. Chuck claims that for any temperature less than 0°C, the temperature in degrees Fahrenheit will always be less than 0°F. Is Chuck's claim true? Justify your answer. 6.EE.2, 6.EE.2c

3. The table shows the total cost of admission to a museum for different numbers of guests. Select whether each statement is true or false. 6.EE.9

Museum Admission	
Number of Guests, x	Total Cost (\$), y
1	9
2	18
3	27
4	36

True	False	
☐	☐	The total cost for 14 guests is \$22.
☐	☐	The total cost for 8 guests is \$72.
☐	☐	The equation $y = x + 8$ can be used to find the total cost for x guests.
☐	☐	The equation $y = 9x$ can be used to find the total cost for x guests.

4. A store's rewards program awards 5 points for joining and 2 points for every item purchased. Select all of the representations that determine the number of reward points earned. 6.EE.9

☐

Items Purchased, x	1	2	3	4
Number of Points, y	7	9	11	13

☐ $y = 5 + 2x$, where y represents the total number of points earned, and x represents the number of items purchased.

☐

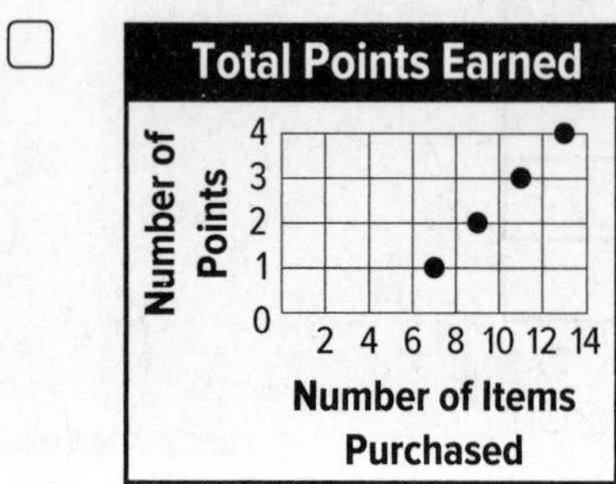

5. An infant car seat manufacturer uses the inequality $w \leq 22$, where w is the infant's weight in pounds, to determine the weight of infants who can be safely transported in their car seats. Sort the names of the infants shown in the table into their appropriate bins based on their weights. 6.EE.5

Name of Infant	Weight (lb)
Marion	20
Taye	18
Quincy	22
Sonia	23
Beth	15
Cory	40

Can be Transported Safely

Cannot be Transported Safely

6. Emilio has at least 6 coins in his piggy bank. Let c represent the number of coins in the bank. 6.EE.6, 6.EE.8

Part A: Write an inequality to represent this situation.

Part B: Graph the inequality on the number line.

7. Consider the inequality $x + 7 \geq 12$. 6.EE.5

Part A: Select whether each value of x makes the inequality true.

Yes	No	
☐	☐	$x = 3.75$
☐	☐	$x = 5$
☐	☐	$x = 8\frac{5}{8}$
☐	☐	$x = -19$

Part B: Kiah claims that all of the values of x that make $x + 7 \geq 12$ true are the same values of x that make $x + 7 > 12$ true. Is Kiah's claim correct? Justify your answer.

8. Five groups of people are standing in line to buy concert tickets. The table shows the number of tickets each group wants to buy. 6.EE.2

Group Number, x	Number of Tickets
1	1
2	4
3	7
4	10
5	13

Part A: The pattern in the table continues. How many tickets does Group 6 want to buy?

Part B: Use the pattern in the table to write a rule for the number of tickets each group wants to buy.

9. Jorge wrote the phrase "7 more than the product of 6 and the number n" to represent the values in an arithmetic sequence. He let n represent a number's position in the sequence. 6.EE.6

Part A: Write the appropriate numbers and symbols to create an expression that represents Jorge's statement.

1 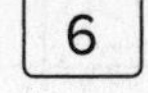 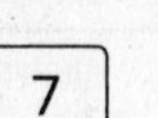 n

+ − × ÷

Part B: What are the first five numbers in the sequence?

10. The library does not charge a fee for books returned no more than 3 days late in a month. The library does charge a monthly late fee represented by $1.25(d – 3) where $d > 3$. The table shows the number of days late d for four months that Margaret borrowed books. Find the total late fees Margaret was charged in the four months. 6.EE.8

Month	Number of Days Late, d
January	5
February	1
March	3
April	7

11. An office box has a height of 1.5 inches. Jen claims that a stack of 9 of these office boxes will have an overall height of 6 inches. Use the rule $h = 1.5n$, where n is the number of boxes and h is the total height, to determine if Jen's claim is true. Justify your answer. 6.EE.9

12. A sales associate at a furniture store receives a bonus of $200 for every couch she sells. Her goal is to earn at least $1,250 in bonuses. 6.EE.6, 6.EE.8

Part A: Write an inequality to represent the number of couches the associate must sell to reach her goal. Identify any variables you include.

Part B: Solve the inequality for your variable. What is the least number of couches the associate must sell to reach her goal?

Inequality: ______ ______ couches

13. The table shows the relationship between x and y. Graph the given ordered pairs. Then complete the table. 6.EE.9

Input (x)	Output (y)
0	0
1	2
1.5	
2	4
3	6
x	

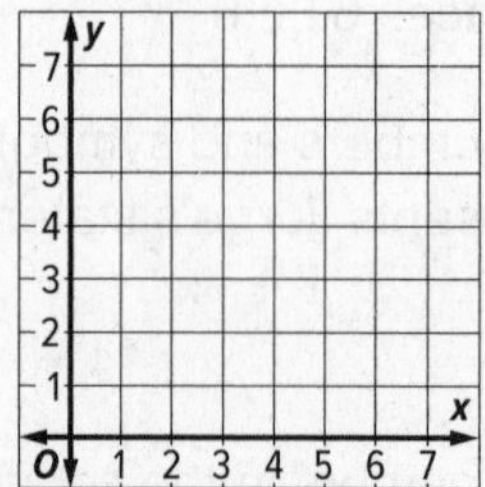

14. Select whether each statement can be represented by the equation $y = 0.1x + 2$. 6.EE.9

Yes	No	
☐	☐	A server earns 10% of a check plus $2.
☐	☐	Students must solve two test items of their choice and 10% of the remaining items.
☐	☐	10% of the workers received 2 bonuses.
☐	☐	A veterinarian wants a dog to lose $\frac{1}{10}$ of its weight plus 2 pounds.
☐	☐	It is 2 degrees cooler than $\frac{1}{10}$ of the temperature in Florida.

15. Sort the values of x into the appropriate bin based on the inequality $17 > 20 - x$. 6.EE.5

$x = 0$ | $x = 2$ | $x = 5$ | $x = 3$ | $x = 6$ | $x = 10$

Solution	Not a Solution

16. A bicyclist takes 3 hours to travel 12 miles to a campsite. He cycles at least 1 mile but no more than 5 miles during the first hour. He cycles at least 2 miles during the second hour. He cycles exactly 3 miles during the third hour. Find the least number of miles the bicyclist could have traveled during the second hour. 6.EE.8

17. Doug earns at most x dollars per day. His wife earns at least twice as much per day as Doug. Select whether each statement is true or false in representing their incomes. 6.EE.6

True	False	
☐	☐	Doug and his wife could earn $3x per day.
☐	☐	Doug and his wife could earn $(3x - 1)$ dollars per day.
☐	☐	If Doug earns $100 in a day, he and his wife could earn a total income of $150 that day.

18. Lorena determined that she weighs 3 pounds more than 4 times the weight of her baby brother Omar. She represented her weight with the expression $4x + 3$, where x is Omar's weight. Lorena weighs 67 pounds. How many more pounds does Lorena weigh than Omar? 6.EE.9

19. Consider the sequence: 1, 4, 16, 64, ... Describe the pattern. Then determine the sixth term in the sequence. 6.EE.9

Sixth term:

20. For each function table, write the corresponding equation in the space provided. 6.EE.9

$y = 5x + 1$ | $y = x + 5$ | $y = x + 1$ | $y = 2x - 1$ | $y = 3x - 2$

Input (x)	1	2	3	4
Output (y)	6	7	8	9

Equation:

Input (x)	1	2	3	4
Output (y)	1	3	5	7

Equation:

Input (x)	1	2	3	4
Output (y)	6	11	16	21

Equation:

NAME ______________________ DATE __________ PERIOD ______ SCORE ______

Chapter 9 Test

1. Select all of the base and height dimensions of a parallelogram with an area of 12 square feet. 6.G.1

- ☐ base = 2 ft, height = 4 ft
- ☐ base = 3 ft, height = 8 ft
- ☐ base = 5 ft, height = 2.4 ft
- ☐ base = 12 ft, height = 1 ft
- ☐ base = 3 ft, height = 3 ft

2. The diagram shows two parallelograms. For what value of *n* is the area of parallelogram B twice the area of parallelogram A? 6.G.1

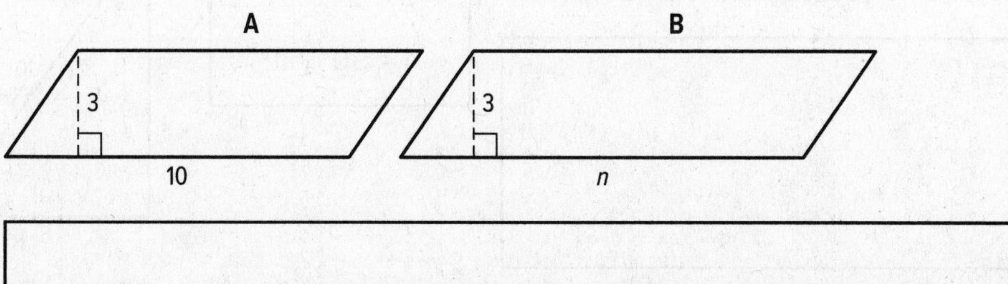

3. The diagram shows a sign that Alice is designing for a restaurant. The sign is in the shape of a parallelogram. 6.G.1

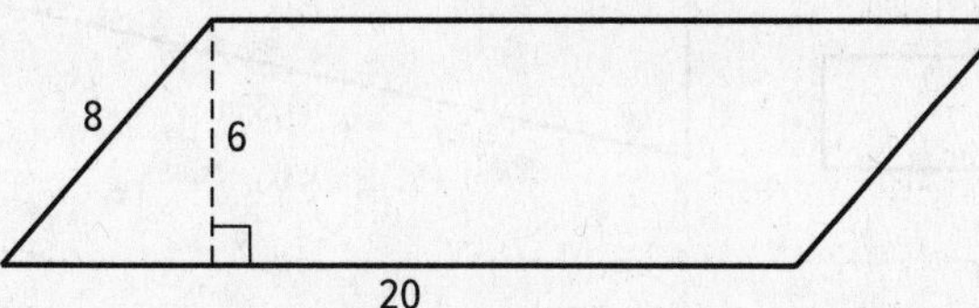

Part A: Alice wants to paint the front of the sign blue before adding white lettering. One quart of paint covers 100 square feet. How many quarts of blue paint does she need to buy? Justify your answer.

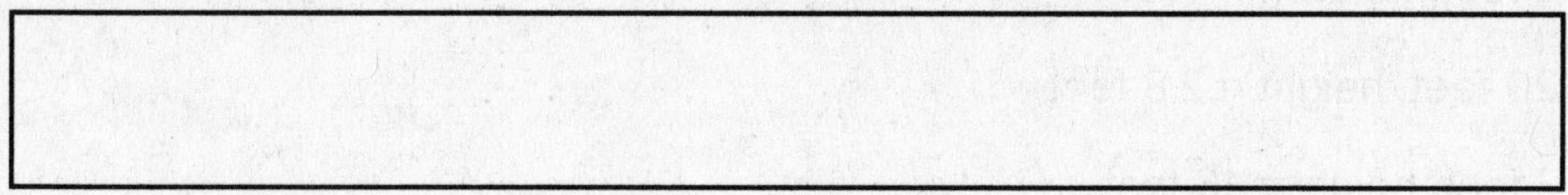

Part B: Alice wants to string lights around the edges of the sign. A box of lights contains 12 linear feet of lights. How many boxes of lights does Alice need to buy? Justify your answer.

4. The two triangles shown have the same area. Select whether each statement is true or false in representing the dimensions of the triangles. 6.G.1

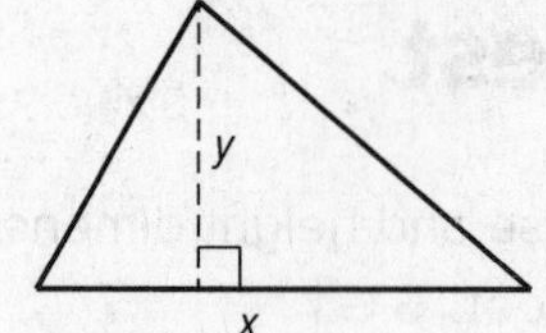

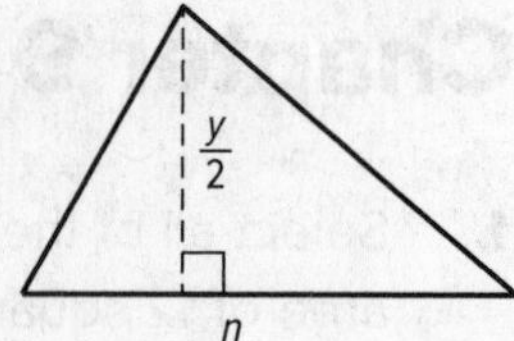

Not drawn to scale.

True	False	
☐	☐	$n = \frac{x}{2}$
☐	☐	$n = x$
☐	☐	$n = 2x$
☐	☐	$n = 4x$
☐	☐	$x = \frac{n}{2}$

5. Andrew found the area of the triangle. His work is shown. Describe and correct Andrew's error. 6.G.1

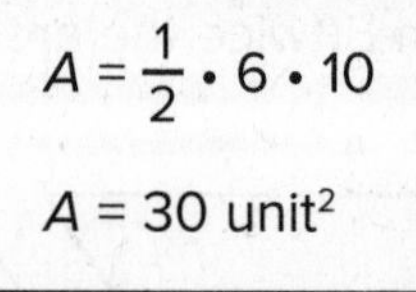

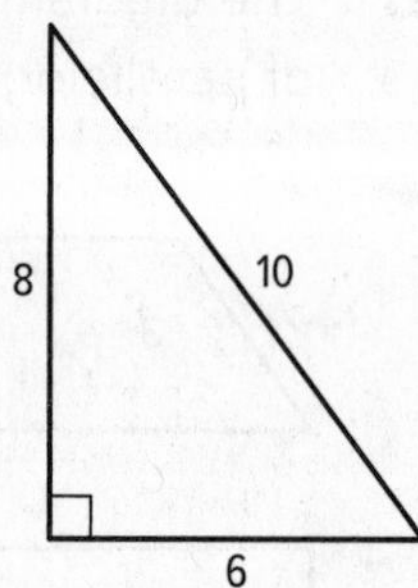

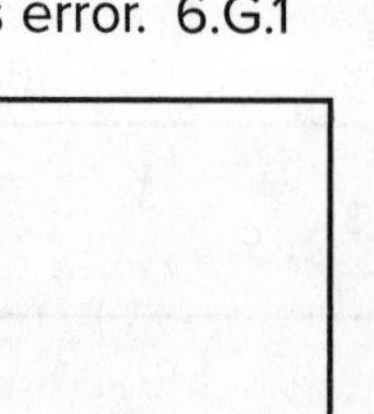

6. The diagram shows the pennant hanging on Henrietta's bedroom wall. How much wall space does the pennant cover? 6.G.1

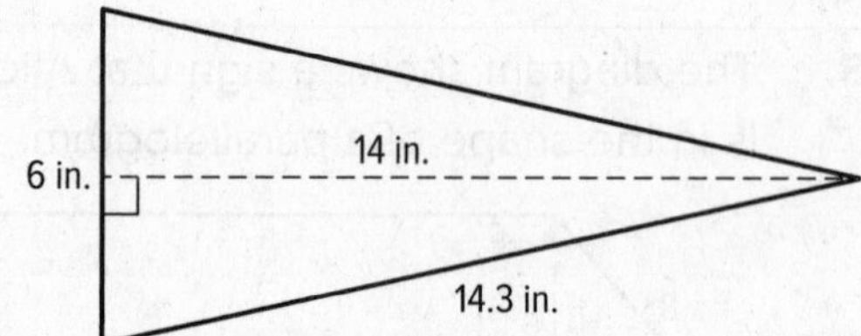

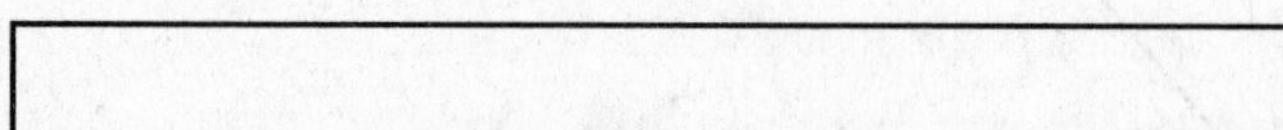

7. The area of the triangular plot in front of Adrianna's house is 28 square feet. Select all of the sets of dimensions that could be the dimensions of the triangular plot. 6.G.1

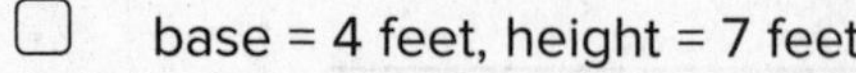

☐ base = 4 feet, height = 7 feet

☐ base = 20 feet, height = 2.8 feet

☐ base = 7 feet, height = 16 feet

☐ base = 14 feet, height = 4 feet

☐ base = 2 feet, height = 7 feet

8. The area of a trapezoid is 20 square units. The sum of the base lengths is 10 units. What is the height of the trapezoid? 6.G.1

9. The stage in a theater is in the shape of a trapezoid. The length of the front of the stage is 80 feet. The length of the back of the stage is 50 feet. The distance from the front to the back of the stage is 40 feet. What is the area of the stage? 6.G.1

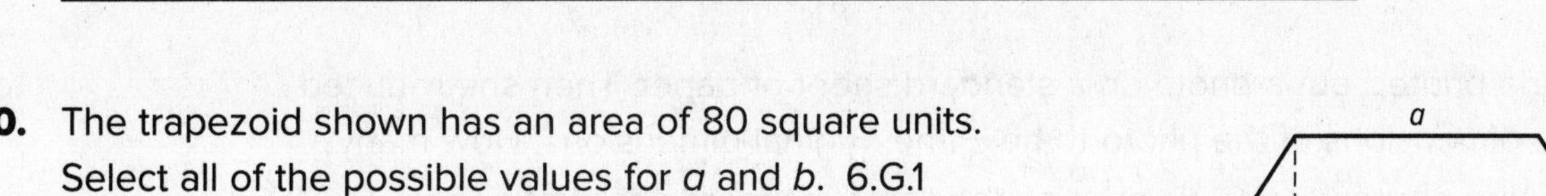

10. The trapezoid shown has an area of 80 square units. Select all of the possible values for a and b. 6.G.1

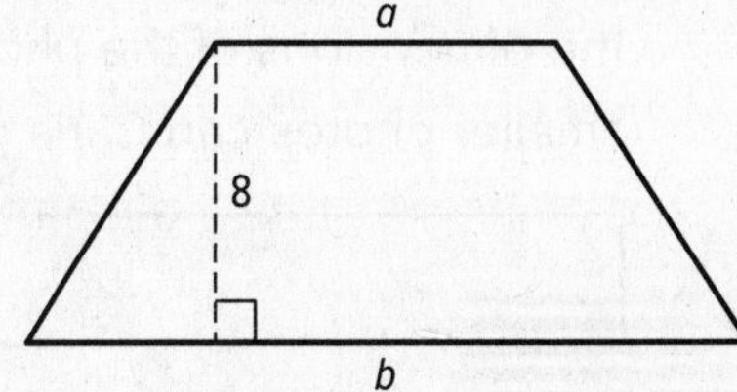

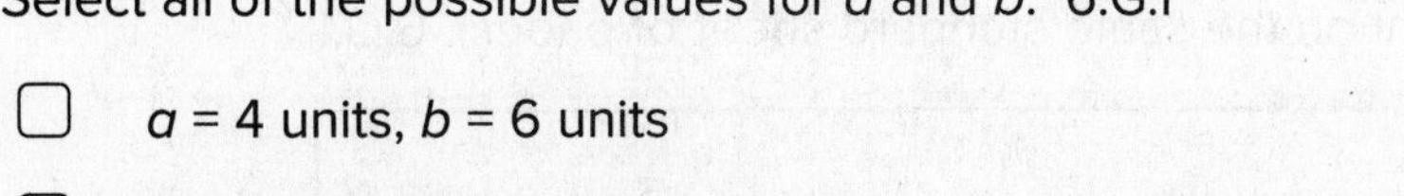

☐ a = 4 units, b = 6 units

☐ a = 5 units, b = 15 units

☐ a = 7 units, b = 9 units

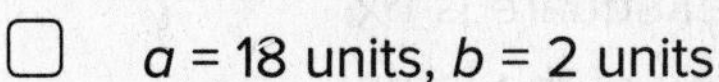

☐ a = 18 units, b = 2 units

11. The dimensions of a rectangular canvas are multiplied by a factor of 5 to create a new canvas. Select whether each statement is true or false in representing how the new canvas compares to the original canvas. 6.G.1

True	False	
☐	☐	The perimeter of the new canvas is 5 times greater.
☐	☐	The perimeter of the new canvas is 10 times greater.
☐	☐	The perimeter of the new canvas is 25 times greater.
☐	☐	The area of the new canvas is 5 times greater.
☐	☐	The area of the new canvas is 25 times greater.

12. The carpeting that Elizabeth has selected for her bedroom floor is sold by the square yard. The floor measures 10 feet by 12 feet. 6.G.1

Part A: How many square feet are in one square yard?

Part B: How many square yards of carpeting will Elizabeth need to carpet the entire bedroom floor?

13. Carla printed out a photo on a standard sheet of paper. Then she reduced the dimensions of the photo to be $\frac{1}{4}$ the original dimensions. How many smaller photos can Carla print on the same standard sheet of paper? 6.G.1

14. The perimeter of one square is $8x$. The perimeter of another square is $6x$. What is the ratio of the area of the smaller square to the area of the larger square? 6.G.1

15. The locations of four corner flags of a soccer field are plotted on the coordinate plane. Diego points out that 1 square unit on the coordinate plane represents 60 square feet. What is the area of the soccer field? Explain how you found your answer. 6.G.1, 6.G.3, 6.NS.8

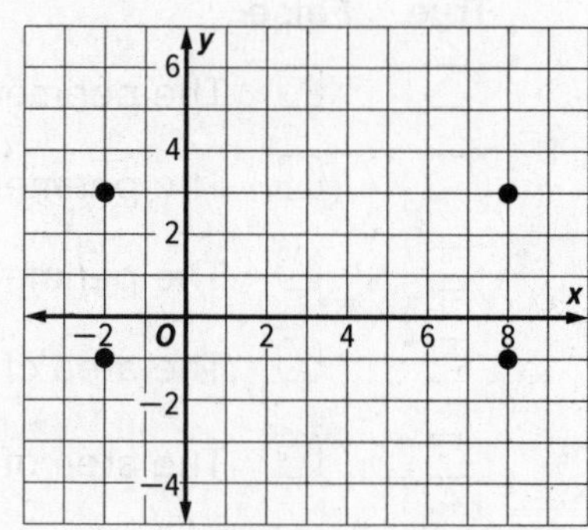

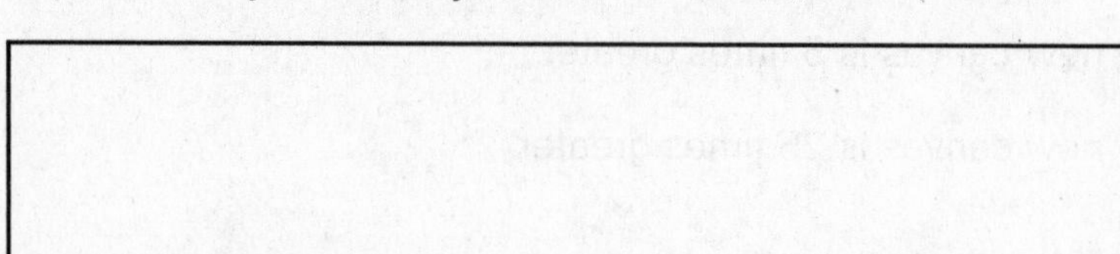

16. Yoruba is creating a logo on a coordinate plane. She identifies the vertices of the logo as (2, –1), (3, 5), (6, 5), and (7, –1). 6.G.1, 6.G.3, 6.NS.8

Part A: Graph the ordered pairs that show the vertices of the logo, and connect the vertices to outline the shape of the logo.

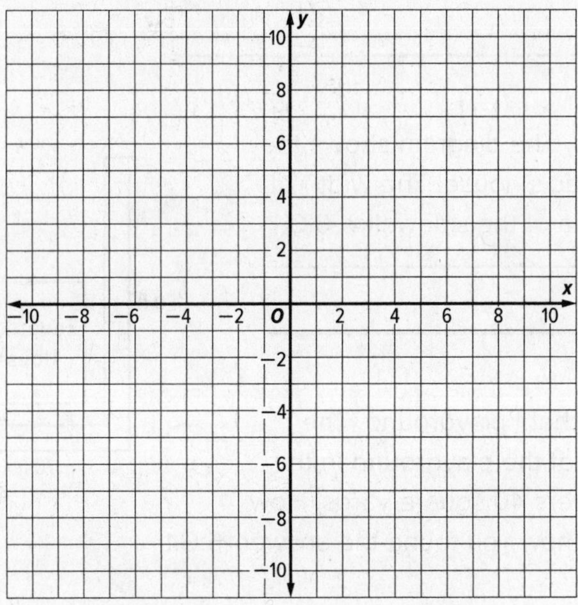

Part B: What is the area of the logo?

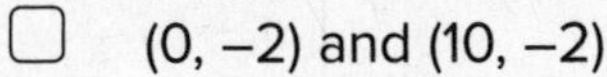

17. A rectangle has a perimeter of 20 units and an area of 21 square units. The coordinate plane shows two vertices of the rectangle. Select all of the ordered pairs that could represent the other two vertices of the rectangle. 6.G.1, 6.G.3, 6.NS.8

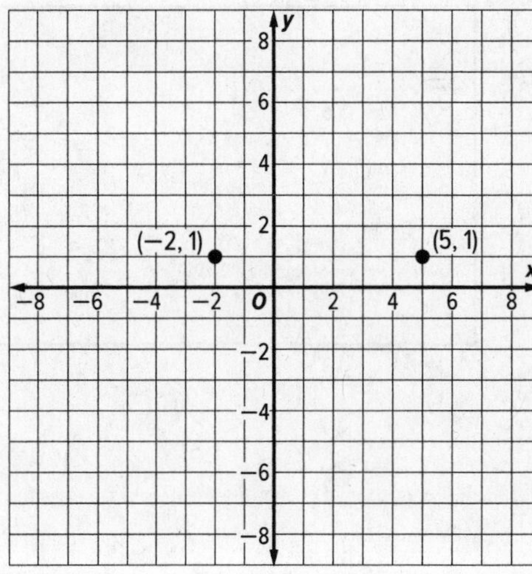

- ☐ (0, –2) and (10, –2)
- ☐ (–2, 4) and (5, 4)
- ☐ (–2, 8) and (5, 8)
- ☐ (–2, –2) and (5, –2)
- ☐ (1, 1) and (8, 1)

18. Aaron wants to paint a wall in his office. There are two windows in the wall. The windows have dimensions of 4 feet by 3 feet. The height of the wall is 8 feet and the width is 12 feet. What area of wall is to be painted? 6.G.1

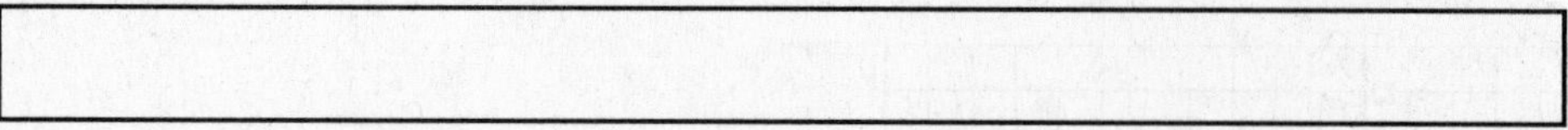

19. Eduardo lives on the corner of two streets. The diagram shows the dimensions of the sidewalk around Eduardo's house. The width of the sidewalk is 3 feet. What is the total area of the sidewalk? 6.G.1

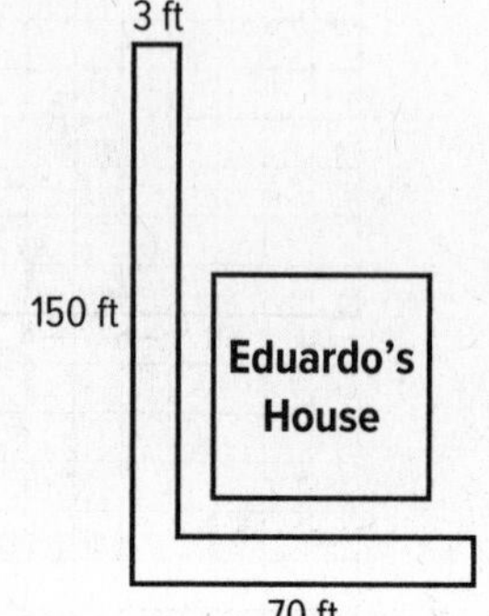

20. The diagram shows the dimensions of a school playground. The student council wants to paint the surface of the playground in the school color. A one-gallon can of paint covers 40 square yards. How many cans of paint will they need? Explain how you found the answer. 6.G.1

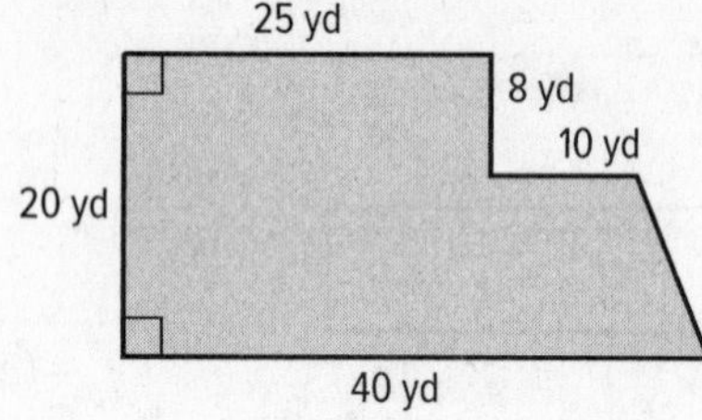

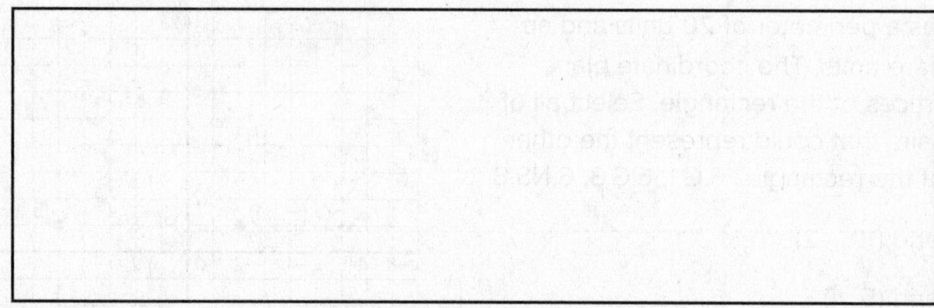

NAME ______________________ DATE ____________ PERIOD ________ SCORE ________

Chapter 10 Test

1. A fish tank has a width of 4 feet, a length of 3 feet, and a height of 2.5 feet. Ariana fills the tank with water until the height of the water is 12 inches from the top of the tank. What is the volume of water in the fish tank? 6.G.2

6	12	18	20
22.5	24	30	144

☐ ft^3

2. The ratio of side lengths of two square prisms is 2:3. What is the ratio of the volumes? 6.G.2

☐

3. A sporting goods company ships products in a 30-inch by 20-inch by 10-inch rectangular carton. Footballs are packaged in a 5-inch by 5-inch by 8-inch box. The company places 20 football boxes in a carton and fills the rest of the space with packing material. What volume of space was filled with packing material? Explain your answer. 6.G.2

☐

4. The volume of the cereal box shown is 121.6 cubic inches. The height of the shelves in Valerie's pantry is 10.75 inches. Is it possible for Valerie to place this cereal box in an upright position on her pantry shelf? Justify your response. 6.G.2

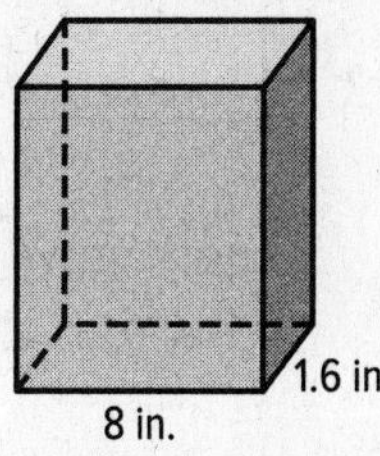

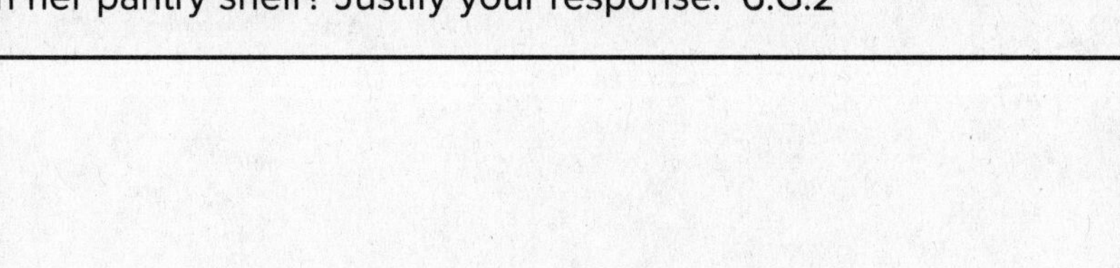

5. Edgardo created a rectangular prism with a square base. The volume of the prism is 45 cubic inches. The dimensions of the prism are all whole numbers. What is the height of the prism? 6.G.2

6. The diagram shows the tent the Wilsons used on a camping trip. The front and back of the tent are isosceles triangles. Write the number and measurement to indicate the capacity of the tent. 6.G.2

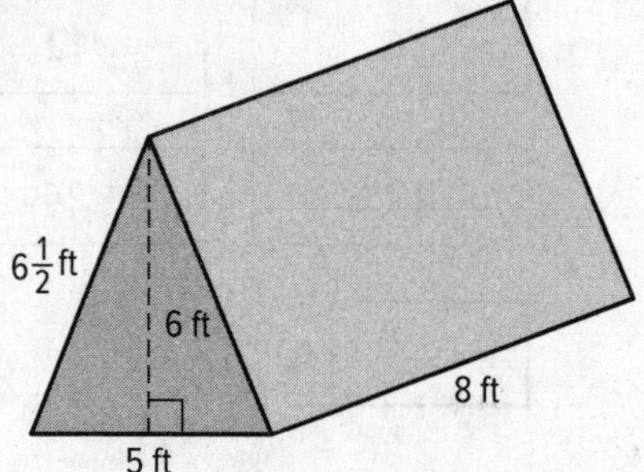

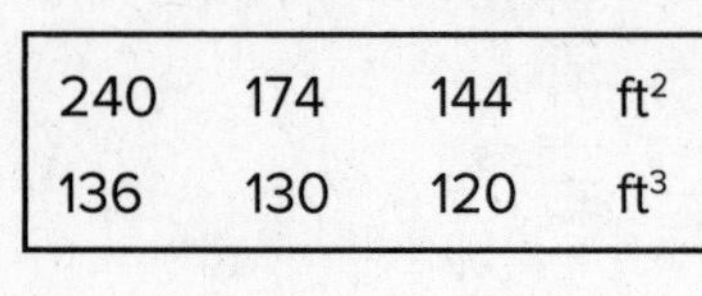

240	174	144	ft²
136	130	120	ft³

7. The diagram shows the dimensions of a triangular prism. Select all of the values for a and b that would give the prism a volume of 90 cubic inches. 6.G.2

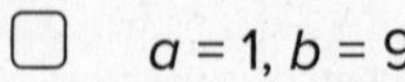

- ☐ $a = 1$, $b = 9$
- ☐ $a = 3$, $b = 6$
- ☐ $a = 4$, $b = 9$
- ☐ $a = 9$, $b = 2$
- ☐ $a = 3$, $b = 3$

b in.
10 in.
a in.

8. The diagram shows the dimensions of a building block. A set of these blocks is packaged in a box 10 inches long, 6 inches wide, and 3 inches high. What is the greatest number of blocks in a set? 6.G.2

6 in.
0.75 in.
2 in.

9. The volume of a triangular prism is equal to half the volume of a rectangular prism. Select whether each statement is true or false. 6.G.2

True	False	
☐	☐	Each dimension of the triangular prism is half the measure of the corresponding dimension of the rectangular prism.
☐	☐	The two prisms have the same dimensions.
☐	☐	Each dimension of the triangular prism is twice the measure of the corresponding dimension of the rectangular prism.
☐	☐	The dimensions of the two prisms are never equal.

10. The diagram shows a 3,300-cubic-foot greenhouse. What is the height of the greenhouse? 6.G.2

80 ft
10 ft

11. The diagram shows the gift box Fernando plans to wrap. He wants to use the least amount of wrapping paper needed to completely cover the box. A sheet of wrapping paper is 600 square inches. How much wrapping paper would Fernando have left after wrapping the box? 6.G.4

1.5 in.
8 in.
10 in.

12. Select whether each statement is a method for finding the surface area of a rectangular prism with length ℓ, width w, and height h. 6.G.4

Yes	No	
☐	☐	Find the product of ℓ, w, and h.
☐	☐	Find ℓwh, and then divide the product by 2.
☐	☐	Find $\ell w + h\ell + wh$, and then multiply the sum by 2.
☐	☐	Find $\ell w + h\ell + wh + wh + h\ell + \ell w$.

13. The dimensions of rectangular prism X are twice the dimensions of rectangular prism Y. 6.G.4

Part A: The surface area of prism X is 100 square inches. What is the surface area of prism Y?

Part B: The dimensions of rectangular prism Z are three times the dimensions of rectangular prism Y. What is the surface area of prism Z?

14. Select all of the situations for which surface area is the appropriate measure. 6.G.4

☐ The amount of water inside a fish tank.

☐ The amount of glass needed to make a fish tank.

☐ The amount of space inside a wooden toy chest.

☐ The amount of stain needed to paint a wooden toy chest.

15. The diagram shows the net of a cardboard box. How much cardboard is needed to make the box? 6.G.4

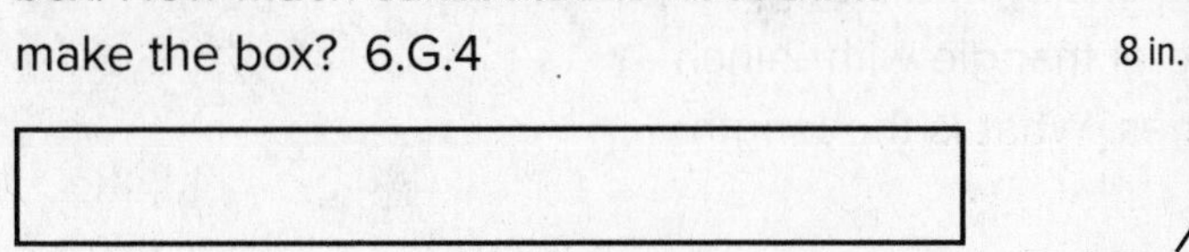

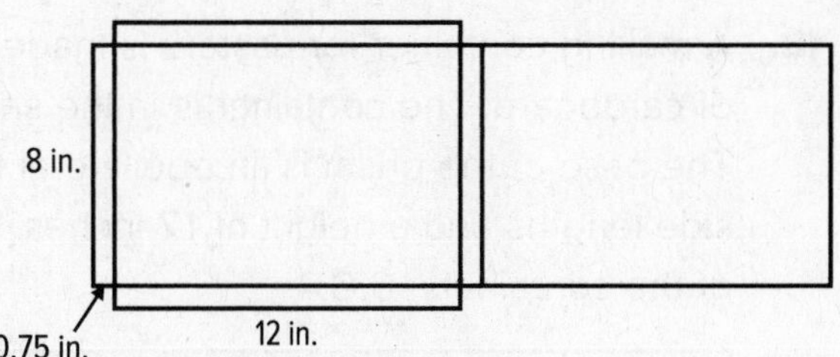

16. The diagram shows the dimensions of a canvas tent. How much canvas fabric does Charlie need to make the tent, including the floor? 6.G.4

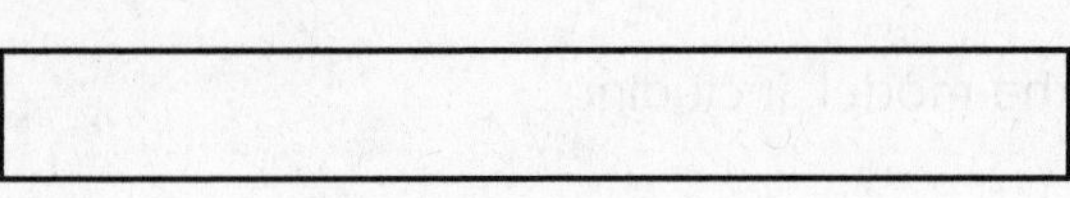

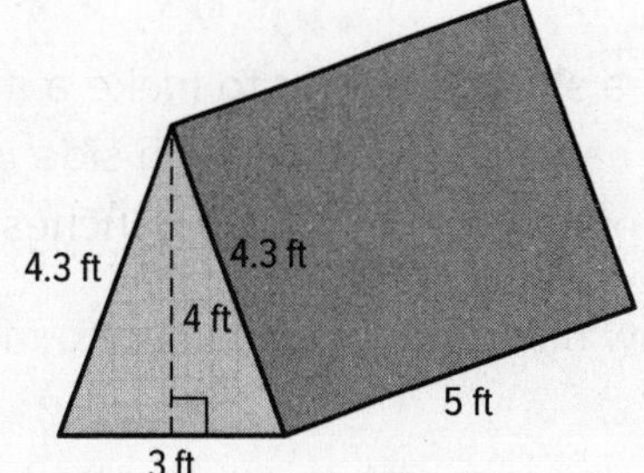

17. The diagram shows the net of a three-dimensional solid. 6.G.2, 6.G.4

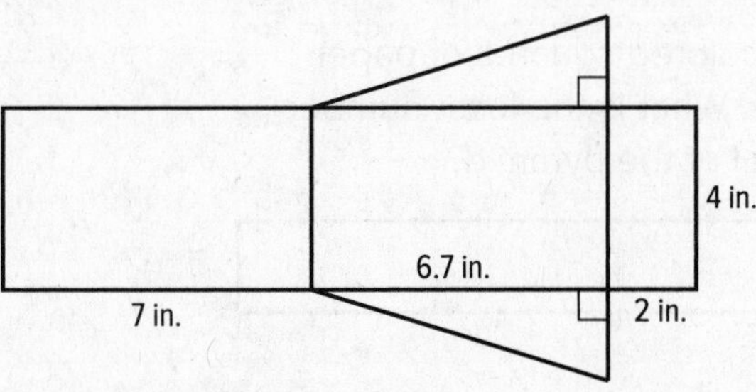

Part A: Identify the name of the solid represented by the net.

Part B: Find the surface area and volume of the solid.

Surface area:

Volume:

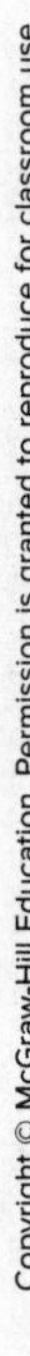

18. A mailing container for posters is made from 87.4 square inches of cardboard. The container is in the shape of a triangular prism. The base of the prism is an equilateral triangle with 2-inch side lengths and a height of 1.7 inches. What is the length of the container? 6.G.4

19. David uses a sheet of paper to make a model of an Egyptian pyramid. The model has a square base with side lengths of 4 inches. The slant height of the model is 5 inches. 6.G.4

Part A: How much paper was used to make the model, including the base?

Part B: David wants to cover his model with colored squares of paper. Each colored square has 1.5-inch side lengths. What is the least number of colored squares needed to cover the model of the pyramid?

20. The diagram shows a net of a triangular pyramid. 6.G.4

Part A: What is the lateral area of the triangular pyramid?

Part B: What additional steps are needed to find the surface area of the triangular pyramid?

NAME _______________ DATE __________ PERIOD ______ SCORE ______

Chapter 11 Test

1. In 7 days, Jessica walked an average of 30 minutes per day. Select whether each set of data has the same average as Jessica. 6.SP.3

Yes	No	
☐	☐	30, 30, 30, 30, 30, 30, 30
☐	☐	20, 24, 25, 30, 31, 32, 35
☐	☐	30, 30, 30, 20, 15, 25, 40
☐	☐	40, 20, 15, 22, 32, 40, 41

2. Greg earned $15, $18, $12, $20, and $25 for each of five lawns he mowed. Greg wants to earn a mean of $20 per lawn. How much must he charge for his next mowing job? Justify your answer. 6.SP.3

3. The table shows the number of personalized greeting cards that artists created to send to veterans. 6.SP.3

Part A: What is the mean number of cards created?

Part B: How does the number of cards Sue made affect the mean of the data?

Greeting Cards Made

Artist	Number of Cards
Gilberto	36
Isabel	35
Taye	40
Selam	38
Kenji	34
Sue	81

4. Larry needs to gather data for a science report. Select whether each question can be classified as a statistical question. 6.SP.1

Yes	No	
☐	☐	What is the distance between Mars and Earth?
☐	☐	How many articles were published in various science magazines about planets last year?
☐	☐	What percent of students know that the sun is a star and not a planet?
☐	☐	How many moons does each planet have?

5. The list shows the number of seconds it took eight phones to receive the same text message. 6.SP.3, 6.SP.5, 6.SP.5c

4 5 7 4 2 6 3 5

Part A: Write the appropriate value(s) for each data measure.

2	5
3	6.5
3.5	7
4	8
4.5	9

number of data values: ☐

mean: ☐

median: ☐

modes: ☐ and ☐

range: ☐

interquartile range: ☐

Part B: What is the mean absolute deviation of the data? Explain how you found your answer.

6. The table shows the shoe sizes of a group of boys. Find and compare the median and mode of the data. 6.SP.5, 6.SP.5c

Shoe Size			
6	8	7	6
10	9	7.5	5
5	5.5	6	7.5

7. The line plot shows the ages of people enrolled in a pottery class. Select all of the data values that are outliers. 6.SP.5, 6.SP.5c

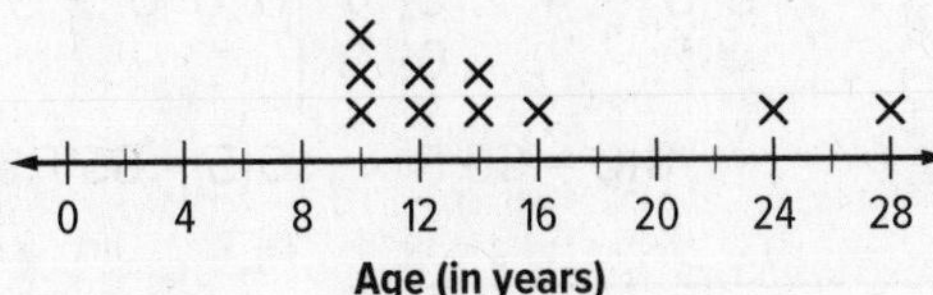

- ☐ 10
- ☐ 12 and 14
- ☐ 16
- ☐ 24
- ☐ 28

8. The table shows the number of trees in some city parks. 6.SP.3, 6.SP.5, 6.SP.5c

Number of Trees in City Parks			
20	22	34	50
42	28	20	52

Part A: Order the values from least to greatest, and find the median.

Part B: Determine the first quartile and third quartile.

Part C: What is the range of the data? What is the interquartile range?

9. A student conducted a survey by asking 20 people, "Do you know how to knit, crochet, do both, or do neither?" The results showed that 7 people knit and 5 people crochet. Of these people, 4 know how to do both. How many of those surveyed do not know how to knit or crochet? 6.SP.1

10. The double stem-and-leaf plot shows the temperature, in degrees Fahrenheit, taken on the hour in two different classrooms. 6.SP.3, 6.SP.5, 6.SP.5c

Room 100		Room 103
8	6	5
8 5 5 4 2 0	7	0 0 0 2 3 3 4
0	8	

8|6 = 68°F   6|5 = 65°F

Part A: What is the median temperature for each room?

Part B: What are the range and interquartile range for each room? Justify your answer.

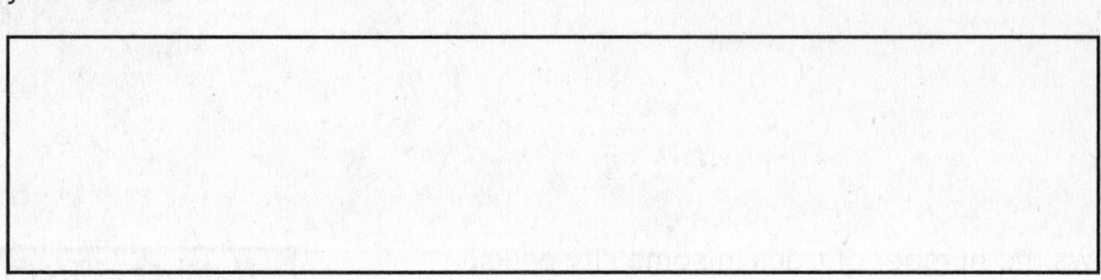

Part C: Compare and contrast the measures of variation for both rooms.

11. The table shows the hourly parking fees of three different garages. Margaret found the mean absolute deviation as 0.75. Explain Margaret's error. 6.SP.5, 6.SP.5b, 6.SP.5c

Hourly Parking Fee	
Garage A	$5.50
Garage B	$9.00
Garage C	$6.50

12. The table shows the maximum speeds of car drivers on a residential road. Circle the values that are more than one mean absolute deviation away from the mean. 6.SP.5, 6.SP.5b, 6.SP.5c

Maximum Speeds (mph)			
35	36	32	40
37	38	29	33

29   32   33   35

36   37   38   40

13. The list shows the number of phone calls made by five people in one month: 132, 28, 40, 35, 20. Select whether each statement is true or false in representing the data. 6.SP.3, 6.SP.5, 6.SP.5c

True	False	
☐	☐	The median better represents the data than the mean.
☐	☐	The mean is less than the median.
☐	☐	The range is affected by the outlier.
☐	☐	The mode is affected by the outlier.

14. A company pays seven employees $10 per hour and one employee $60 per hour. 6.SP.5, 6.SP.5c

Part A: Find the median and mean of the hourly wages.

Part B: The company claims that their employees earn an average of $16.25 per hour. Assume you were interviewing for a job at this company. What question should you ask to validate the claim?

Part C: Which measure(s) of center best describe(s) the data? Explain.

15. For each data set, write the most appropriate measure of center. Use each answer once. 6.SP.5, 6.SP.5d

mean
median
mode

☐ Club fees: $35, $225, $36, $45, $60

☐ Age of dancers: 51, 25, 64, 51, 51, 51

☐ Number of lunges: 9, 9, 17, 24, 20, 16, 30

16. Fatima asked, "How tall is the tallest female in your household?" Is her question a statistical question? If so, explain why it is statistical. If not, rephrase it so it is a statistical question. 6.SP.1

17. The list shows the number of homework problems out of ten that Juan answered correctly for eight assignments: 9, 4, 10, 6, 10, 8, 7, 10. Select whether each statement is true or false in representing the data. 6.SP.3

True	False	
☐	☐	10 is a mode of the data set.
☐	☐	8 is the median of the data set.
☐	☐	8.5 is the mean of the data set.
☐	☐	There is no mode in the data set.

18. Use the data: 27, 21, 22, 20, 21, 23, 25, 25, 25, 26, 26, 27. Write the appropriate term to correctly complete each statement. 6.SP.5, 6.SP.5b, 6.SP.5c

interquartile range

mean

median

mean absolute deviation

The ________ is approximately 2.

The ________ is 25.

The ________ is 24.

19. The data show the time, in seconds, that members of a track team ran 100 meters: 11, 12, 11, 10, 20, 12, 12, 11. Sort the terms into the appropriate bin based on the effect of the outlier. 6.SP.3

mean

median

mode

Affected by the Outlier	Not Affected by the Outlier

20. The table shows the number of times students have visited their state capital. Describe the effect on the mean when the outlier is removed from the data. Justify your answer. 6.SP.5, 6.SP.5d

Visits to the State Capital		
0	1	3
2	4	3
2	1	11

NAME ______________________ DATE ____________ PERIOD ________ SCORE ________

Chapter 12 Test

1. Select whether each statement is true or false about data represented by a line plot. 6.SP.5, 6.SP.5a, 6.SP.5b

True	False	
☐	☐	Each individual data value is shown.
☐	☐	The mean is more easily determined than the mode.
☐	☐	The median cannot be computed.
☐	☐	The range can be easily computed.

2. The table shows the amount of time 15 students spent reading last night. 6.SP.4, 6.SP.5, 6.SP.5c

Time Spent Reading (min)				
45	38	27	15	45
30	40	27	18	24
15	45	18	22	27

Part A: Complete the line plot to represent the data.

Time Spent Reading (min)

10 15 20 25 30 35 40 45 50

Part B: Find the median, the mode(s), and the interquartile range.

3. Select whether each statement is true or false about data represented by a histogram with intervals on the horizontal axis. 6.SP.5, 6.SP.5a, 6.SP.5b

True	False	
☐	☐	Each individual data value is shown.
☐	☐	The median can be easily identified.
☐	☐	The mode can be easily identified.
☐	☐	The bars touch each other because the data are in ranges with consecutive intervals.

4. The histogram shows test scores for one class. Select whether each statement is true or false. 6.SP.5, 6.SP.5c

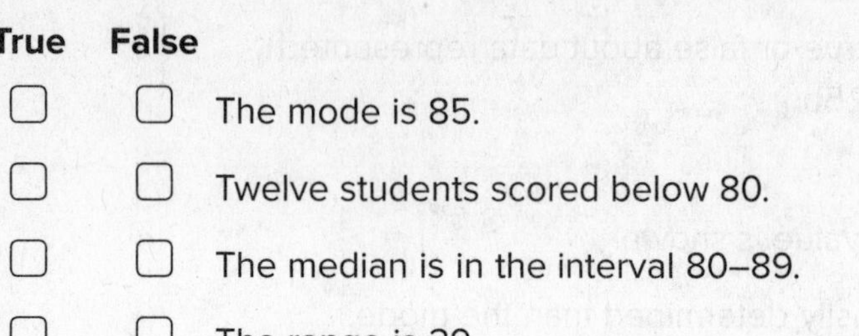

True	False	
☐	☐	The mode is 85.
☐	☐	Twelve students scored below 80.
☐	☐	The median is in the interval 80–89.
☐	☐	The range is 39.

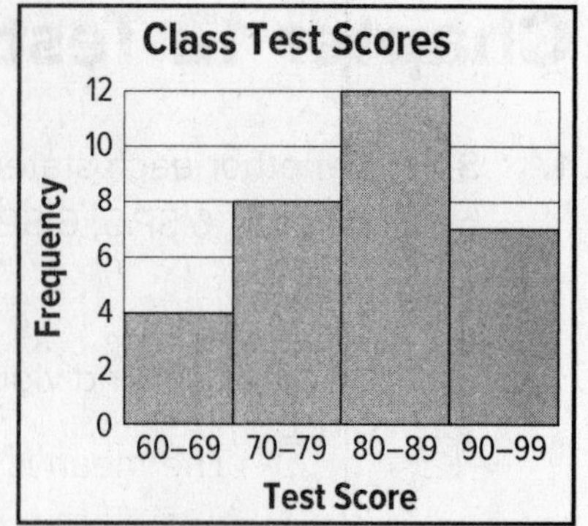

5. The table shows the number of points Michael scored in each of 20 games. 6.SP.4, 6.SP.5, 6.SP.5a

Number of Points Scored				
22	15	0	9	16
9	11	22	30	27
15	18	31	15	2
10	16	8	27	23

Part A: Complete the histogram to represent the data.

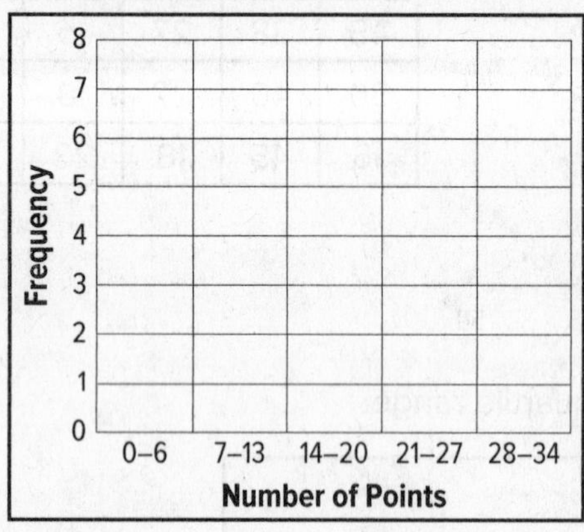

Part B: In how many games did Michael score more than 13 points?

6. Select whether each statement is true or false in representing data by a box-and-whisker plot. 6.SP.5, 6.SP.5a, 6.SP.5b

True	False	
☐	☐	The mean is located outside of the box.
☐	☐	The median can be easily determined.
☐	☐	The mode is always a point inside of the box.
☐	☐	The range can be computed from two of the plotted points.
☐	☐	The number of data values can be determined.

7. The box-and-whisker plot shows the number of books checked out of a library each day. Select all of the statements that are valid. 6.SP.5, 6.SP.5c

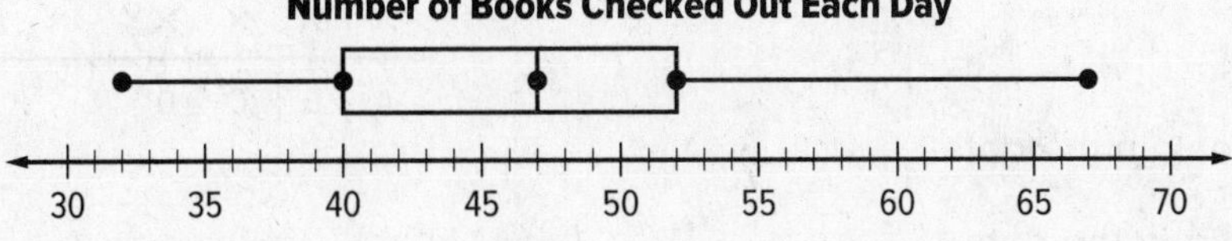

- ☐ There are more data values from 52 to 67 than from 32 to 40.
- ☐ Half the values are between 40 and 52.
- ☐ The least number of books checked out is 32.
- ☐ There are the same number of values between 47 and 52 as from 52 to 67.

8. The table shows the heights, in inches, of 15 students. 6.SP.4, 6.SP.5, 6.SP.5c

Heights of Students (in.)				
50	60	58	64	62
52	61	54	60	50
53	62	58	55	60

Part A: Complete the box-and-whisker plot to represent the data.

Heights of Students (in.)

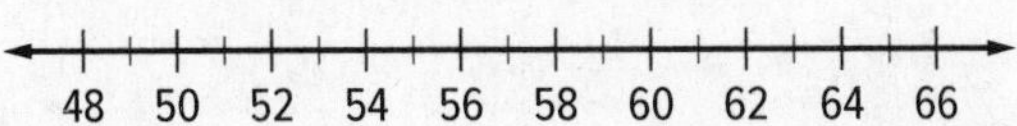

Part B: What is the interquartile range?

9. The diagram shows some points on a box-and-whisker plot. Write the appropriate point or expression that corresponds to each measure. 6.SP.5, 6.SP.5c

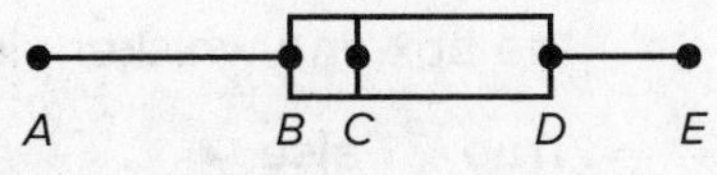

$D - B$	$E - A$	A to C	E	D to E	C

Median: ______ Range: ______

Interquartile range: ______ Greatest value: ______

Same number of values as from A to B:

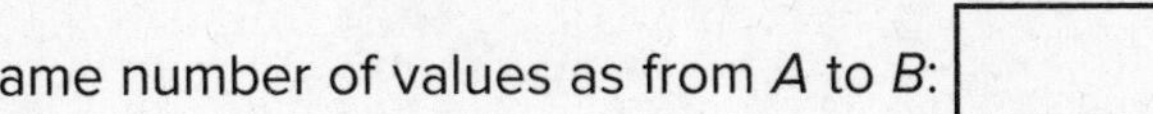

10. Piano students were asked to name their favorite musical note. The line plot shows the survey results. Select whether each statement is true or false. 6.SP.2, 6.SP.5, 6.SP.5c

Favorite Musical Notes of Piano Students

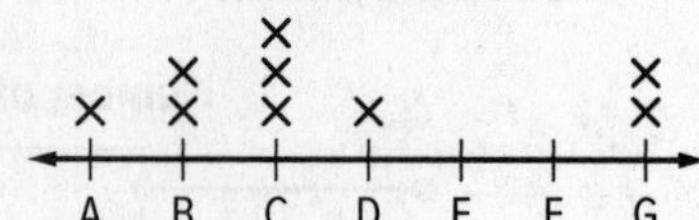

True **False**

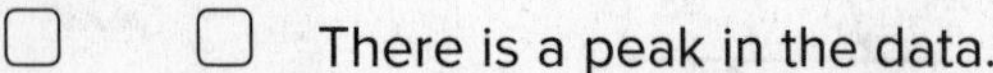

☐ ☐ There is a peak in the data.

☐ ☐ There is a gap in the data.

☐ ☐ The distribution is symmetrical.

☐ ☐ There is a data cluster.

11. A survey asked students how many sit-ups they completed in a physical education class. The histogram shows the results. Answer each question about the data in the histogram. 6.SP.2, 6.SP.5, 6.SP.5c

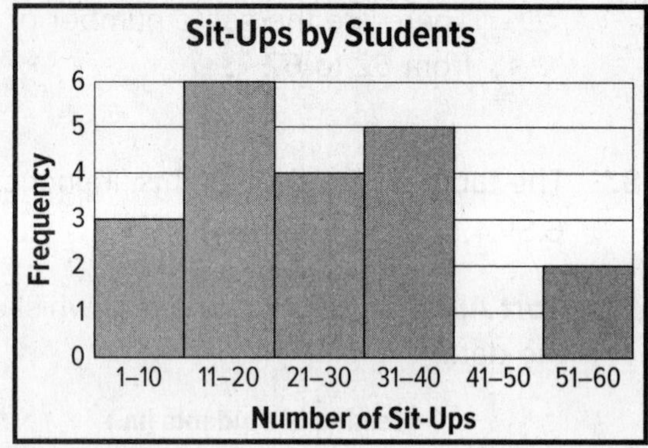

Yes **No**

☐ ☐ Is there an outlier in the interval 51–60?

☐ ☐ Is there a gap from 41–50?

☐ ☐ Is the distribution symmetrical?

☐ ☐ Is the peak 15 sit-ups?

☐ ☐ Is there a cluster from 1–40?

12. Select whether each statement is true or false in representing the data shown by the box-and-whisker plot. 6.SP.5, 6.SP.5c

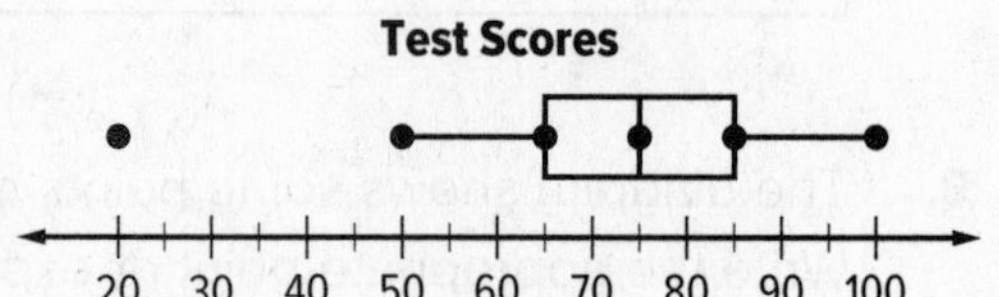

True **False**

☐ ☐ There is an outlier at 20.

☐ ☐ There is a peak at 75.

☐ ☐ The distribution is symmetrical.

☐ ☐ There is a gap from 20 to 50.

13. Select all of the situations that are best represented with a line graph. 6.SP.4

- ☐ the high temperature recorded each day for a week
- ☐ the test scores of students in a class
- ☐ the population in a town for each of eight years
- ☐ the amount of protein in a protein bar

14. Joseph wants to make a data display so that the median is easily identifiable. What type of data display should he use? Explain. 6.SP.4, 6.SP.5, 6.SP.5d

15. Juanita wants to display her standardized test scores for the last few years. What type of display should she use? Explain. 6.SP.4

16. Harold created a line plot to show research data. He now wants to present the data using a different type of display that shows the data in categories. 6.SP.4

Part A: What other type of display should Harold use?

Part B: Compare the line plot with the display you identified in Part A. How are the two displays alike and how are they different?

17. A principal wants to make a data display of the amount of time the 500 students in the school spend on homework each evening. What type of data display should the principal use? Explain your choice. 6.SP.4

18. A set of data has an outlier. Which measures of center and spread would be more appropriate to represent the data: mean and mean absolute deviation, or median and interquartile range? Explain your reasoning. 6.SP.5, 6.SP.5c, 6.SP.5d

19. Select all of the displays that show individual data values. 6.SP.4, 6.SP.5, 6.SP.5a

- ☐ bar graph
- ☐ histogram
- ☐ line plot
- ☐ line graph
- ☐ box-and-whisker plot

20. Select all of the statements that are valid in representing the data shown in the line graph. 6.SP.4

- ☐ The temperatures increase from June to July.
- ☐ The temperatures increase from August to September.
- ☐ The greatest change in temperature is between September and October.
- ☐ The highest temperatures are in August.

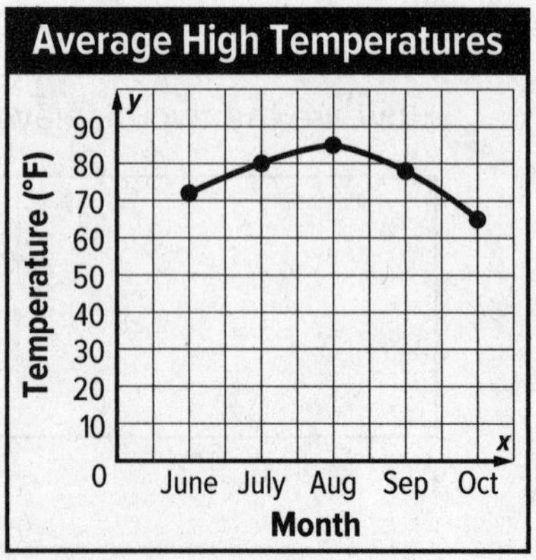

Average High Temperatures

NAME ____________________ DATE __________ PERIOD ______ SCORE ______

Chapter 1 Performance Task

Triathlon Bound

Mr. Jackson coaches the junior varsity track team. He has entered his athletes in a triathlon. He needs information to help him motivate and prepare his athletes for this challenging event.

The triathlon consists of 1 mile of swimming, 25 miles of biking, and 6 miles of running. Mr. Jackson estimates that the average time spent on each phase of the race will be 30 minutes for swimming, 75 minutes for biking, and 60 minutes for running. He sets up a training schedule that includes two sports each day.

Monday	Tuesday	Wednesday	Thursday	Friday
Swim, Bike	Run, Bike	Swim, Run	Run, Bike	Swim, Bike

Write your answers on another piece of paper. Show all your work to receive full credit.

Part A

Mr. Jackson wants to use the average times in the race as a basis for daily training times. On each day of training, the time spent on the two sports will be in the same ratio as the time expected in the actual race. Write a ratio for the amount of time that will be spent in the race for each pair of sports. Use ratio language to explain how Mr. Jackson should set up each day of training.

Part B

Make a table of values for each ratio found in Part A to show different amounts of time that could be spent on the sports during training days. Each table should have 5 pairs of values relating the two sports. The maximum values in each table should be the average time spent on the sports in the race.

Part C

Graph the ordered pairs from the tables on the same coordinate plane. Describe how the ratios of the times for each pair of sports compare.

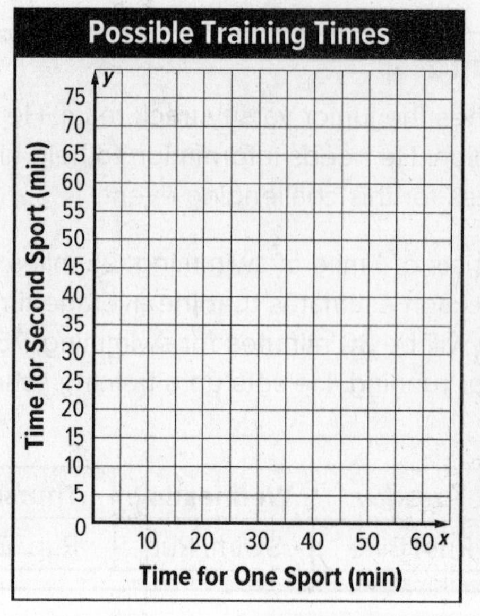

Part D

Mr. Jackson would like to know the average speed for each sport. Use the average time Mr. Jackson originally estimated would be spent on each phase of the actual race. Find the average speed for each sport as a unit rate of miles per hour (mph).

Part E

Mr. Jackson wants to find out how far an athlete will swim on Monday and bike and run on Tuesday of the first week of training compared to the fourth week of training. Each week of training corresponds to the entries listed in your ratio tables. For example, the first week of training uses the first set of times in your tables in Part B, and the second week of training uses the second set of times in your tables. Find the distances for the first and fourth weeks of training for each sport. Use the speeds found in Part D.

NAME ______________________ DATE ____________ PERIOD ________ SCORE ________

Chapter 2 Performance Task

Home Interior Paint

Ava is working in the paint department at a home improvement store. She creates custom paint colors for customers using three different pigment colors: red, blue, and yellow. The paint color that Ava creates depends on the ratio of the three pigment colors she adds to a can of white base paint.

Write your answers on another piece of paper. Show all your work to receive full credit.

Part A

Ava is helping a customer decide between three custom colors of paint. The customer plans to select the paint color that has the lowest percentage of red pigment. The table shows the number of drops of each pigment needed to create one gallon of the designated paint color.

Paint Color	Red Pigment (drops)	Blue Pigment (drops)	Yellow Pigment (drops)
Coral Paradise	8	1	10
Sunset Shine	5	1	7
Peach Pie	6	0	12

Which paint color should Ava advise the customer to select based on the lowest percentage of red pigment? Explain how you found your answer.

Part B

What is the least number of drops of red, blue, and yellow pigment that Ava can add to a gallon of white paint so that the custom color consists of 25% red, 35% blue, and 40% yellow pigment? Use a bar diagram to solve.

Part C

Ava needs help correcting a mistake she made with the pigments while creating the custom color Royal Purple. This custom color is supposed to consist of 75% red pigment and 25% blue pigment. However, Ava only added 8 drops of red pigment and 4 drops of blue pigment into the gallon of white paint. How many drops of red pigment should she add to the gallon of paint to correct her mistake?

One of Ava's job responsibilities at the home improvement store is to place an order for pigment each month. Last month she ordered these amounts of each pigment.

Pigment	Red	Blue	Yellow
Amount Ordered (oz)	8	12	12

Part D

What percent of the total amount of pigment ordered last month was red pigment? blue pigment? yellow pigment?

Part E

This month custom paint sales at the home improvement store have increased by 25%. Ava needs to order 25% more of each pigment than she did last month. Complete the table to show how many ounces of each color she should order this month. Then find the total amount of pigment.

Pigment Color	Amount Ordered Last Month	Amount to Order This Month
Red	8 oz	
Blue	12 oz	
Yellow	12 oz	

Part F

The company that supplies the pigment for the home improvement store charges $30.50 per ounce, plus $7.99 shipping. Ava purchased 40 ounces of pigment. The sales tax rate on the pigment, excluding shipping, is 6%. How much money did Ava pay in sales tax?

NAME ______________________ DATE ____________ PERIOD ________ SCORE ________

Chapter 3 Performance Task

Welcome to our School Store!

The sign shown is posted outside the school store. The sign lists the prices of all items for sale in the store.

School Supplies		Clothing		Electronic	
Portfolio	$24.59	School sweatshirt	$32.00	Mouse pad	$2.14
Eraser	$0.59	School sweatpants	$14.00	Music case	$1.25
Pencil	$0.99	School t-shirt	$11.00	Phone case	$1.99
Pen	$0.99			Scientific calculator	$175.65
Copy paper	$2.99			Graphing calculator	$205.12
Notebook	$2.48				
Notebook paper	$2.99				
Binder	$12.92				

All items are taxable at a rate of 6%.

Write your answers on another piece of paper. Show all your work to receive full credit.

Part A

A student uses three $20 bills for a purchase of 2 binders, 2 packs of copy paper, 3 notebooks, and 5 pens. All of these items are taxable. What amount of change should the student receive?

Part B

The football team is purchasing 12 t-shirts, 12 sweatpants, and 12 sweatshirts to give to a charity. They will not pay tax on the items. The cost will be divided equally among 37 players and coaches. What is the cost for each person?

Part C

The computer club is purchasing 14 portfolios, 14 binders, 14 school sweatshirts, 14 music cases, 14 phone cases, and 14 mouse pads. The club will pay for 40% of the cost. The 14 members are equally responsible for the rest of the cost. All items are taxable. How much will each member owe?

The profit the school makes is found by subtracting the cost that the store paid for an item, known as the wholesale cost, from the selling price of the item. The table shows the wholesale cost of some of the items in the school store.

Item	Portfolio	Notebook	Binder	Pen	Pencil	Mouse Pad	Eraser	Scientific Calculator
Wholesale Cost	$16.00	$2.00	$9.00	$0.50	$0.70	$1.75	$0.30	$150.00

Part D

In the first week of school, the store sold 3 portfolios, 15 notebooks, 12 binders, 22 pens, 34 pencils, and 11 mouse pads. What is the total profit for that week?

Part E

Profits from the store are equally distributed among 6 after-school programs. How much money would each after-school program receive from school profits of 3 scientific calculators, 15 portfolios, 48 notebooks, 12 mouse pads, 57 erasers, and 26 binders?

NAME _______________ DATE _______ PERIOD _____ SCORE _____

Chapter 4 Performance Task

Treasure Box

Mr. Penny's class will be constructing wooden treasure boxes. Each student will construct a box that consists of 4 rectangular pieces for the sides that are $8\frac{1}{4}$ inches long and $6\frac{3}{4}$ inches wide, and 2 rectangular pieces for the top and bottom bases that are $8\frac{1}{4}$ inches long and $8\frac{1}{4}$ inches wide. Prior to class, Mr. Penny plans to cut a wooden plank into the required pieces of wood so the students have the necessary materials at the start of class.

Write your answers on another piece of paper. Show all your work to receive full credit.

Part A

How many side pieces $8\frac{1}{4}$ inches long and $6\frac{3}{4}$ inches wide can Mr. Penny cut from a wooden plank $9\frac{5}{8}$ feet long and $\frac{9}{16}$ foot wide?

Part B

How many base pieces $8\frac{1}{4}$ inches long and $8\frac{1}{4}$ inches wide can Mr. Penny cut from a wooden plank $4\frac{1}{8}$ feet long and $4\frac{1}{8}$ feet wide? Draw a diagram to support your answer.

Part C

The rectangular sides of the treasure box will be cut from wooden planks $9\frac{5}{8}$ feet long and $\frac{9}{16}$ foot wide. How many planks will Mr. Penny need so that his 18 students can each construct one treasure box?

Part D

The rectangular bases of the treasure box will be cut from wooden planks $4\frac{1}{8}$ feet long and $4\frac{1}{8}$ feet wide. How many planks will Mr. Penny need for his 18 students to each make one treasure box?

Part E

Each treasure box will need 3 pieces of decorative ribbon $4\frac{1}{2}$ inches, or $\frac{3}{8}$ foot, long. The ribbon pieces will be cut from a long ribbon with length $2\frac{1}{4}$ feet. Use a model to find the quotient $2\frac{1}{4}$ feet $\div \frac{3}{8}$ foot. How many ribbon pieces can Mr. Penny cut from one long ribbon?

Part F

How many long ribbons will Mr. Penny need for his 18 students to each decorate one treasure box?

Part G

Mr. Penny pays $\frac{1}{10}$ of a dollar for every $\frac{1}{4}$ inch of ribbon. Find the total cost of the ribbons needed for the treasure box project.

NAME ______________________ DATE ____________ PERIOD ________ SCORE ________

Chapter 5 Performance Task

Adventure Party

Valentina is having an adventure party. She and a few friends will skydive, rappel, and complete a scavenger hunt. The skydiving will occur in a vertical wind tunnel, and the rappelling will take them into a cave below the ground. Some of the party participants are skydiving while others are rappelling. The table shows each person's position with respect to ground level after 1 hour.

Name	Valentina	Grace	Sheila	Nannette	Kendra
Location (ft)	68	–34	27	–85	–51

Write your answers on another piece of paper. Show all your work to receive full credit.

Part A

Plot each person's location on a vertical number line. Label each point with the first letter of the name. Explain what 0 represents on the number line and why.

Part B

Explain the position of each person after she perform these actions. Then use integers to justify your answers.

- Nannette moves upward 85 feet.
- Sheila moves upward 27 feet.
- Grace moves opposite to Kendra's location.

Part C

The rate at which each person descends into the cave is compared to the day's record of 11 feet per second. The table shows the difference between the person's rate and the record rate. Explain the meaning of the signs on each rate difference. Then order the participants' rates from slowest to fastest.

Name	Valentina	Grace	Sheila	Nannette	Kendra
Rate Difference (ft/s)	–0.8	–2.5	$-1\frac{2}{5}$	1.25	$-1\frac{3}{4}$

For the scavenger hunt, the party participants divide into two groups. The first group travels to locations designated on the coordinate plane as points *A*, *B*, and *C*. Their final destination, point *G*, is a reflection of *C* across the *x*-axis. Each square on the coordinate plane represents one block in Valentina's neighborhood.

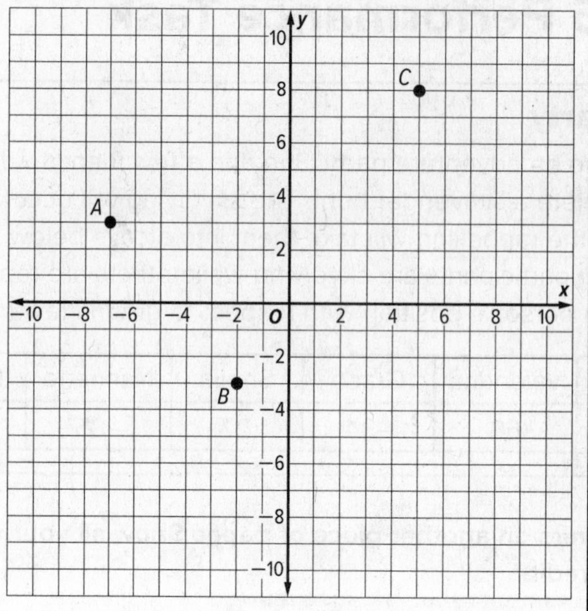

Part D

Identify each location the first group traveled to by writing the ordered pair for points *A*, *B*, *C*, and *G*. Name the quadrant in which each point lies. Explain how you located point *G*.

Part E

The second group travels from *D*(2, 5) to *E*(2, –9) to *F*(–6, 5) and then back to point *D*. Plot the group's locations on the coordinate plane. About how many square blocks did the group's travel pattern enclose? Use absolute value to explain how you determined your answer.

Part F

Valentina provides a fruit pizza for her friends to have as a snack. The shaded region represents the part of the pizza that is left at the end of the party. Represent the amount of fruit pizza the party participants consumed, using both a fraction and a decimal. Explain how you found the answer.

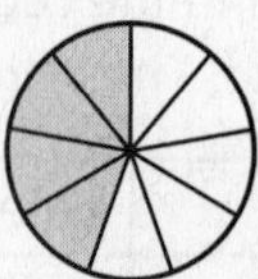

NAME ________________ DATE ________ PERIOD ______ SCORE ______

Chapter 6 Performance Task

Movie Night

Imani hosts a movie night to raise money for the drama club. The movie is viewed in the school auditorium and the snacks are purchased at the concession stand in the school cafeteria.

Write your answers on another piece of paper. Show all your work to receive full credit.

Part A

Tickets for the movie night are $4 for students and $6.50 for adults. Write an algebraic expression in simplest form to represent the total amount of ticket sales for *a* adults and 132 students. Later Paige heard that 76 adults attended the movie night. She calculates the total ticket sales for adults and students to be $3,926. Do you agree with Paige's amount? Prove your response with a calculation.

Part B

The movie projector sits on a stand that is in the shape of a rectangular prism. The length and width of the stand are both 18 inches. Use the volume formula for a rectangular prism, $V = \ell wh$, to write an expression for the volume of the stand. Then rewrite the expression using exponents. The volume of the stand is 11,664 cubic inches. What is the height? Explain how you found the answer.

Part C

Imani notices that the movie stand looks like two cubes stacked on each other. Use this fact to write an expression, using powers, for the volume of the stand. Explain your answer.

The sign shows the prices of snacks and sandwiches at the concession stand.

Snacks, Drinks		Build your own sandwich!	
Popcorn	$0.75	Bread	$$x$
Fruit	$0.50	Meat	$0.60
Drink	$1.25	Cheese	$0.40
		Vegetables	$0.35

Part D

Paulo orders two popcorns, a piece of fruit, and four drinks for his family. Write and evaluate an expression to find his cost. Laurie orders a piece of fruit, four drinks, and two popcorns for her family. How will their bills compare? Use algebraic properties to justify your answer.

Part E

Michael ordered two sandwiches, each with meat, cheese, and vegetables. Laurie says the cost is $2(x + 0.60 + 0.40 + 0.35)$, but Michael thought the cost would be $2x + 2(0.60) + 2(0.40) + 2(0.35)$. Who is correct? Explain why. Simplify each expression as part of your explanation.

NAME ______________________ DATE __________ PERIOD ______ SCORE ______

Chapter 7 Performance Task

Selling Scones

The students in the chorus will be performing at an amusement park. After the performance, the students will get to go on the rides. The students sell scones at breakfast during the school year to help raise money for the trip.

Part A

Parents volunteer to make the scones. They are given a recipe. The recipe calls for $6\frac{1}{2}$ cups of flour. Duyi has already added $2\frac{3}{4}$ cups of flour. How much more flour will he need to add? Use a bar diagram to model this situation. Then write and solve an addition equation to find the answer. How can you check your answer? Explain.

Part B

Kijika recorded students' flavor preferences last year in a table. However, the number of students that preferred almond is unreadable. Kijika remembers that the number of students who liked vanilla was $\frac{1}{5}$ of the number who liked almond. Write and solve an equation to find the number of students who preferred almond. Explain how you could use both a multiplication and a division equation to find the answer.

Preferred Flavor	Number of Students
Lemon	24
Vanilla	11
Almond	p

Part C

The chorus started selling scones when Kijika was in sixth grade. For his eighth-grade year, he projects that they will sell 140 more scones than in the previous two years combined.

Year	Number Sold
Sixth grade	146
Seventh grade	225
Eighth grade	m

Kijika writes an equation to find the number of scones they will sell this year. He first writes $m - (146 + 225) = 140$ and simplifies that to $m - 371 = 140$. He solves the simplified equation and finds that they will sell 231 scones this year. Explain what error he made in solving the equation. Then, show that 231 is not a solution of the equation. Finally, solve the equation to find the number of scones they will sell this year.

Part D

Each scone sells for $1.50. The chorus' profits are 80% of their sales. Their current profits are $578.40. How many scones have they sold? Write and solve equations to find the answer.

Part E

On cold days the chorus also sells hot tea for $2 a cup. A science teacher bought a cup of hot tea and some scones. She spent $8. How many scones did she purchase? Write and solve an equation to find the number of scones. Compare this equation to the others you have been solving in Parts A, B, C, and D.

NAME ______________________ DATE ____________ PERIOD ________ SCORE ________

Chapter 8 Performance Task

Field Trip Meeting

Mr. Ahmed is in charge of student field trips. He schedules a meeting with the students to inform them about the costs and details of an upcoming trip.

Write your answers on another piece of paper. Show all your work to receive full credit.

Part A

Mr. Ahmed records the number of students who have arrived at the meeting prior to the meeting start time. The table shows his findings.

Time Before Meeting Starts (min)	Number of Students Present
10	45
8	46
4	48

Write a function rule to represent the number of students at the meeting x minutes before the meeting begins. Does the rule make sense for all positive integers? Explain why or why not.

Part B

Mr. Ahmed will start the meeting only when at least 40 students are present. Let s be the number of students present. Write and graph an inequality to represent this situation.

Students planning to attend the field trip are required to make a $20 deposit toward the cost of the trip by the end of the meeting. Mr. Ahmed displays the graph to show the students the monthly payment plan for the field trip.

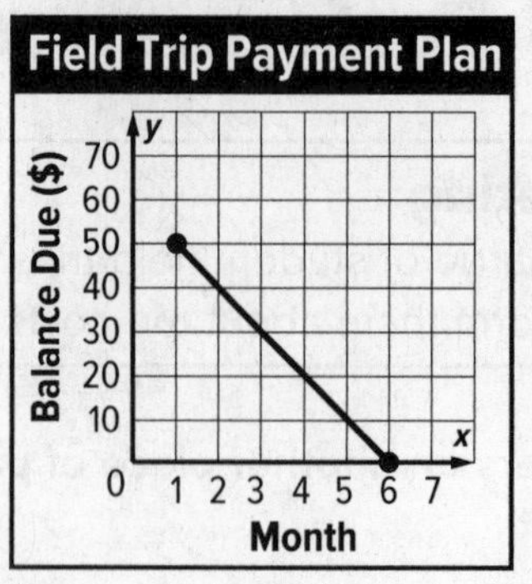

Part C

Use the graph to complete the table. Write an equation that represents the balance due y for the cost of the trip at month x. What is the balance due at month 3? Explain how you determined your answer using the graph and the equation.

Month	Balance ($)
1	
2	
4	

Part D

What is the total cost of the field trip for each student?

Part E

Jake plans to take $60 in spending money on the field trip. The table shows how much he plans to save by the end of each week for the trip. Do you think Jake will have enough spending money saved by the end of week 6? Explain your reasoning.

Week	Total Amount Saved ($)
1	2
2	4
3	8
4	16
5	32

NAME ______________________ DATE __________ PERIOD ______ SCORE ______

Chapter 9 Performance Task

The Recreation Room

Madison's father hires an architect to turn a non-rectangular space in their home into a recreation room. Madison wants the recreation room to include a dance floor.

Write your answers on another piece of paper. Show all your work to receive full credit.

Part A

The architect represents the room on a blueprint as figure *ABCD*. Plot and connect the vertices of figure *ABCD* on the coordinate plane: *A*(–4, 5), *B*(8, 5), *C*(10, –4), and *D*(–10, –4). Identify the type of figure *ABCD* is, and compute the area of the room.

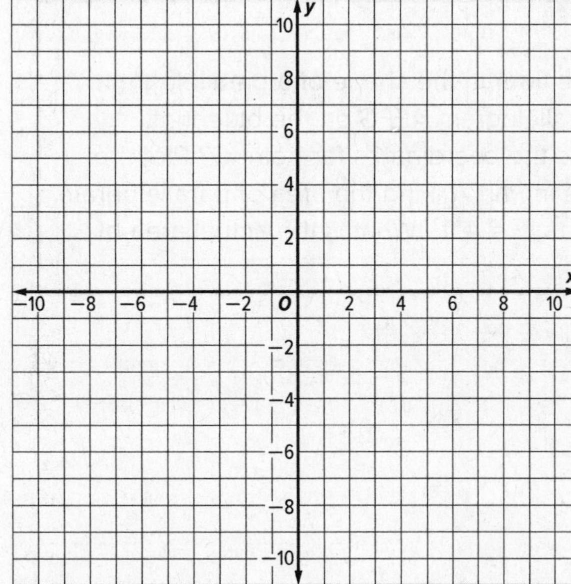

Part B

Decompose figure *ABCD* into triangles and parallelograms. Use these shapes to prove that the area you found in Part A is correct.

Part C

Originally, the space in the house designated for the recreation room was much smaller. Figure *ABCD* shown on the blueprint in Part A is based on the shape of the original designated space, but with twice the length of each side. How do the perimeter and the area of figure *ABCD* on the blueprint compare to the perimeter and the area of the original designated space? What was the area of the original designated space? Explain. The perimeter of the original designated space was approximately 26 units. What is the approximate perimeter of figure *ABCD* on the blueprint?

Part D

The architect is designing the dance floor in the shape of a parallelogram. He plots three of the vertices of parallelogram *AEFG* on the blueprint: *A*(–4, 5), *E*(2, 5), and *F*(0, 1). What are the coordinates for point *G*? Plot the dance floor on the coordinate plane in Part A. Find the area of parallelogram *AEFG*. The key on the blueprint is 1 unit^2 = 4 ft^2. What is the actual area of the dance floor?

Part E

Madison chooses wood flooring for the dance floor and carpet for the rest of the area. The flooring costs $4.99 per square foot, and the carpet costs $7.99 per square foot. Madison's dad budgeted $4,500 for flooring materials. Did Madison stay within or go over the flooring budget, and by how much? Support your answer.

NAME _______________ DATE ________ PERIOD ______ SCORE ______

Chapter 10 Performance Task

Math Crunchies

A new cereal is being marketed to those who love mathematics. Math Crunchies is a whole-grain cereal in the shape of operations signs: +, –, ×, and ÷. Osamu, Vajra, Kanuna, and Deondre are on the packaging design team.

Write your answers on another piece of paper. Show all your work to receive full credit.

Part A

Osamu designs a cereal box for a single-sized serving. Draw and label a net of the cereal box. What is the least amount of cardboard needed to make one box?

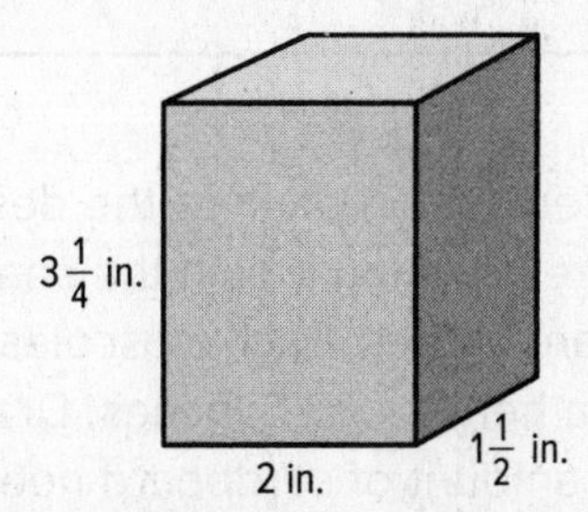

Part B

Vajra triples each dimension of Osamu's cereal box. What are the dimensions and surface area of the new box? How many times more cardboard is needed to make Vajra's cereal box than Osamu's cereal box?

Part C

Find the number of cereal servings that can fit inside of Vajra's cereal box. Justify your answer.

Part D

Kanuna takes a different approach to the design of the cereal box. He designs a single-sized serving box in the shape of a square pyramid. The base area is 9 square inches. Each isosceles triangular face has a perimeter of 10.8 inches and a height of 3.6 inches. Draw and label a net of this box. Calculate the least amount of cardboard needed to create this box.

Part E

Deondre designs a cereal box in the shape of a triangular prism. His cereal box has the same volume and height as Osamu's cereal box. Determine the possible dimensions for the base of the prism. Explain your reasoning.

NAME ______________________ DATE ____________ PERIOD ________ SCORE ________

Chapter 11 Performance Task

Bird Watching

Sofia's favorite part of hiking is bird watching. She dreams of vacationing in Costa Rica and viewing the famous quetzal. She polls her friends to find out how many birds each can identify. She records the results in the table.

Number of Identifiable Birds				
22	17	24	56	19
34	8	28	25	21
33	24	18	29	24

Write your answers on another piece of paper. Show all your work to receive full credit.

Part A

Based on the results of Sofia's survey, what is the mean number of birds that can be identified? Round your answer to the nearest tenth. Sofia can identify 27 birds. Suppose Sofia includes her data value in the survey results. How will the mean be affected? Explain.

Part B

Based on the results in the table, what is the median number of birds that can be identified? How does adding Sofia's value of 27 birds affect the median? Explain.

Part C

What is the range of the data, including Sofia's value of 27 birds? What is the IQR? Explain how you found your answer. Is there an outlier in the data? Justify your answer.

Sofia also enjoys fishing. She knows how to identify 12 different types of fish. She polls her friends to find out how many fish each can identify. She records the results of her survey in the table.

Number of Identifiable Fish				
10	12	13	11	15
15	8	11	12	13
14	10	12	12	9

Part D

Find and interpret the mode of the fish data in the table. Explain how you determined the value of the mode.

Part E

The mean absolute deviation (MAD) for the fish data is 6.7. Sofia can identify 12 fish. Including Sofia's data value, what is the MAD for the fish data? Do not round your calculations until the final step. Use the MAD values to compare the bird data and the fish data.

Part F

What is the most appropriate measure of center (mean, median, or mode) for each set of data? Justify your answer.

NAME ____________________ DATE ____________ PERIOD ________ SCORE ________

Chapter 12 Performance Task

For this Performance Task, your teacher will ask you to do some research to provide the data you will use for your calculations.

Wagging the Dog

Dog shows include many types of dogs. The judges observe, evaluate, and measure different aspects of each dog type.

Research ten different breeds of dogs. Find the ideal weight of each type of dog, in pounds.

Write your answers on another piece of paper. Show all your work to receive full credit.

Part A

Create a line plot of the data. Describe the distribution. What does the distribution tell you about the weights of the dogs?

Part B

Create a frequency table using appropriate intervals for the data. Then use the frequency table to create a histogram.

Part C

Compare the line plot and the histogram. State some advantages and disadvantages for displaying the data in each type of plot. Which of these two data displays is better suited for this type of data? Justify your answer.

Part D

Are there any outliers in your data? Explain your answer.

Part E

Create a box-and-whisker plot of the data. Describe how you would use the box-and-whisker plot to find the answer to this question: The ideal weight of half of the dogs is at least how many pounds?

Part F

Explain why you would *not* use a line graph to display the data. Describe data related to a dog that could be displayed on a line graph.

NAME ________________ DATE ________ PERIOD ______ SCORE ______

Benchmark Test, Chapters 1–4

1. Namid works for a florist and is making flower arrangements for the tables at a reception. He has 36 roses, 48 tulips, and 72 carnations. Each vase must contain the same number of each type of flower. How many vases will Namid need? How many of each type of flower will he put in one vase? 6.NS.4

Vases:

Flowers:

2. On a map, 3 centimeters represents 500 miles. 6.RP.3

Part A: Two cities are 9 centimeters apart on the map. How many miles apart are the two cities?

Part B: Two national parks are 750 miles apart. How many centimeters apart are the two parks on the map?

3. A restaurant sells an 8-oz drink for $2.56 and a 12-oz drink for $3.66. Which drink is the better buy? Justify your answer. 6.RP.2, 6.RP.3, 6.RP.3b

4. Desta reads at a constant rate of 3 pages in 8 minutes. 6.RP.3, 6.RP.3a

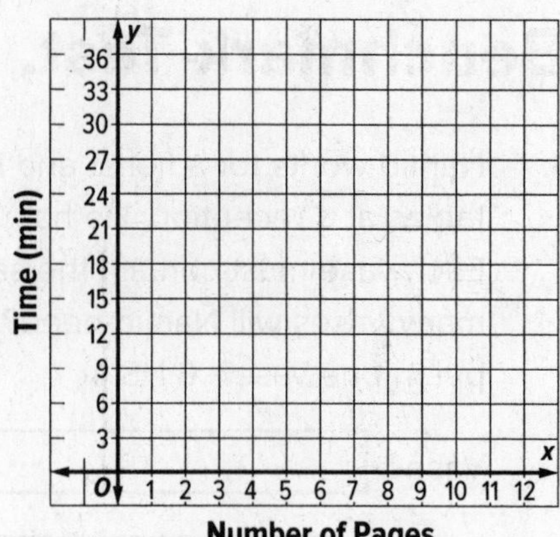

Part A: Complete the ratio table for Desta's reading rate.

Number of Pages	3	6		12
Time (min)	8		24	

Part B: Graph the ordered pairs that show the time it takes Desta to read 3, 6, 9, and 12 pages.

5. A train travels at a rate of 84 miles per hour. Select all of the rates that are equivalent to the train's speed. 6.RP.2, 6.NS.2

- ☐ 162 miles in 2 hours
- ☐ 252 miles in 3 hours
- ☐ 378 miles in 4.5 hours
- ☐ 489 miles in 6 hours
- ☐ 621.6 miles in 7.4 hours

6. Sort the decimals into the appropriate bins by their percent values. 6.RP.3

1.3	0.9	89.2
0.398	1	0.095

Greater than 90%	Equal to 90%	Less than 90%

7. A student conducted a survey of other students to find the number of sports they play. The table shows the results of the survey. 6.RP.3

Number of Sports Played	0	1	2	3+
Portion of Responses	0.25	$\frac{1}{5}$	$\frac{3}{8}$	17.5%

Complete the table to order the responses from least to greatest percent of students.

	Number of Sports Played	**Percent of Students**
Least		
Greatest		

8. Mr. Guerrero counted 60 students wearing a school shirt. Select all the expressions that represent this value. 6.RP.3, 6.RP.3c

- ☐ 10% of 600 students
- ☐ 15% of 500 students
- ☐ 20% of 400 students
- ☐ 25% of 240 students
- ☐ 40% of 150 students

9. A sewing needle manufacturer states that an average of $\frac{1}{5}$% of the needles produced will be defective. Last week, 150,000 needles were produced. Predict the number of needles that were defective. 6.RP.3, 6.RP.3c

10. In the first football game, the quarterback completed 18 out of the 24 passes he attempted. 6.RP.3, 6.RP.3c

Part A: What percent of the passes did the quarterback complete?

Part B: In the next game, the quarterback completed 19 of the 26 passes he attempted. Explain the change in the quarterback's overall percentage of completion for the two games compared to his completion percentage from the first game.

11. Amadahy wants to buy a card and two gifts for her friend. Cards cost $3.49 each and gifts cost $10.63 each. Amadahy has a $20 bill. Does she have enough money to buy these items? If so, how much change will she receive? If not, how much more money does she need? Explain. 6.NS.3

12. Select all of the expressions that have a product with only two decimal places. 6.NS.3

- ☐ 0.45 × 37
- ☐ 6.7 × 5.3
- ☐ 2.17 × 3.48
- ☐ 6.148 × 6.32
- ☐ 5.02 × 8.04
- ☐ 7.54 × 14.5

13. The rectangles have the same area. What is the length of the unknown side? 6.NS.3

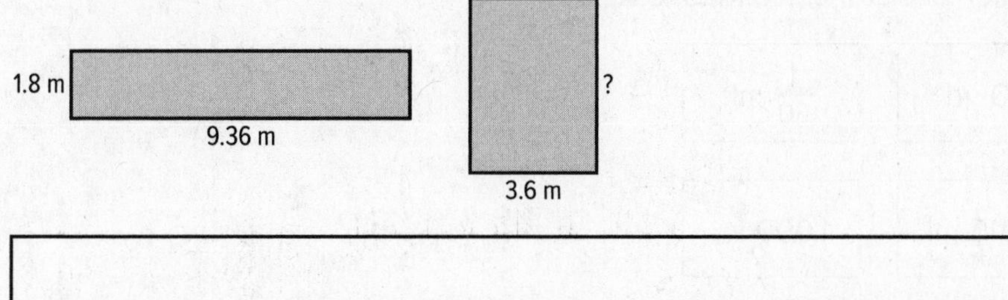

14. The table shows Amiri's jogging workouts for four days. Complete the table to order the days from Amiri's slowest to fastest jogging rate. 6.RP.3, 6.RP.3b

Day	Distance (mi)	Time (h)
Monday	4.75	1.25
Wednesday	6.21	1.8
Friday	8.64	2.4
Sunday	9.13	2.2

	Day	Rate (mph)
Slowest		
Fastest		

15. One machine at a manufacturer makes 81,600 paper clips in a day. 6.NS.2

Part A: The machine runs at a constant speed all day. How many paper clips are made each hour?

Part B: One size box can hold 40 paper clips. How many boxes are filled each hour?

16. On a baseball diamond, the distance from home plate to first base is 90 feet. Sort the lengths into the appropriate bins by how each length compares to the baseball distance. 6.RP.3, 6.RP.3d

360 ft	30 yd	$\frac{1}{50}$ mi
900 in.	0.015 mi	1,090 in.

Less than 90 ft	Equal to 90 ft	Greater than 90 ft

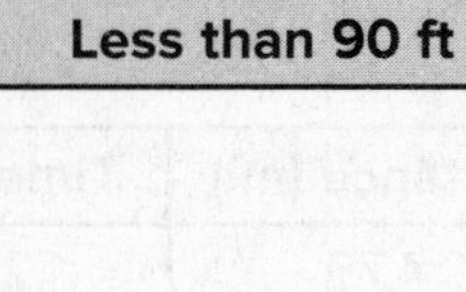

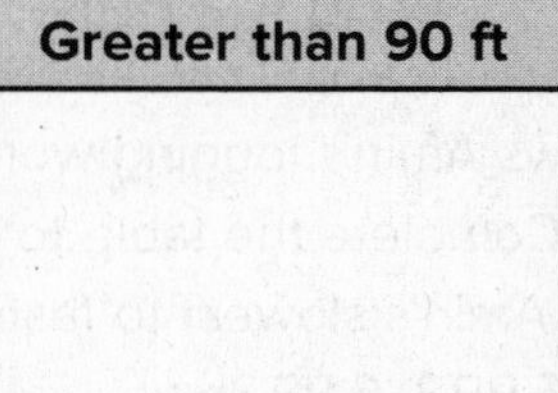

17. Mrs. Harris took 6 oranges out of the refrigerator and cut them into wedges. Each wedge represents $\frac{1}{6}$ of the entire orange. Her children ate $\frac{3}{4}$ of the wedges. How many wedges are left? Justify your answer. 6.NS.1

18. A salami is $2\frac{3}{5}$ inches long. The salami is cut into $\frac{1}{8}$-inch thick slices. 6.NS.1

Part A: How many slices of salami were cut?

Part B: Write the correct numbers to identify the length of the leftover piece of salami. You can write 1 or 2 numbers in each box to make either a 1-digit or a 2-digit number.

1	2	3	4	5
6	7	8	9	0

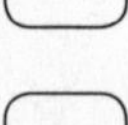

$\frac{\square}{\square}$ inch

19. Two numbers are multiplied and the product is $\frac{3}{8}$. 6.NS.1

Part A: Select whether each statement is true or false.

True	False	
☐	☐	Both factors are less than $\frac{3}{8}$.
☐	☐	One factor is less than $\frac{3}{8}$; the other factor is greater than $\frac{3}{8}$.
☐	☐	Both factors are greater than $\frac{3}{8}$.

Part B: Give an example to support a true statement.

20. There are 75 boys in the sixth grade. The number of boys is $\frac{5}{12}$ of the students in the sixth grade. How many of the sixth-grade students are girls? 6.NS.1

NAME ______________________ DATE ____________ PERIOD ________ SCORE ________

Benchmark Test, Performance Task, Chapters 1–4

For this Performance Task, your teacher will ask you to do some research to provide the data you will use for your calculations.

The Stock Market

Owning stock in a company is one way to invest your money.

For this task, research stock information for three different companies. Find the price of the stock, the amount of increase or decrease from the previous day, the P/E ratio, a five-day history, and a five-year history of the stock price.

Write your answers on another piece of paper. Show all your work to receive full credit.

Part A

For each company, use ratio language to describe the price-to-earnings (P/E) ratio. Then explain how these ratios compare to one another.

Part B

For each company, find what percentage of today's stock price is the previous day's stock price. Write your answers as sentences.

Part C

For each company, determine the relationship between the total value of a stock today and the number of shares. Express one of the relationships as an equation, one as a table, and one as a graph on the coordinate plane. Then find the value of 15 shares of each stock.

Part D

For each company, find the difference between the current year's highest stock price and the highest stock price during the year five years ago. Explain each of your answers in a sentence.

NAME ______________________ DATE __________ PERIOD ________ SCORE ________

Benchmark Test, Performance Task, Chapters 5–8

1. Mark owes Veronica $19 for building a doghouse for his dog. Veronica has eight $1 bills in her purse. Explain the meaning of 0 in this situation. 6.NS.5

2. Last week, the town of Maineville was behind the average weekly rainfall by 3 inches. After today's rainfall, the town was ahead of the average weekly rainfall by 4 inches. Graph both points on the number line. 6.NS.6

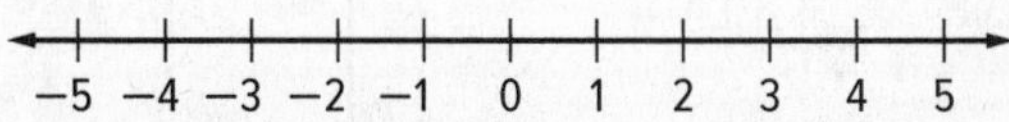

3. Circle all of the phrases that can be described by the same absolute value. 6.NS.7, 6.NS.7c

a loss of 12°　　an increase in a room's temperature by 12°

12° above freezing　　an increase in an oven's temperature by 10°

4. The table shows the melting points of five different elements to the nearest degree Celsius. Is the absolute value of the highest melting point greater than, less than, or equal to the absolute value of the lowest melting point? Justify your reasoning. 6.NS.7, 6.NS.7c

Element	Melting Point (°C)
Bromine	−7
Francium	27
Radon	−71
Rubidium	39
Mercury	−39

5. A contractor needs bricks that are 8 inches long for a project. The table shows the difference between 8 inches and the actual length of four types of bricks. 6.NS.7, 6.NS.7a

Brick	Difference (in.)
A	$-0.\overline{6}$
B	$\frac{2}{3}$
C	$\frac{5}{6}$
D	-0.625

Part A: Which bricks are longer than what the contractor needs? Order the differences from least to greatest.

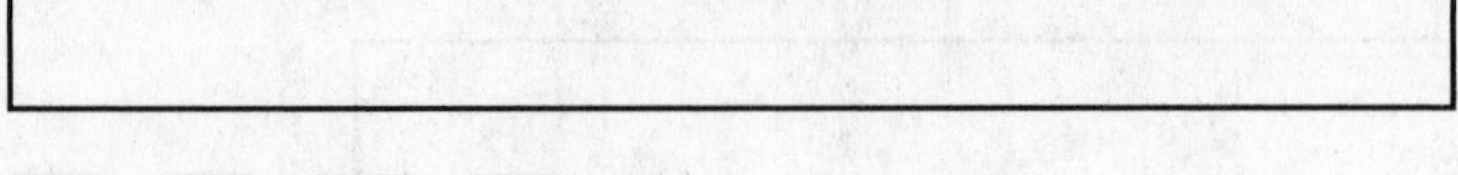

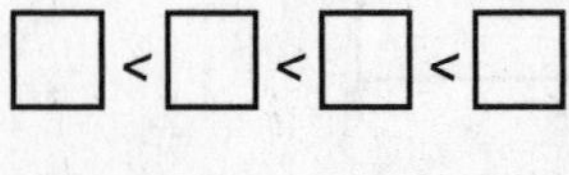

Part B: Between which two bricks is the brick size that the contractor needs? Justify your response.

6. The base of Ricardo's house is in the shape of a rectangle. The points *A*, *B*, and *C* represent three corners of the base of the house. 6.NS.6, 6.NS.6b, 6.NS.6c

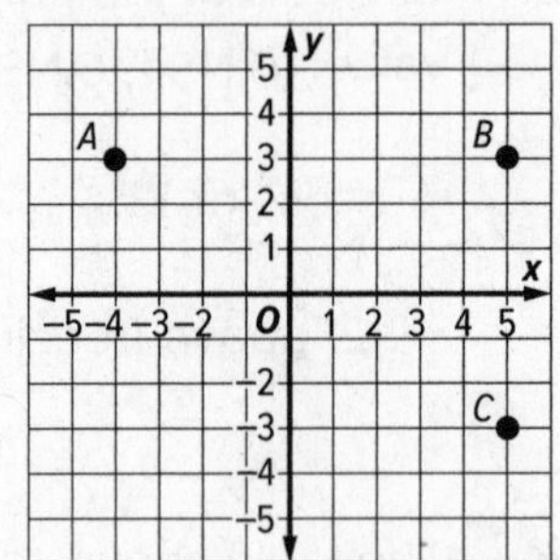

Part A: Complete the table by identifying the ordered pair that names each point. Then identify the quadrant in which each point is located.

Point	Ordered Pair	Quadrant
A		
B		
C		

Part B: Identify the ordered pair for point *D*, the fourth corner of the base of the house.

7. Which expression is not equivalent to the other three? Justify your response. 6.EE.1, 6.NS.3

$0.3^2 + 8$	$2^3 + 0.09$	$2^3 + 0.03^2$	$3^2 \div 10^2 + 2^3$

8. The table shows the pounds of corn picked by each of Shani's cousins at an All-You-Can-Pick corn farm. The cousins picked a total of 85 pounds of corn. 6.EE.2, 6.EE.6

Name	Corn Picked (lb)
Ann	x
Ben	23
Chris	35
David	15

Part A: Write the appropriate numbers, variables, and symbols in the expression to represent the total number of pounds of corn picked by the cousins.

+	–	×	÷	x
23	35	15	85	73

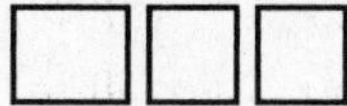

Part B: How many pounds of corn did Ann pick?

9. Each row in the table shows a pair of expressions.

Part A: Complete the second column in the table. Write whether the pairs of expressions in each row are equivalent.

Expressions	Equivalent? Yes or No	Property
7 – 3 and 3 – 7		
$d \times 1$ and d		
$(3 + y) + 2$ and $(y + 3) + 2$		
$(3 + y) + 2$ and $3 + (y + 2)$		
$0 \times m$ and m		

Part B: Complete the third column in the table. Write the property that is applied for each pair of equivalent expressions. 6.EE.3

- Associative Property of Add.
- Associative Property of Mult.
- Commutative Property of Add.
- Commutative Property of Mult.
- Identity Property of Add.
- Identity Property of Mult.
- Distributive Property
- Addition Property of Equality

10. Marta and four friends went to a movie. The movie tickets were $7 each. Each person also paid y dollars for a snack and a drink. 6.EE.3, 6.NS.4

Part A: Write the appropriate numbers and variables in the expression to represent the amount they spent altogether.

☐ × (☐ + ☐)

4	5	7
12	28	y

Part B: Write the expression in simplified form.

☐

11. For a small-sized box, a shipping company charges x dollars to ship the package, y dollars to wrap the package, and $6 to insure the package. The expression $5x + 5y + 30 + x + y$ represents the total cost of shipping, packaging, and insuring 5 packages, and shipping and packaging 1 package without insurance. 6.EE.2, 6.EE.2b, 6.EE.4

List all the terms of the expression.

List the coefficients of the expression.

List the constant(s) of the expression.

Write the expression in simplified form.

☐

12. Select all of the equations that have a solution of 4. 6.EE.5

- ☐ $g - 3 = 7$
- ☐ $\frac{20}{g} = 5$
- ☐ $12 + g = 16$
- ☐ $\frac{g}{2} = 8$
- ☐ $8g = 32$
- ☐ $4(5 - g) = g$

13. Yang is y years old. His brother is 4.5 years younger than Yang. His brother is 9.5 years old. 6.EE.7

Part A: Write a subtraction equation to model the situation.

Part B: Solve the equation to find Yang's age.

14. Mrs. Ruiz travels a distance of 144 miles to attend a business meeting. She drives for 3 hours at an average speed of r miles per hour. 6.EE.7, 6.RP.3

Part A: Write the appropriate numbers, symbols, and variables to represent the situation with an equation.

r	144	3	1
+	−	×	÷

☐ = ☐ ☐ ☐

Part B: What is Mrs. Ruiz's average speed in miles per hour?

15. Kathy rode her bike 8 miles today. This was $\frac{1}{4}$ of the miles she rode this month. How many miles m did Kathy ride her bike this month? Justify your answer using an equation. 6.EE.7

16. Todd's car consumes an average of 1 gallon of gas for every 25 miles he drives. Select all of the representations that model this function. 6.EE.9

☐ 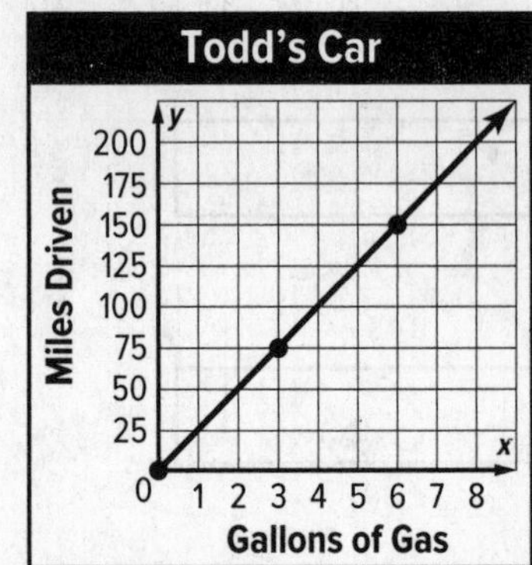

☐ $y = 20x + 5$, where y represents the total number of miles driven and x represents the number of gallons of gas

☐

Miles Driven	250	300	480	600
Gallons of Gas	10	12	19.2	24

17. A recycling company uses the inequality $t \geq 3.5$, where t is the mass of paper recycled per month, to determine whether they recycle enough paper to make a profit that month. Sort the months into the appropriate bins based on whether the company made a profit that month recycling paper. 6.EE.5

Month	Mass of Paper, t
January	4.2
February	1.8
March	3.9
April	3.5
May	1.5
June	0.75

January	February	March
April	May	June

Made a Profit	Did Not Make a Profit

18. The construction crew has less than 7 days left to complete the road repairs. Let *d* represent the number of days left to complete the road repairs. 6.EE.6, 6.EE.8

Part A: Write an inequality to represent this situation.

Part B: Graph the solution of the inequality on the number line.

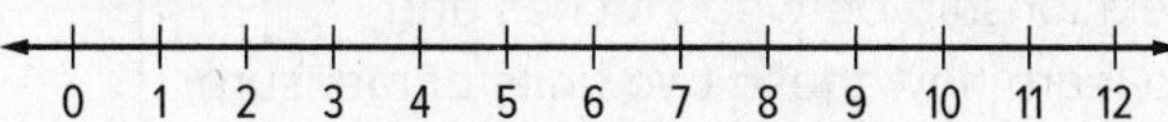

19. Akeelah buys an $18 binder for her baseball cards. The baseball cards she purchases cost $12 per box. 6.EE.2, 6.EE.2c

Part A: Complete the table to find the cost when Akeelah buys 2, 3, 5, and 7 boxes of cards.

Number of Boxes, *x*	$12x + 18$	Cost ($), *y*
2		
3		
5		
7		

Part B: What is the cost of 10 boxes of baseball cards and a binder?

20. All entrees cost $10 at the Roadside Diner. Each side dish is an additional $2. The equation $y = 2x + 10$ describes the total cost, *y*, for the number of side dishes, *x*. Graph the equation of the line. 6.EE.9

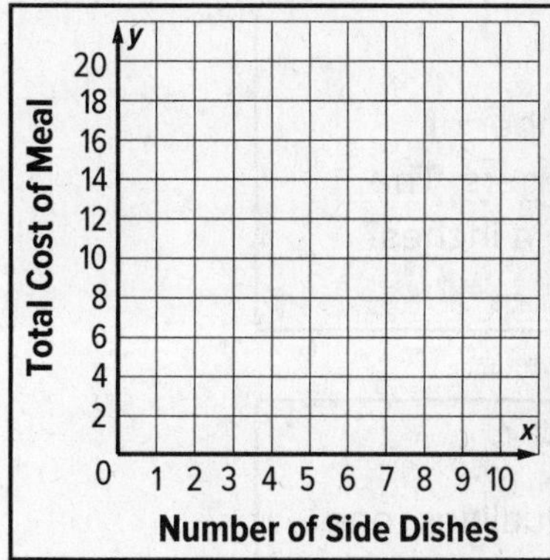

NAME _______________ DATE _______ PERIOD _______ SCORE _______

Benchmark Test, Performance Task, Chapters 5–8

For this Performance Task, your teacher will ask you to collect some data that you will use for your calculations.

Big Foot

Have you ever wondered about the relationship between inches and centimeters? You can use your data to learn how these two units of measure are related.

For this task, collect data by measuring the foot length of 10 other students. You should measure from the back of the heel to the top of the longest toe. Measure the length of each student's foot to the nearest $\frac{1}{8}$ inch and to the nearest tenth of a centimeter.

Write your answers on another piece of paper. Show all your work to receive full credit.

Part A

Create a table to record your data. Label the first row or column *Length (in.)* and the second row or column *Length (cm)*. Then graph your data on a coordinate plane. Let the *x*-axis be the length in inches and the *y*-axis be the length in centimeters.

Part B

Describe the relationship between the number of inches and the number of centimeters. Represent this relationship as an algebraic expression. Caro's father's foot is 13 inches long. What is this length in centimeters?

Part C

Write a function that relates the number of *x* inches to the number of *y* centimeters. Explain why this rule would not apply for all integers. The length of Baily's foot is 23.125 centimeters. What is this length in inches? Explain how you used your function to find the answer.

Part D

Let *f* be the length of a student's foot in inches. Write two inequalities, one using ≥ and the other using <, that are true for the data you collected. Then graph each inequality. Would a student's foot that is 45 centimeters long make your inequalities true? Explain.

NAME ______________________ DATE ____________ PERIOD ________ SCORE ________

Benchmark Test A, Chapters 1–12

1. The Andersons drove 175 miles in $3\frac{1}{2}$ hours. 6.RP.2, 6.RP.3, 6.RP.3b, 6.RP.3d

Part A: What is their average driving rate, in miles per hour?

Part B: At this rate, how many miles will the Andersons drive in $8\frac{1}{2}$ hours?

Part C: What is the Andersons' driving rate in feet per second? Round to the nearest tenth.

2. A bookstore advertises 4 paperback books for $18.00. Select all of the equivalent ratios. 6.RP.1, 6.RP.3, 6.RP.3a

- ☐ 1 book for $4.00
- ☐ 3 books for $13.50
- ☐ 6 books for $25.00
- ☐ 9 books for $40.50
- ☐ 10 books for $45.00

3. Students at a middle school were surveyed to determine how they arrive at school each day. The table shows the results of the survey. Complete the table to order the responses from least to greatest percent of students. 6.RP.3

How Students Arrive at School	Portion of Students
Walk	29%
Bicycle	$\frac{1}{4}$
Dropped off	0.06
Bus	$\frac{2}{5}$

	How Students Arrive at School	Percent of Students
Least		
Greatest		

4. A principal estimated that 100 students attended the school's play. Select all of the statements that could represent this estimate. 6.RP.3, 6.RP.3c

- ☐ 65% of 150 students
- ☐ 24% of 394 students
- ☐ 52% of 140 students
- ☐ 78% of 211 students

5. A store reduces the price of a jacket by 40%. The sale price of the jacket is marked as $30.00. 6.RP.3, 6.RP.3c

Part A: What percent of the original price is the sale price?

Part B: What was the original price of the jacket?

6. Decide whether each product will have 3 decimal places. 6.NS.3

Yes	No	
☐	☐	42.7 × 3.5
☐	☐	6 × 1.732
☐	☐	1.85 × 10.7
☐	☐	20.34 × 5.02
☐	☐	6.217 × 5.384

7. Sebastian ran 8.64 miles in 2.4 hours at a steady pace. 6.NS.2, 6.NS.3, 6.RP.3, 6.RP.3d

Part A: How many miles did Sebastian run in 1 hour?

Part B: How many miles did Sebastian run in the last 24 minutes? Justify your answer.

8. Decide whether each product is less than 1, equal to 1, or greater than 1. Sort the products into the appropriate bins. 6.NS.1

$\frac{2}{3} \times \frac{3}{4}$ | $\frac{4}{5} \times 1\frac{1}{4}$ | $\frac{1}{6} \times 6\frac{1}{2}$

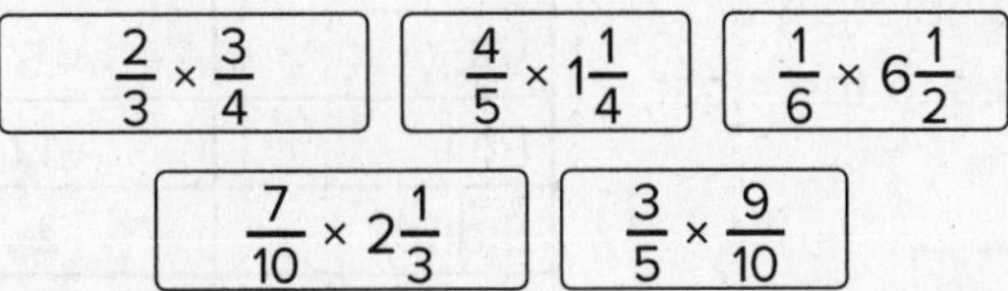

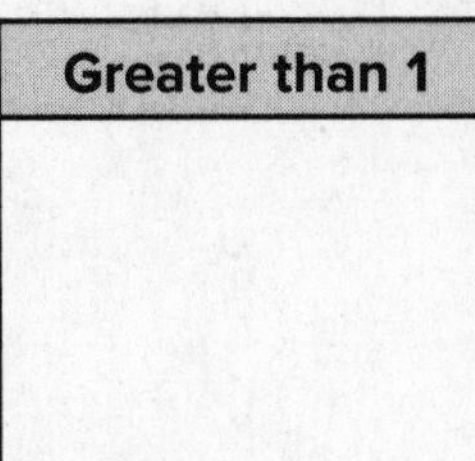

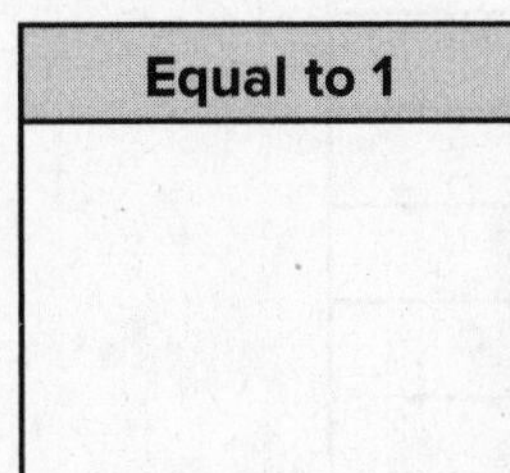

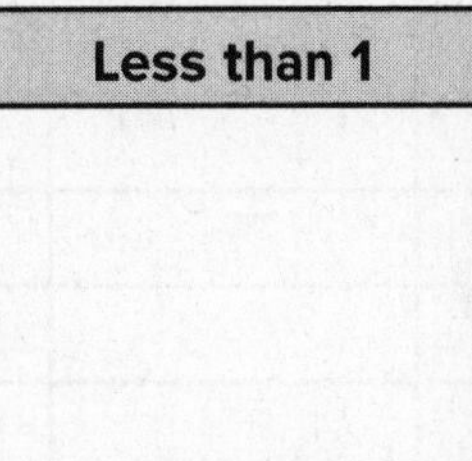

9. A baker cuts pies into equal slices as shown in the diagram. Select all of the expressions the baker can use to find the total number of pie slices. 6.NS.1

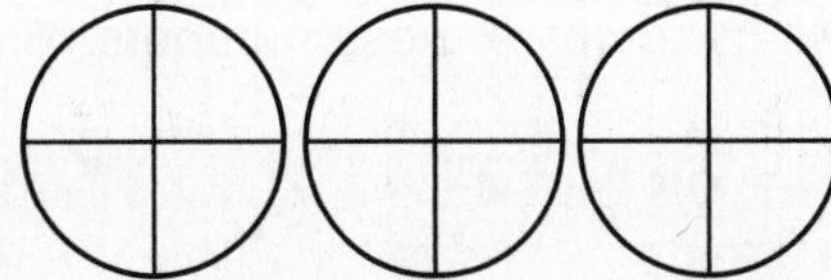

- ☐ $3 \div \frac{1}{4} = \frac{3}{4}$
- ☐ $3 \div \frac{1}{4} = 12$
- ☐ $12 \div \frac{1}{3} = 4$
- ☐ $12 \div \frac{1}{4} = 3$

10. The length of Rosie's garden is $21\frac{1}{4}$ feet. Fencing comes in pieces $2\frac{1}{8}$ feet long. 6.NS.1

Part A: How many pieces of fencing will Rosie need along the length of her garden?

Part B: For each piece of fencing, 4 stakes are used to secure it in place. The stakes are equally spaced along the fencing piece, with one stake at each end. How far apart are the stakes on one piece of fencing?

11. The table shows the scores of five golfers at the end of a tournament. The integer 0 represents par. The greater the score, the more golf strokes a player makes. Complete the table to order the players from the fewest strokes to the most strokes. 6.NS.7, 6.NS.7b

Player	Golf Score
Isao	7
Vijay	–5
Phil	–12
Eldrick	2
Jack	0

	Score	Player
Fewest strokes		
Most strokes		

12. A student wants to compare these numbers. 6.NS.6, 6.NS.6c, 6.NS.7, 6.NS.7a

2	–1.3	0.4	$-1\frac{1}{2}$
–3.1	1.3	–2	4.0

Part A: Graph the points on the number line. Label the points.

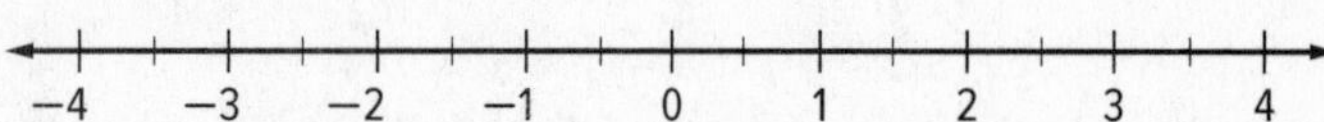

Part B: Compare the numbers by writing them in the inequality.

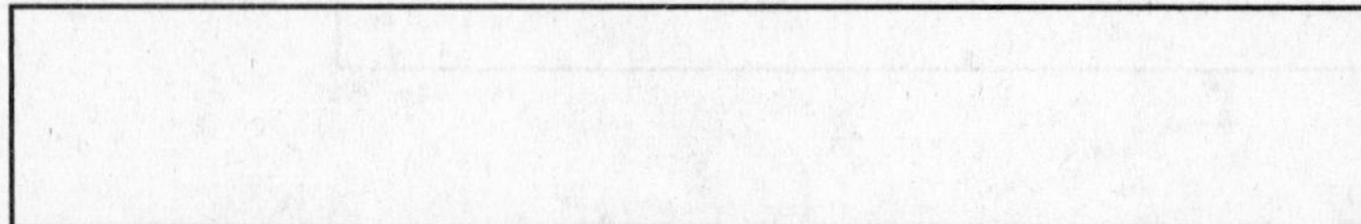

13. Mr. Wong graphed points *A* and *B* on the coordinate plane and then connected them. 6.NS.6, 6.NS.6b, 6.NS.8

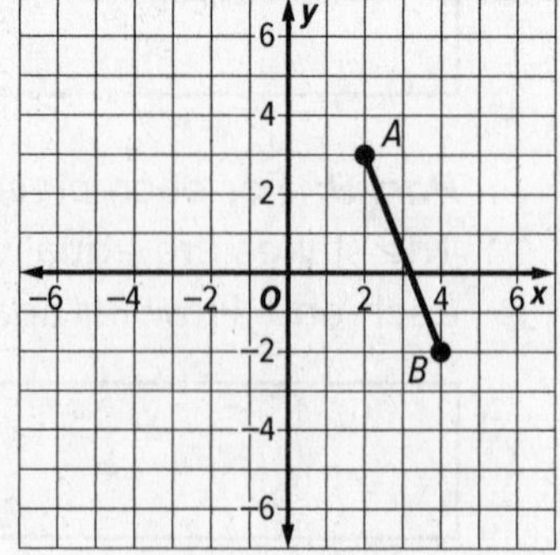

Part A: Reflect points *A* and *B* over the *y*-axis and then connect them.

Part B: How do the coordinates of the reflected points compare to the coordinates of the original points *A* and *B*?

14. Powers have a base and an exponent. Sort each power into the appropriate bin based on how the value compares to 16. 6.EE.1

4^2	5^3	3^5
2^4	3^2	8^2

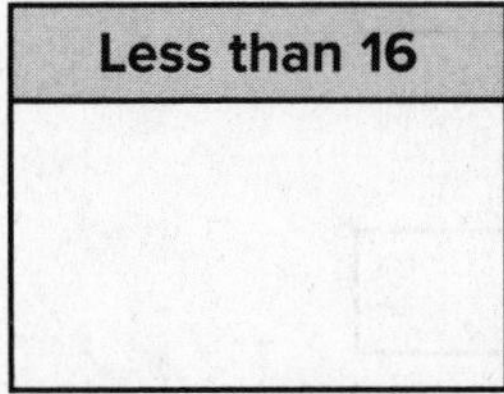

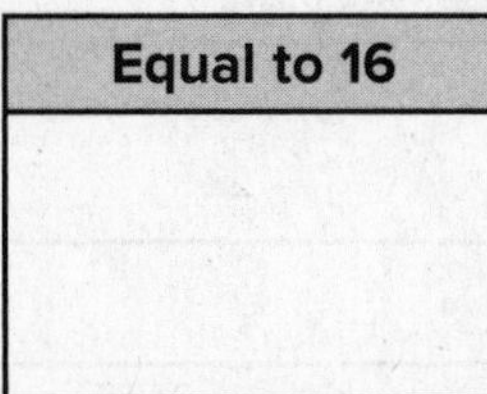

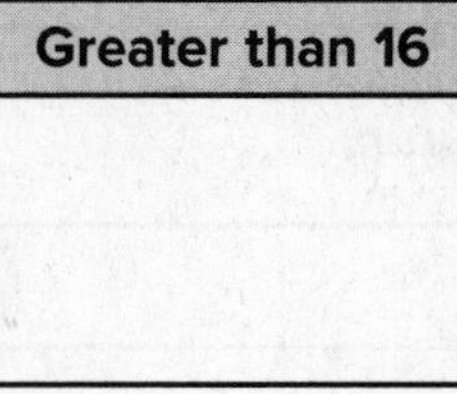

15. Five friends went to an amusement park. The cost of admission per person is x dollars. Three friends paid $30 each for a front-of-line pass. The group had a $20 coupon off the total price. Circle all of the expressions that represent the total cost. 6.EE.2, 6.EE.2a, 6.EE.4

$5x + 30 - 20$	$3(30) + 2x - 20$	$5(x + 30) - 20$	$5x + 70$
$2x + 70$	$3(x + 30) + 2x - 20$	$3(x + 30 - 20) + 2x$	$5x + 10$
$3(x + 10) + 2x$	$3x + 30 + 2x - 20$	$3x + 90 + 2x - 20$	$5x + 30$

16. The rent for an apartment is $800 per month. The landlord charges one month's rent as a deposit plus a nonrefundable damage cost of $250. The expression $800(n + 1) + 250$ represents the cost of the renting the apartment for n months. 6.EE.2, 6.EE.2c, 6.EE.3

Simplify the expression.

[ ]

How much does the apartment cost to rent for 2 years?

[ ]

17. A teacher said that the solution of an equation is $n = 6$. Select all of the equations that have 6 as the solution. 6.EE.5

- ☐ $n + 8 = 14$
- ☐ $5n = 11$
- ☐ $\frac{n}{3} = 18$
- ☐ $\frac{60}{n} = 10$
- ☐ $15 - n = 9$

18. Nicole has run 2.75 miles so far in a race. The race is 10.5 miles. Write an addition equation and then solve to find out how much farther Nicole has to run. 6.EE.7

Addition equation:

Miles Nicole has to run:

19. A bus traveled 744 miles between two cities. The bus traveled at a speed of 48 miles per hour. Write a multiplication equation and then solve to find out how many hours it took for the bus to arrive at its destination. 6.EE.7

Multiplication equation:

Hours the bus takes to arrive:

20. A health-club membership costs \$30 to join and \$40 per month. Select all of the representations of this function. 6.EE.9

☐ 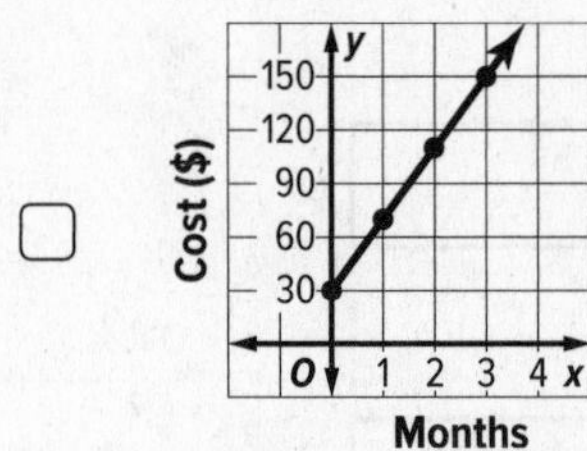

☐ $y = 40 + 30x$, where y represents the total cost and x represents the number of months

☐

Number of Months	1	3	5	10
Cost (\$)	70	150	230	430

21. Jeremy has $20 to spend. He wants to buy some t-shirts that cost $6.25 each. 6.EE.6, 6.EE.8

Part A: Write an inequality to find out how many t-shirts Jeremy can buy. Identify any variables you include.

Part B: Solve the inequality. At most, how many t-shirts can Jeremy buy?

22. Lakeesha says that the area of the parallelogram she is looking at is 24 square feet. Samantha says that the area of the triangle she is looking at is also 24 square feet. The girls exclaim, "How can this be?" Select whether each statement is true or false. 6.G.1

True	False	
☐	☐	The heights are the same, and the base of the parallelogram is twice the base of the triangle.
☐	☐	The base and the height of the parallelogram are both twice the base and height of the triangle.
☐	☐	The bases are the same, and the height of the parallelogram is half the height of the triangle.
☐	☐	The base and height of both figures are the same.

23. The figure shows the dimensions of a rectangular garden that Consuela originally planned to create. She realizes that a garden of this size will not be large enough for all of the vegetables and flowers that she wants to plant. Consuela considers tripling the length and width of the garden and thinks that the new garden size would be large enough for her plants. Select all of the statements that are true for Consuela's garden. 6.G.1

5 ft

8 ft

☐ Consuela needs 3 times the length of fencing to enclose the larger garden than the smaller garden.

☐ Consuela needs 12 times the length of fencing to enclose the larger garden than the smaller garden.

☐ Consuela will have 3 times as much space for her plants with the larger garden than with the smaller garden.

☐ Consuela will have 9 times as much space for her vegetables and flowers with the larger garden than with the smaller garden.

24. The diagram shows the outline of a school's playground. What is the area of the playground? 6.G.1

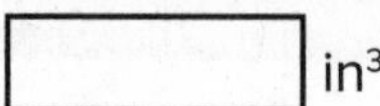 ft^2

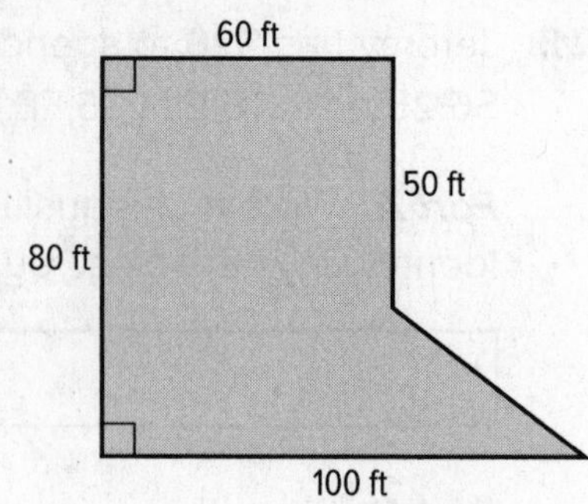

25. The diagram shows the dimensions of Paloma's fish tank. 6.G.2

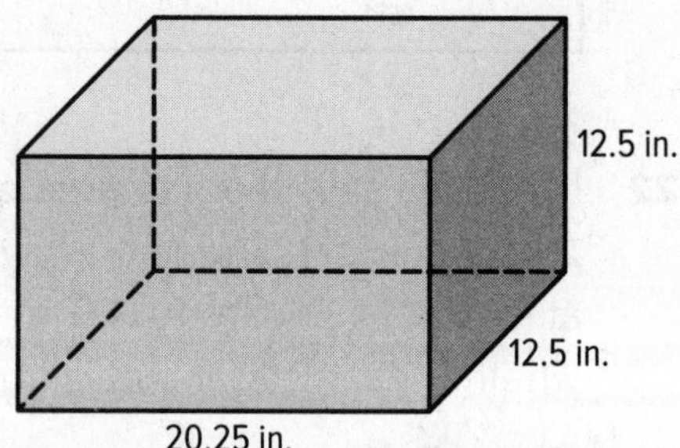

Part A: What is the greatest volume of water that the fish tank can hold? Round to the nearest tenth.

 in^3

Part B: Paloma fills the fish tank with water to a height of 8 inches. How much more water can she put into the fish tank? Round to the nearest tenth.

in^3

26. The points $A(-5, 3)$ and $B(3, -2)$ are the endpoints of the hypotenuse of a right triangle graphed on a coordinate plane. 6.G.3

Part A: What point can be graphed to make a right triangle whose hypotenuse is segment AB?

Use the coordinates of the point in Part A to find the lengths of the two sides that form the right angle in the triangle.

Part B: Is there another point that can be graphed to make a different right triangle than the one described in Part A? Explain.

27. Sheila purchases the gift box shown. What is the least amount of wrapping paper that Sheila needs to completely cover the box? 6.G.4

0.75 in.
6 in.
8 in.

[ ]

28. The list shows a student's quiz scores. 6.SP.3, 6.SP.5, 6.SP.5a

6 10 5 6 6 10 8 9

Part A: Write the appropriate number for each data measure.

3.5	7.5
4	8
5	8.5
6	9.5
7	10

number of data values: [ ]

mean of quiz scores: [ ]

median of quiz scores: [ ]

mode of quiz scores: [ ]

range of quiz scores: [ ]

interquartile range of quiz scores: [ ]

Part B: What is the mean absolute deviation of the scores? Explain how you found your answer.

[ ]

29. Jenna's bowling scores for five games are listed. Select whether each statement is true or false. 6.SP.3, 6.SP.5, 6.SP.5c

142 138 35 140 142

True	False	
☐	☐	The mean is a better measure to represent the data than the median.
☐	☐	The mean is less than the median.
☐	☐	The range is affected by the lowest score.
☐	☐	The mode is affected by the score that is an outlier.

30. The box-and-whisker plot represents the test scores in Ms. Alvarez's class. Select all of the statements that describe the data. 6.SP.4, 6.SP.5, 6.SP.5d

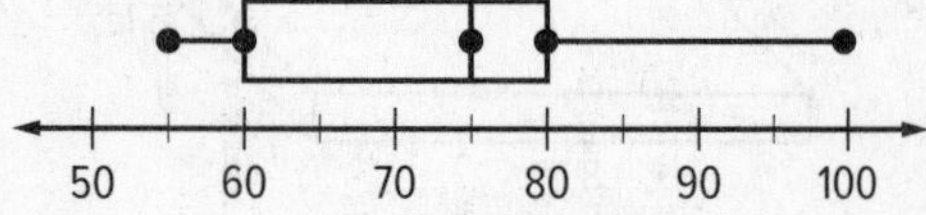

- ☐ The median score is 75.
- ☐ The range of the scores is 45.
- ☐ The box plot shows clusters and gaps in the data.
- ☐ The same number of scores occurs between 55 and 60 as between 80 and 100.
- ☐ The shape of the data distribution is symmetric.
- ☐ Half the scores are between 60 and 80.
- ☐ The most appropriate measures of center and spread to describe the data distribution are mean and mean absolute variation.

31. Students in one middle school class kept track of the books they read during summer vacation. The results are in the table. 6.SP.1, 6.SP.2, 6.SP.4

Books Read During Summer Vacation		
1	5	6
4	3	0
3	7	5
4	3	1
3	7	5
5	4	3

Part A: Complete the line plot by graphing points for the data values.

0 1 2 3 4 5 6 7

Number of Books Read

Part B: Is the question "How many books did the students read during summer vacation?" a statistical question?

Describe the shape of the data distribution.

Which two measures are the same? Explain.

NAME _______________ DATE _______ PERIOD _____ SCORE _____

Benchmark Test A, Performance Task, Chapters 1–12

Boxes R Us

Isaiah owns a company that manufactures and sells various sizes of packaging boxes. His company specializes in standard sizes of boxes as well as custom boxes.

Write your answers on another piece of paper. Show all your work to receive full credit.

Part A

A customer has requested that Isaiah's company manufacture a custom box. The customer specified the following: The box must be a rectangular prism, the volume of the box needs to be 84 cubic inches, and at least one side of the box must measure a value that is not a whole number. Sketch and label a net for this box.

Part B

Another customer requests a box with a volume of 336 cubic inches. How can Isaiah create the box by changing one dimension of the base of the box in Part A? two dimensions? Use the formula for volume of a prism, $V = Bh$, to explain how changing the area of the base of the box changes the volume of the box.

Part C

Isaiah is creating a table to display in a company brochure. Customers will be able to quickly see the volume of a cubic box for a variety of side lengths. Complete the table. Then write an equation that relates the volume of a cubic box, V_1, to the volume of a cubic box, V_2, with side lengths that are twice as long.

Side Length (in.)	1	2	3	4	5	6	7	8	9	10
Volume (in³)	1	8	27							

Isaiah keeps a variety of small boxes in stock on a shelving unit in his warehouse. The line plot shows the number of boxes, by volume, that he keeps in stock.

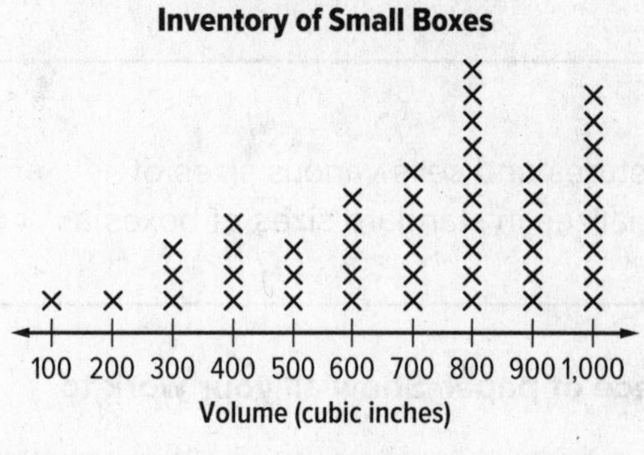

Part D

How many small boxes does Isaiah keep in stock? Find the mean, median, and mode of the data in the line plot. Which measure of center best represents the volume of boxes in stock? Explain your answer.

Part E

Isaiah plans to use this statement on the front of the company brochure.

> "Our warehouse shelves are lined with large quantities of all sizes of small boxes to meet your every need: from rings to bowling balls."

Is this an accurate statement? Explain your answer. What suggestions would you make to Isaiah before he prints this statement on the company brochure?

NAME ______________________ DATE ____________ PERIOD ________ SCORE ________

Benchmark Test B, Chapters 1–12

1. A bus driver drove 190 miles in $3\frac{4}{5}$ hours at a constant speed. Select whether each statement is true or false about the driver's rate of speed. 6.RP.3, 6.RP.3b, 6.RP.3d

True	False	
☐	☐	The average rate of speed was 50 miles per hour.
☐	☐	The average rate of speed was 60 miles per hour.
☐	☐	The bus driver drove 75 miles in $1\frac{1}{2}$ hours.
☐	☐	The bus traveled at a rate of 4,400 feet per minute.

2. A grocery store advertises 5 avocados for $6.25. Select all of the prices that are equivalent to the store's advertisement. 6.RP.1, 6.RP.3, 6.RP.3a

- ☐ 1 avocado for $1.25
- ☐ 3 avocados for $2.75
- ☐ 6 avocados for $7.50
- ☐ 8 avocados for $9.00
- ☐ 10 avocados for $12.50

3. Children at a daycare center were surveyed to determine which activity is their favorite. The table shows the results of the survey. Complete the table by ordering the activities from the least to greatest percent of children. 6.RP.3

Activity	Portion of Children
Finger Paint	0.07
Outdoor Play	$\frac{2}{5}$
Read	23%
Build with Blocks	$\frac{3}{10}$

	Activity	Percent of Children
Least		
Greatest		

4. The manager of a retail store reported that on Friday, 100 shoppers used a coupon. 6.RP.3, 6.RP.3c

Part A: There were 400 shoppers on Friday. Is it likely that 25% of them used a coupon? Justify your answer.

Part B: There were 240 shoppers on Friday. Approximately what percent of the shoppers used a coupon? Explain your answer.

5. A store discounts the price of a beanbag chair by 20%. The price of the beanbag chair is marked as $16. What was the original price of the beanbag chair? 6.RP.3, 6.RP.3c

6. Select whether each product is less than both factors. 6.NS.3

Yes	No	
☐	☐	4.27 × 0.15
☐	☐	0.06 × 0.73
☐	☐	1.65 × 1.0007
☐	☐	0.0203 × 0.75
☐	☐	0.99 × 0.99

7. Arianna runs 3.5 miles in 1.25 hours. Select all of the rates that have the same constant rate of change as Arianna's rate. 6.NS.2, 6.NS.3, 6.RP.3, 6.RP.3d

☐ 4.9 miles in 1.75 hours

☐ 6.5 miles in 2.5 hours

☐ 0.84 mile in 18 minutes

☐ 0.7 mile in 15 minutes

8. Sort the expressions into the appropriate bins by the value of their products. 6.NS.1

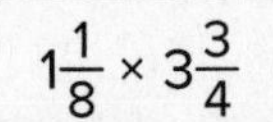

$1\frac{1}{8} \times 3\frac{3}{4}$	$3\frac{3}{4} \times \frac{5}{4}$	$\frac{2}{13} \times 6\frac{1}{2}$	$\frac{9}{10} \times \frac{1}{3}$	$\frac{2}{3} \times \frac{10}{15}$

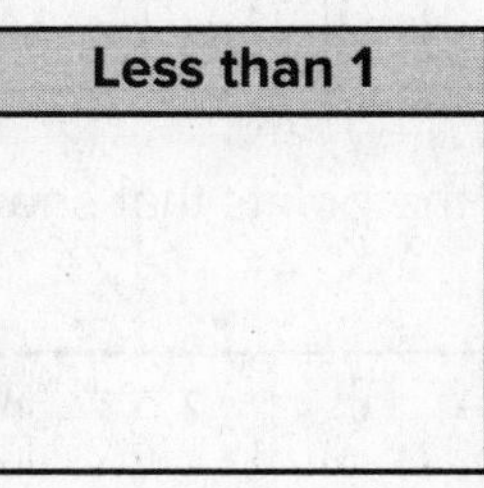

Greater than 1	Equal to 1	Less than 1

9. A carpenter has 8 boards of equal length. The diagram shows how he cuts each board into 6 pieces, each with a length of 2 feet. 6.NS.1

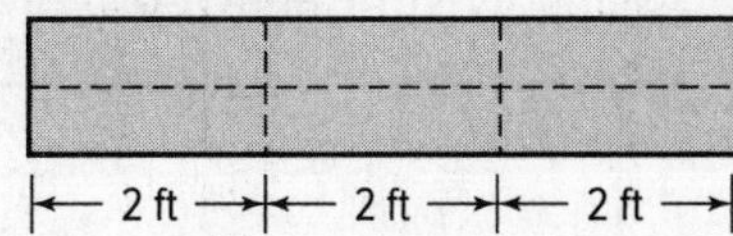

Part A: Write the appropriate numbers to show how to find the total number of pieces of board that the carpenter will cut.

$\square \div \frac{\square}{\square} = \square$

1	2	6	8	14	48

Part B: The carpenter plans to cut one of the 2-foot boards into $\frac{2}{5}$-foot long pieces. What is the greatest number of pieces he can cut from one 2-foot board? Explain your answer.

10. The length of a parking lot is $76\frac{1}{2}$ feet. Cars are parked perpendicular to the edge of the lot in parking spots that are $8\frac{1}{2}$ feet wide. 6.NS.1

Part A: How many parking spots are along the length of the lot?

Part B: There are 13 light poles equally spaced along the length of the lot, including one light pole at each end. Find the distance between light poles.

11. The table shows the location of each of four divers relative to sea level. The integer 0 represents sea level. 6.NS.6, 6.NS.6c, 6.NS.7, 6.NS.7b

Diver	A	B	C	D
Depth (ft)	2	−5	0	−3

Part A: Graph the points that show the locations of the divers.

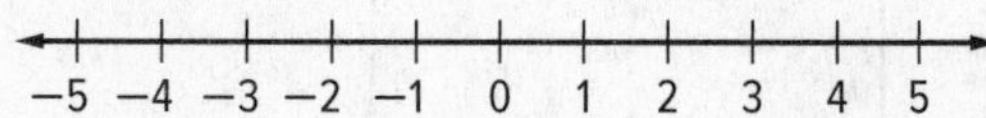

Part B: Which diver is farther from sea level, Diver A or Diver D? Justify your answer.

12. Gordon correctly answered 12 out of 18 questions. Circle the values that are equivalent to the ratio of questions that Gordon got correct. 6.NS.6

$\frac{20}{30}$ $\frac{6}{10}$ $\frac{3}{4}$ $\frac{4}{6}$ 0.1218 $\frac{22}{33}$

13. On a coordinate plane, a flagpole is represented by point (6, −2.5). A traffic light is represented by the point that is a reflection of (6, −2.5) across the *x*-axis. 6.NS.6, 6.NS.6b, 6.NS.8

Part A: Write the location of the traffic light as an ordered pair.

Part B: What is the distance from the flagpole to the traffic light?

14. Sort the expressions into the appropriate bins based on how the values compare to 64. 6.EE.1

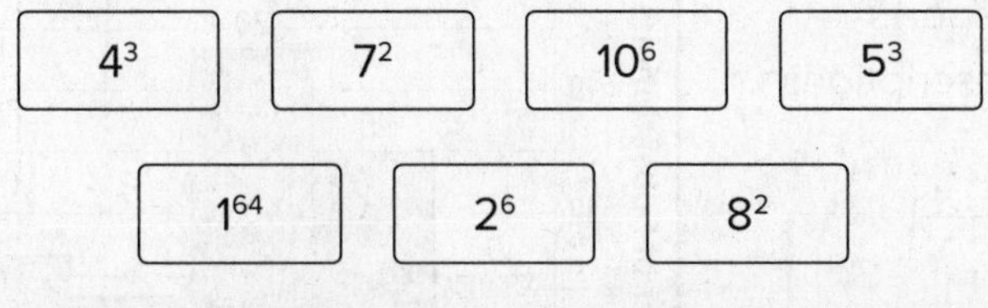

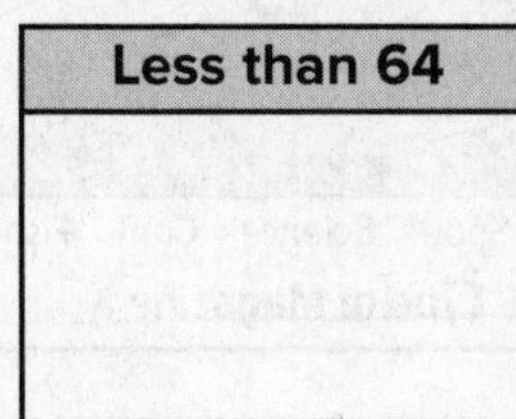

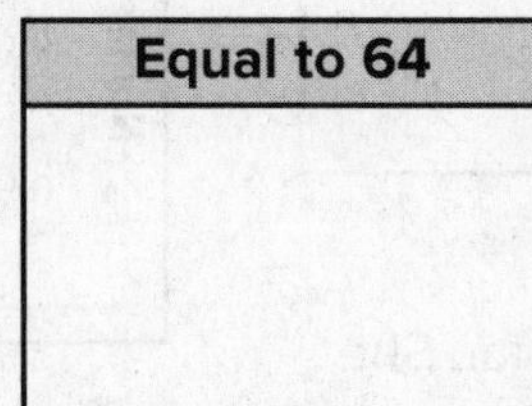

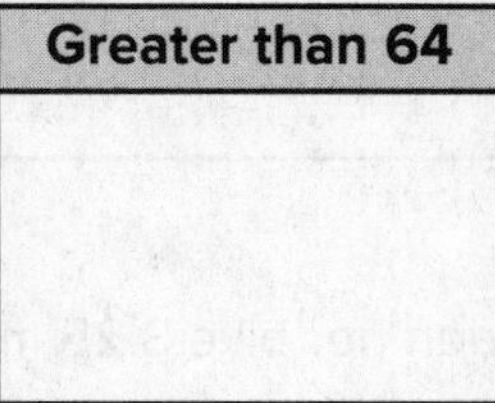

15. The table shows the amount 6 friends spent at the fair. Together, they spent a total of $215. Select whether each statement is true or false. 6.EE.2, 6.EE.6, 6.EE.7

Name	Amount Spent ($)
Rafi	35
Esi	21
Ron	28
Julie	x
Charo	50
Mario	37

True	False	
☐	☐	The expression $(56 + x)$ represents the total amount Rafi, Esi, and Julie spent.
☐	☐	The total amount the 6 friends spent is $215x$.
☐	☐	Julie spent $44 at the fair.
☐	☐	Julie spent the least amount at the fair.

16. Jennifer and three of her friends bought the same pair of jeans and the same t-shirt. The table shows the cost of each item. 6.EE.3, 6.NS.4

Item	Cost ($)
T-shirt	15
Jeans	35

Part A: Write the appropriate numbers to represent the amount they spent altogether.

2 3 4 15 20 35

☐ × (☐ + ☐)

Part B: Is the expression $20(3 + 7)$ equivalent to the total amount Jennifer and her friends spent? Explain your answer.

17. The graph shows the number of magazine subscriptions sold. Write and solve an equation to find the difference d in the number of sports subscriptions and the number of craft subscriptions sold. 6.EE.5, 6.EE.7

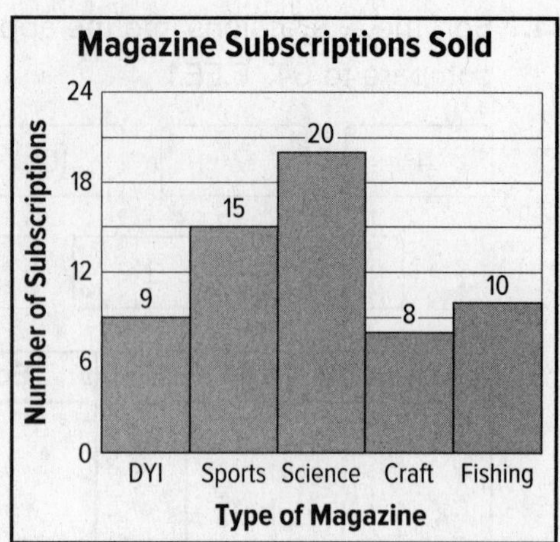

18. Talutah has ridden her bike 3.25 miles so far. She plans to ride 7.75 miles in all. Let d represent how much farther she has to ride. Select whether each statement is true or false. 6.EE.7

True	False	
☐	☐	The equation $d + 3.25 = 7.75$ models the situation.
☐	☐	The equation $7.75 - 3.25 = d$ models the situation.
☐	☐	Talutah has 11 miles left to ride.
☐	☐	Talutah has 4.5 miles left to ride.

19. Danilo took 900 breaths in one hour. Write and solve a multiplication equation to find Danilo's average number of breaths per minute. 6.EE.7, 6.RP.3

Multiplication equation:

Number of breaths per minute:

20. A cell phone company charges an initial fee of \$50 plus \$30 per month for unlimited minutes of phone usage. Complete the table to show the relationship for the total cost t of using a cell phone for m months. Then write an equation to represent the relationship between the total cost and the time in months. 6.EE.9

Number of Months, *m*	1	2	3	4
Total Cost (\$), *t*				

Equation:

21. A bag can hold at most 45 kilograms of rice. Currently, there are 15 kilograms of rice in the bag. 6.EE.6, 6.EE.8

Part A: Write an inequality that represents how many more kilograms of rice k can be added to the bag.

Part B: Then graph the solution of the inequality.

22. The diagram shows the top view of a wading pool. A fabric cover is used to cover the top of the pool. The cover is the same shape as the pool, but the base dimension is 1 foot longer, and the height is 2 feet longer than the pool. What is the area of the pool cover? 6.G.1

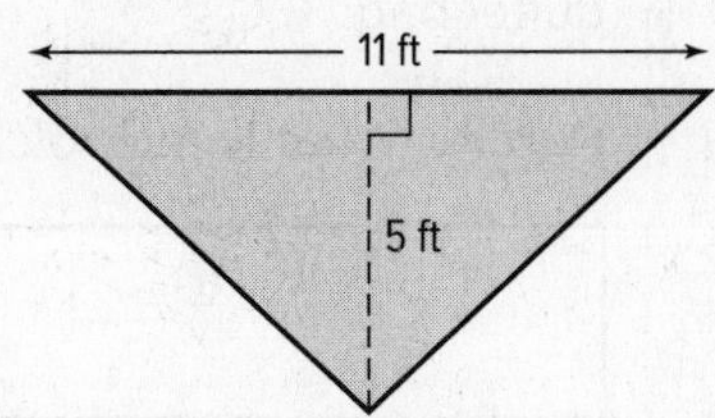

23. The dimensions of a child-sized, rectangular tabletop are $\frac{1}{3}$ the dimensions of an adult-sized tabletop. The adult-sized tabletop has an area of 2,268 square inches and a length of 63 inches. What are the dimensions of the child-sized tabletop? Justify your answer. 6.G.1

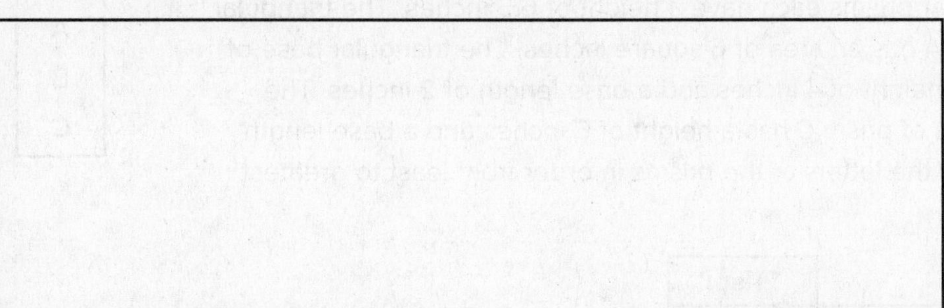

24. The diagram shows the dimensions of an attic wall in David's house. Select all of the expressions that represent the area of the wall in square feet. 6.G.1

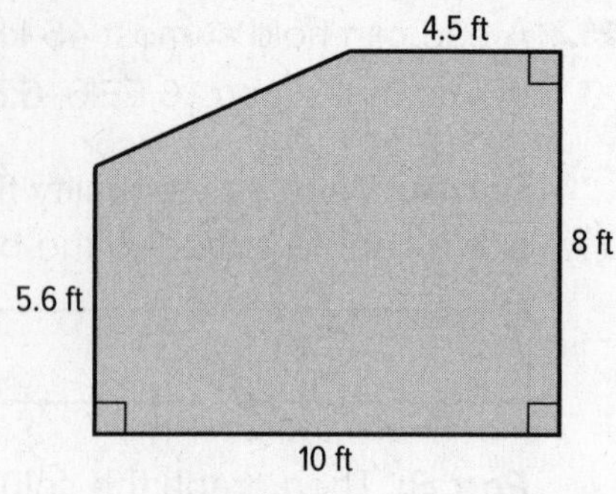

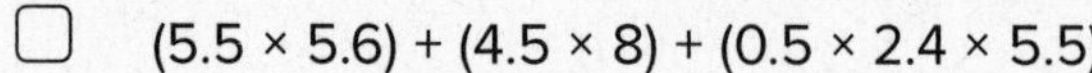

- ☐ (5.5 × 5.6) + (4.5 × 8) + (0.5 × 2.4 × 5.5)
- ☐ (10 × 8) – (0.5 × 2.4 × 5.5)
- ☐ (5.5 × 5.6) + (4.5 × 5.6) + (2.4 × 8) + (0.5 × 2.4 × 5.5)
- ☐ (10 × 5.6) + (4.5 × 8) + (0.5 × 2.4 × 5.5)

25. The diagram shows the dimensions of Elizabeth's rolling duffel bag. 6.G.2

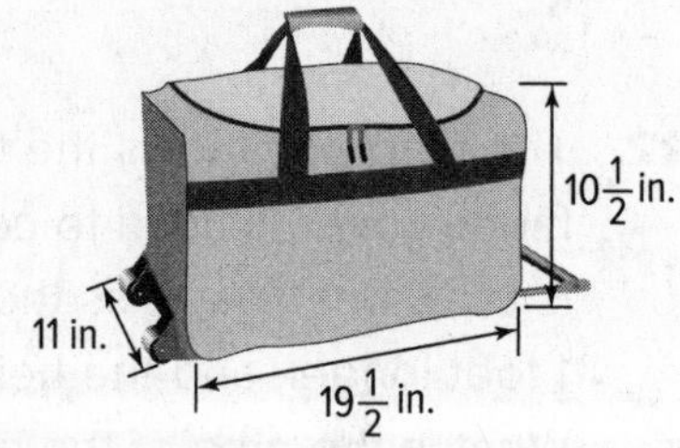

Part A: What is the volume of the duffel bag?

Part B: Elizabeth fills the bag to a height of 9 inches. How much space is left empty in her bag?

26. Three triangular prisms each have a height of 6.5 inches. The triangular base of prism *A* has an area of 6 square inches. The triangular base of prism *B* has a height of 4 inches and a base length of 2 inches. The triangular base of prism *C* has a height of 6 inches and a base length of 1 inch. Write the letters of the prisms in order from least to greatest volume. 6.G.3

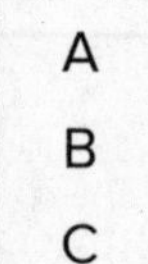

	Prism
Least volume	
Greatest volume	

27. The diagram shows the dimensions of a museum display case. All faces of the case are made of glass and are covered with a protective scratch-proof coating. Write the appropriate numbers to find the total amount of protective coating needed to cover each glass face. 6.G.4

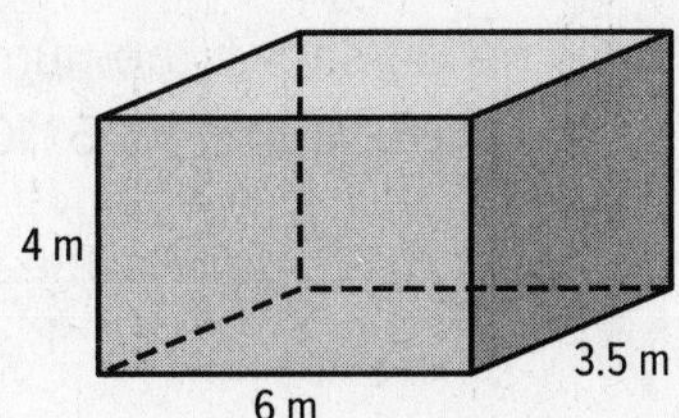

3.5	4	6	14	21	24
28	42	48	59	118	128

Surface area of front and back = 2 (☐)(☐) = ☐

Surface area of top and bottom = 2 (☐)(☐) = ☐

Surface area of the two sides = 2 (☐)(☐) = ☐

Total amount of protective coating needed:

☐ + ☐ + ☐, or ☐ square meters

28. The list shows the number of students absent each day that school was in session in August: 8, 7, 9, 5, 5, 12, 2, 0. Select all of the statements that are valid based on the data. 6.SP.3, 6.SP.5, 6.SP.5c

- ☐ The range is 10.
- ☐ The mean number of students absent is 6.
- ☐ The median number of students absent is 6.
- ☐ The mean absolute deviation of the data is 3.
- ☐ There is no mode.

29. The list shows the ages in years of seven sea turtles: 58, 62, 38, 60, 59, 63, 61. Identify the outlier in the data set. Explain which measure of center best describes the data with and without the outlier. 6.SP.3, 6.SP.5, 6.SP.5c, 6.SP.5d

30. The list shows the number of books sold each hour a bookstore was open: 9, 12, 18, 10, 5, 10, 12, 2. 6.SP.4, 6.SP.5, 6.SP.5a

Part A: Complete the box-and-whisker plot to represent the data.

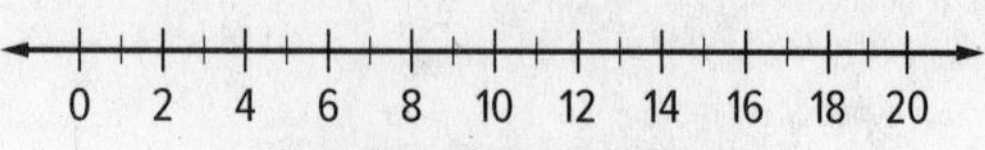

Part B: Between which two values are 50% of the data found?

31. The line plot shows the results of a survey question posed to fifth-grade students, "How many cavities did you have last year?" 6.SP.1, 6.SP.2, 6. SP.5, 6.SP.5d

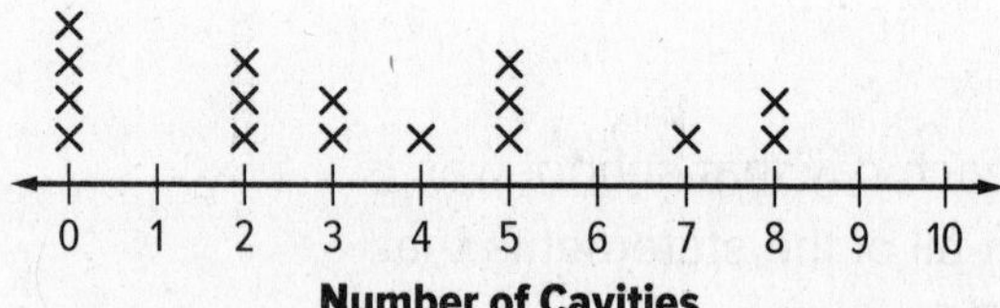

Part A: Why is the question a statistical question?

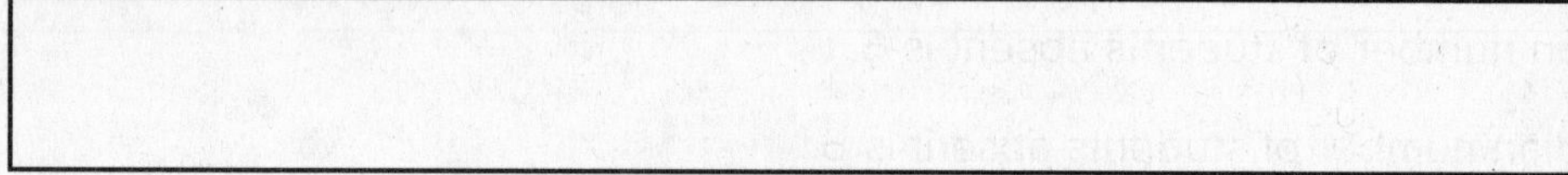

Part B: Interpret what the mode represents in the data.

Part C: Describe the shape of the data distribution.

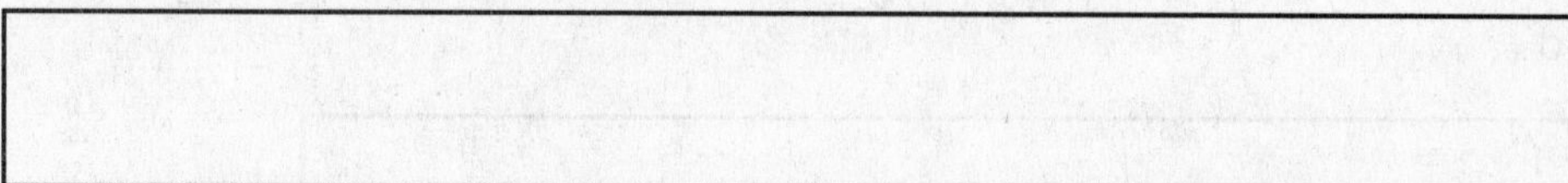

NAME _______________ DATE _______ PERIOD _______ SCORE _______

Benchmark Test B, Performance Task, Chapters 1–12

The Fruit Stand

Andy owns a fruit stand where many people buy their afternoon snacks. The table shows the prices that are posted on his fruit stand.

Fruit	Price
Apple	\$1.62 for 3
Banana	2 for 64¢
Orange	46¢ each
Kiwi	4 for \$1.44

Write your answers on another piece of paper. Show all your work to receive full credit.

Part A

What is the unit price, in cents per piece of fruit, of each type of fruit sold? Then find the mean unit price for the fruit stand.

Part B

Use integers to represent the difference between each fruit's unit price and the mean unit price. Explain what the positive or negative signs represent. Then plot each difference on a number line.

Part C

Use the differences you calculated in Part B to find which fruit has a difference less than –7. Write an inequality to represent this statement. Then explain how it relates to that fruit using the phrase "greater than" or "more than."

Andy prepares two bags of fruit for people looking to buy a variety of fruits.

- Bag 1 contains 2 apples, 3 kiwis, and 1 banana.
- Bag 2 contains 4 oranges and 5 bananas.

Andy also prepares *b* identical bags of fruit for delivery to a restaurant. The cost of the bags can be represented by the expression $6b(0.32 + 0.36 + 0.54)$.

Part D

Write a numerical expression for the cost of each bag of variety fruit to be sold. Then evaluate each expression, and write the total cost in dollars.

Part E

What type of fruit is in each bag for the restaurant delivery? Use the Distributive Property to write an equivalent expression for the cost of the bags. Andy is paid no more than $25. How many bags could the restaurant purchase? Write and solve an inequality to explain your answer.

Part F

The bags that Andy uses, when opened, are in the shape of a rectangular prism. The volume of an empty bag is $1{,}212\frac{3}{4}$ cubic inches. When a bag is placed upright on a table, the base of the bag covers a surface of $67\frac{3}{8}$ square inches. What is the height of each bag? Explain your answer.

Assessment Item Types

You will encounter selected-response, constructed response, and technology-enhanced item types when taking an online assessment. Use these next several pages to become familiar with these item types. With each type, there is one for you to try on your own.

Selected-Response Items

You will be asked to select one or more given responses for a set of options.

Multiple True/False or Multiple Yes/No

The quotient $\frac{a}{b} \div \frac{c}{d}$ is found. Select whether each statement is true or false. 6.NS.1

True	False	
☐	■	The quotient is always greater than 1.
☐	■	The quotient is equal to $\frac{db}{ca}$.
■	☐	To find the quotient, multiply $\frac{a}{b} \times \frac{d}{c}$.
■	☐	$\frac{a}{b} \div \frac{c}{d} = \frac{ad}{cb}$ because $\frac{c}{d} \times \frac{ad}{cb} = \frac{a}{b}$.

ONLINE EXPERIENCE Click the appropriate box for each statement.

HELPFUL HINT There are usually several statements, as opposed to one true-false statement. *All* of the statements must be selected correctly.

Try On Your Own!

The graph shows the rate at which L'Shaundra reads a novel. She continues to read at this rate until she finishes a 174-page novel. Select the appropriate box to indicate whether the answer to each question is yes or no. 6.EE.9

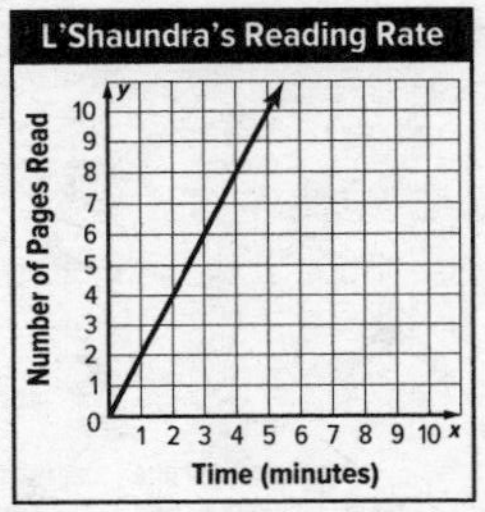

Yes	No	
■	☐	Will L'Shaundra finish reading the novel in 1 hour 27 minutes?
☐	■	Does the equation $p = 0.5m$ represent the relationship between the number of pages p and the number of minutes m?
■	☐	Will L'Shaundra have read 88 pages after 44 minutes?
☐	■	Are all three points (14, 28), (26, 52), and (56, 122) found on the graph of the line?

Another example of a selected-response item is shown below.

Multiple Correct Answers

A representative sample of students from Jones Middle School is surveyed as to how many servings of vegetables they eat each day. The dot plot shows the responses. 6.SP.5, 6.SP.5a, 6.SP.5c

Servings of Vegetables per Day

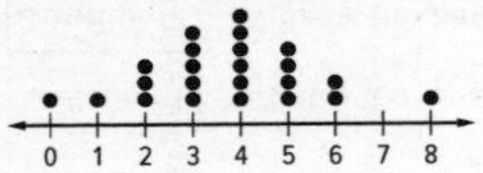

ONLINE EXPERIENCE Click *all* of the correct answer choices.

HELPFUL HINT Read *each* answer choice carefully. There is often more than one correct answer, as opposed to a single correct answer for a traditional multiple-choice problem.

Select all of the statements that are valid based on the survey results.

- ■ There were 23 students surveyed.
- ■ Fewer than one fourth of the students failed to meet the goal of at least 3 servings per day.
- ☐ The mean number of servings is 4.1.
- ■ The interquartile range is 6 less than the range.
- ☐ Due to the outlier, the median is the measure that best represents the data.

Try On Your Own!

Miguel plans to build a wooden crate to store pool toys. He first draws a net as his blueprint. He wants the crate to be 6 feet by 4 feet by 3 feet when it is finished. Select all of the statements that are true. 6.G.4

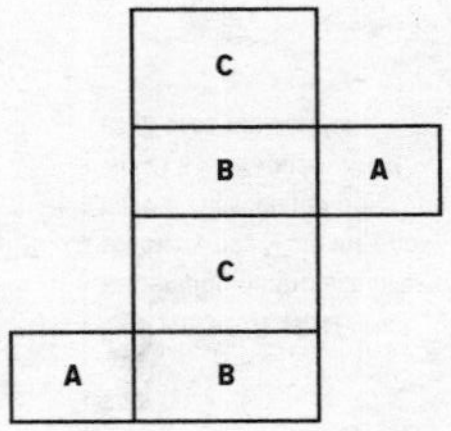

- ☐ The crate represented by the blueprint will not have a lid.
- ☐ The volume of the crate is greater than 100 ft^3.
- ■ Miguel will need 108 ft^2 of wood to make the crate.
- ■ A can of paint covers 75 ft^2. Miguel will need 3 cans to paint the inside and outside of the box.
- ■ The surface area of the crate is represented by the expression 2[(6)(4) + (6)(3) + (4)(3)].

Constructed-Response Items

You will be asked to generate a response, using letters, numbers, and mathematical symbols.

Type Entry

ONLINE EXPERIENCE Use a keypad or keyboard to enter a response that may or may not contain variables and math symbols.

One leg of a right isosceles triangle is 12 centimeters long. Another right triangle has twice the area of the first isosceles triangle. What is the height of the second right triangle? 6.G.1

12 cm

16 cm

18 cm

Try On Your Own!

Ms. Hernandez is collecting chicken eggs from students who raise chickens. She wants to collect 5 dozen eggs to sell at the Farmer's Market. The table shows the number of eggs she has collected so far. Let x represent the number of eggs left to collect. Write an equation in the form of $x + p = q$ that represents how many more eggs Ms. Hernandez needs to collect. 6.EE.7

Child	Eggs Collected
José	8
Kendrick	Twice as many as José
Caro	Three fewer than Kendrick

$x + 37 = 60$

Technology-Enhanced Items

Many of the items on online tests are technology-enhanced items. In these items you will be asked to use computer-based technology, such as dragging and drawing objects, to solve the problem presented.

Bin Sort

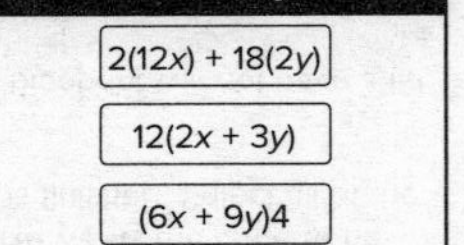
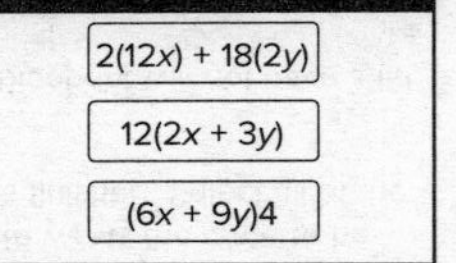
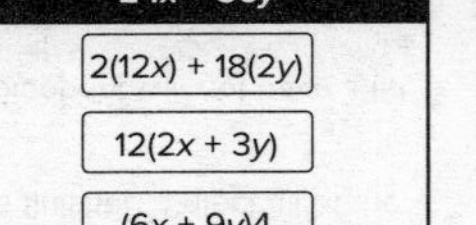
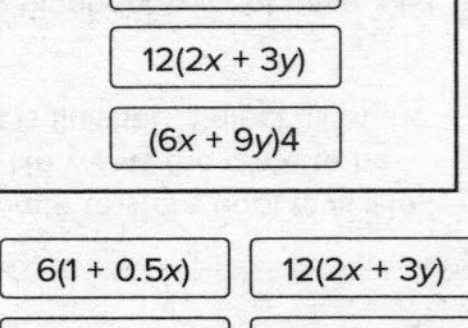

ONLINE EXPERIENCE Sort objects by dragging them into their appropriate bins.

HELPFUL HINT Depending on the actual problem, every bin may not have an associated object to which it is dragged. Read each problem carefully.

Sort the expressions listed at the bottom into the category that correctly shows an equivalent expression. 6.EE.3

$6 + 3x$	$24x + 36y$
$3(x + 2)$	$2(12x) + 18(2y)$
$6(1 + 0.5x)$	$12(2x + 3y)$
$x + 6 + 2x$	$(6x + 9y)4$

$2(12x) + 18(2y)$ | $3(x + 2)$ | $6(1 + 0.5x)$ | $12(2x + 3y)$

$6(18x + 30y)$ | $6(1 - 3x)$ | $(6x + 9y)4$ | $x + 6 + 2x$

Try On Your Own!

Destiny wants to conduct a survey, and she wants to be sure that she asks a statistical question. Sort the questions into the category that correctly describes whether or not the question is a statistical question. 6.SP.A.1

Statistical Question	Not a Statistical Question
Question 1 Question 4 Question 5	Question 2 Question 3

Question 1 What is the favorite card game of each person in our class?

Question 2 When is the birthday of the oldest student in your math class?

Question 3 How many boys are on the A-Team?

Question 4 How tall are the girls at your school?

Question 5 How many annual concerts are held in each U.S. state capital?

Another example of a technology-enhanced item is shown below.

Drag and Drop

Allison claims that different powers can be equivalent. Drag digits into the boxes to create an expression that supports Allison's claim. 6.EE.1

0	1	2	3	4
5	6	7	8	9

A sample answer is shown.

$2^6 = \boxed{8}^2 = \boxed{4}^{\boxed{3}}$

ONLINE EXPERIENCE
Drag objects to their appropriate locations, not necessarily in bins. In this book, write or draw the object in its appropriate location as opposed to dragging it.

HELPFUL HINT
Depending on the actual problem, not all of the objects are dragged to complete the problem correctly. Read each problem carefully.

Try On Your Own!

A *fortnight* is a unit of time that is commonly used in Great Britain. Six fortnights is the same as 84 days. Drag the correct numbers to complete the table to show how the number of fortnights and the number of days are related. 6.RP.1, 6.RP.3, 6.RP.3a

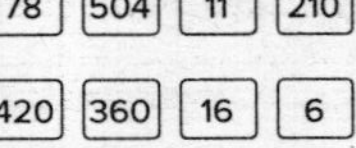

14 12 168 78 504 11 210 93

24 28 180 420 360 16 6 13

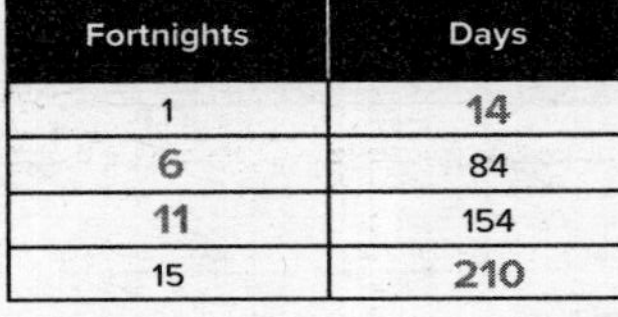

Fortnights	Days
1	14
6	84
11	154
15	210

Some problems on an online assessment will require you to complete multiple parts. One or more parts may be technology-enhanced. An example is below.

Construct Statistical Graphs

The table shows the average amount 20 teens collected per hour at a fundraiser. Coleman predicted that most teens collected $6 or more per hour. 6.SP.4

ONLINE EXPERIENCE
Click to shade sections of the graph. If you make a mistake, click to deselect a section that you selected.

Average Amount Collected per Hour			
$5.00	$3.50	$3.20	$4.25
$7.50	$4.00	$9.10	$7.75
$6.50	$5.00	$5.25	$6.15
$8.00	$7.75	$6.60	$5.50
$2.50	$3.50	$4.85	$7.40

Part A: Complete a histogram to represent the data.

Average Amount Collected per Hour
Frequency: 0, 3, 6, 9, 12
Dollars: 0–2.99, 3–5.99, 6–8.99, 9–11.99

Part B: Is Coleman's prediction valid? Select yes or no.

Yes No

Try On Your Own!

The table shows the average number of texts sent per day by students in Scarlett's class. Scarlett predicted that more people sent 80 to 99 texts than 0 to 19 texts per day. 6.SP.4

Number of Texts per Day			
52	34	68	21
66	52	87	99
45	78	77	49
51	69	81	56
75	64	95	88
27	39	56	19

Part A: Complete a histogram to represent the data.

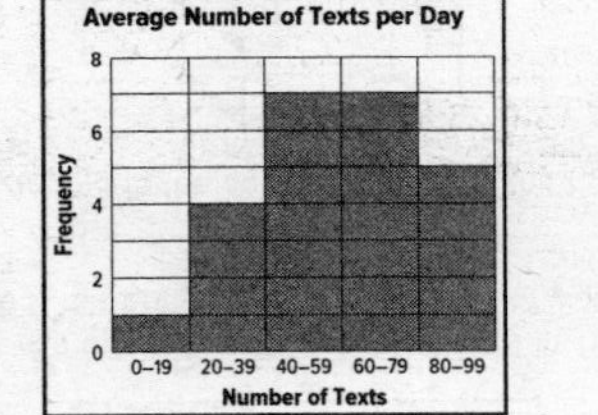

Part B: Is Scarlett's prediction valid? Select yes or no.

Yes No

Another example of a technology-enhanced item is shown below.

Coordinate Plane

Jake works half an hour each day and makes $3 per day babysitting. Graph the ordered pairs that show how much money Jake has after working 1, 2, and 3 days. 6.NS.8, 6.EE.9

ONLINE EXPERIENCE Click the buttons **Add Point** and **Connect Line** to plot points and draw lines on a coordinate plane.

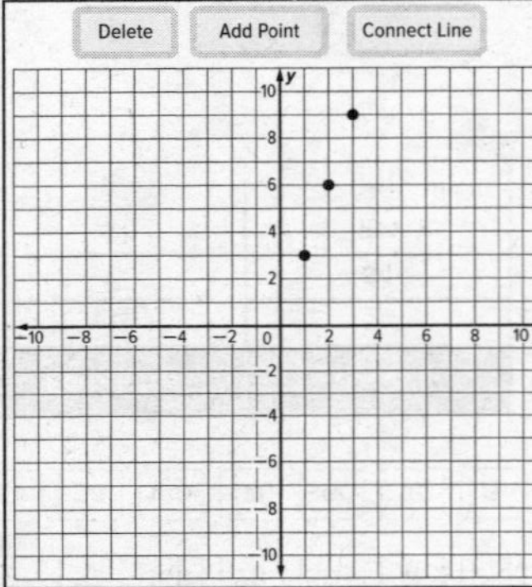

Try On Your Own!

Karl starts to graph a rectangle by plotting two vertices. Graph the other two vertices and the sides to complete one possible rectangle. 6.NS.8, 6.G.3

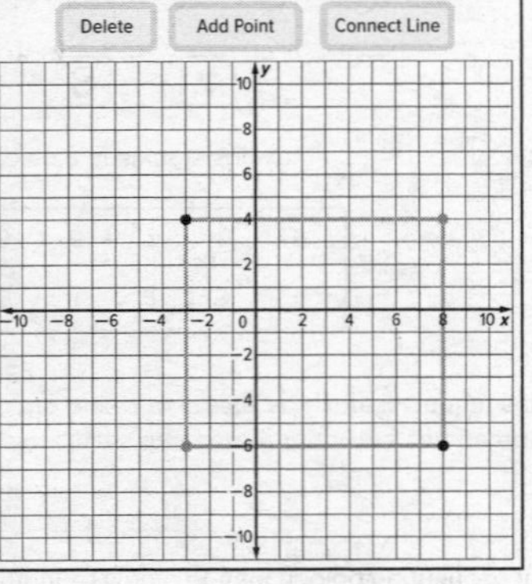

Another example of a multipart technology-enhanced item is shown below.

Volume of Solids

The base of an aquarium measures 24 inches by 10 inches. There is currently 3,840 cubic inches of water in the aquarium. 6.G.2

Part A: Shade the aquarium to show the height of the water.

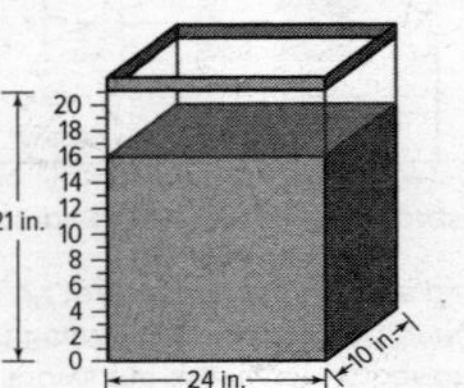

Part B: Another aquarium has a base that is twice as long and twice as wide as the aquarium shown. The water from the first aquarium is poured into it. To what vertical height, in inches, does the water reach?

4

ONLINE EXPERIENCE Click to shade sections of a solid. If you make a mistake, click to deselect the sections you selected.

HELPFUL HINT There may be more than one part to a problem. Be sure to read and complete all parts of the problem.

Try On Your Own!

Georgia stacks 14 packs of 8.5-inch by 11-inch paper. Each pack is 2 inches thick. Then she stacks the same volume of legal-sized paper, which is 8.5 inches by 14 inches. Each legal pack is also 2 inches thick. 6.G.2

Part A: Shade the prism to show the number of packs of 8.5-inch by 14-inch paper she stacked.

Part B: What is the combined volume of paper in the two stacks?

5,236 in³

Performance Tasks

These tasks measure your ability to integrate knowledge and skills across multiple topics, which helps prepare you for college and future careers. An example of a performance task is shown below, with guidance about how to complete it.

Movie Time 6.RP.3, 6.NS.3, 6.NS.8, 6.EE.2, 6.EE.2a, 6.EE.2c, 6.EE.5, 6.EE.6, 6.EE.7, 6.EE.9

The local movie theater offers some summer packages.

Package A is $8 per movie.
Package B is $25 per month and $5 per movie.
Package C is $50 per month for unlimited movies.

This performance task has 5 parts, Parts A–E. Read each part and follow the guiding instructions for how to complete it.

Part A

Grayson wants to evaluate each package. Let x be the number of movies he plans to see. Write an expression to represent the cost of each package. Identify whether each expression is numeric or algebraic. Explain your answer.

Write an expression for the cost of Package A.

$8x$

Write an expression for the cost of Package B.

$25 + 5x$

Write an expression for the cost of Package C.

50

Identify each expression as numeric or algebraic. Explain your answer.

Because they have variables, both $8x$ and $25 + 5x$ are algebraic expressions; 50 is numeric because there is no variable.

Part B

Grayson thinks that he will probably see 6 movies each month. Which package should he choose? Justify your answer.

Calculate how much Grayson will spend with each package. Show your work.

Package A: $8x = 8(6) = 48$
Package B: $25 + 5x = 25 + 5(6) = 25 + 30 = 55$
Package C: 50, for any number of movies

Grayson sees 6 movies each month. He would spend $ 48 with Package A, $ 55 with Package B, and $ 50 with Package C.

How do the costs compare? Which package should Grayson choose? Justify your answer.

All of the costs are close to or equal to $50. Grayson should choose Package A because it costs the least amount of money.

Part C

Grayson chooses Package A. He spends $72 at the movies one month. How many movies did he see? Write and solve an equation to find the answer. Would either of the other packages have been a better choice for this number of movies? Explain your answer.

Write and solve an equation to find the number of movies Grayson saw. Show your work.

$8x = 72$
$x = 9$
He saw 9 movies.

Would either of the other packages have been a better choice? Explain your answer.

Package C would have been a better choice because Grayson would have paid only $50. Package B would have been $2 less than Package A, because 25 + 5(9) = $70. So, either package would have been a better choice.

Part D

Grayson wants to know how many movies he would need to see each month so that the cost of Package B would equal the cost of Package C. Complete the table for each package, and then graph each function on the coordinate plane. For what number of movies is the cost the same? How does the graph show this number?

Complete each table to show the number of movies or cost in each package.

Package B	
Number of Movies	**Cost ($)**
2	35
8	65
12	85

Package C	
Number of Movies	**Cost ($)**
4	50
9	50
Any number	50

Graph the function for each movie package on the coordinate plane. Be sure to label the functions.

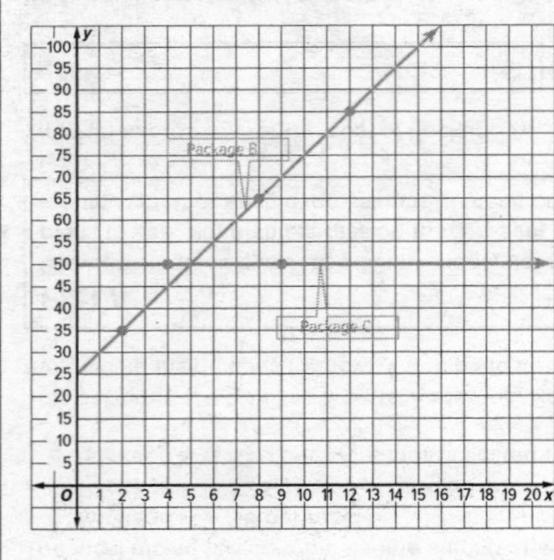

For what number of movies will the cost be the same? How does the graph show this number?

5 movies; The lines intersect at $x = 5$, where both dependent values are 50.

Part E

Grayson maps the theater on a coordinate plane, plotting each seat at a gridline intersection and using the axes to represent aisles. He plots his favorite seat as well as where he and his friend had to sit today. How far is Grayson's seat today from his favorite seat? How far is he sitting from his friend today? Use absolute value expressions to justify your answers.

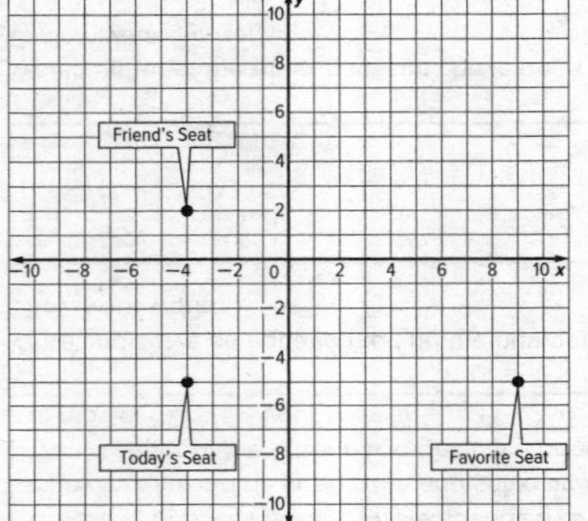

HELPFUL HINT Use the graph to double-check your answers.

Write and evaluate an expression using absolute value to represent the distance from Grayson's seat today to the aisle represented by the *y*-axis.

$|-4| = 4$, or 4 seats

Write and evaluate an expression using absolute value to represent the distance from Grayson's favorite seat to the aisle represented by the *y*-axis.

$|9| = 9$, or 9 seats

What is the distance between Grayson's seat today and his favorite seat? Explain how you determined this distance.

13 seats; I added the distances to the aisle; $4 + 9 = 13$.

What is the distance between Grayson's seat today and his friend's seat? Explain how you determined this distance.

7 seats; The distance between today's seat and the aisle represented by the *x*-axis is $|-5| = 5$, or 5 seats. The distance between his friend's seat and the aisle represented by the *x*-axis is $|2| = 2$, or 2 seats. I added the distances between each seat and the aisle; $5 + 2 = 7$.

NAME ________________ DATE ________ PERIOD ______ SCORE ______

Countdown: 20 Weeks

1. In Raphael's class there are 14 boys and 10 girls. Select whether each statement is true or false. 6.RP.1

True	False	
■	☐	The ratio of boys to girls is 14:10.
☐	■	The ratio of girls to boys is 7:5.
■	☐	The ratio of boys to girls is $\frac{7}{5}$.
■	☐	The ratio of girls to boys is $\frac{30}{42}$.

Online Test Tip
On an online test, you might be asked to click the appropriate box for each statement. In this book, you will be asked to shade in the boxes instead.

2. Rita wants to buy a sweater that was originally priced at $25.00. Today the sweater is on sale for 40% off the original price. 6.RP.3, 6.RP.3c

Part A: What is the sale price of the sweater?

$15.00

Part B: Rita has a coupon for an additional 10% off the sale price. How much will Rita pay for the sweater before taxes?

$13.50

3. A seagull flies 15 feet above the surface of the ocean. The table shows the location of several other objects in relation to the ocean's surface. Sort the objects into the appropriate bins by their distances to the ocean surface as compared to the seagull's distance. 6.NS.7, 6.NS.7c

Object	Location in Comparison to the Ocean's Surface (feet)
Fish	−6
Shark	−50
Airplane	150
Submarine	−218
Pelican	9

Submarine | Fish | Shark | Pelican | Airplane

Farther from the Ocean's Surface than the Seagull is	Closer to the Ocean's Surface than the Seagull is
Shark Airplane Submarine	Fish Pelican

4. Nicholas is driving his car at a constant rate of 55 miles per hour. Select whether Nicholas could achieve the distances listed in the given times. 6.RP.3, 6.RP.3b

Yes	No	
■	☐	165 miles in 3 hours
☐	■	240 miles in 4 hours
■	☐	330 miles in 6 hours
☐	■	504 miles in 9 hours

5. Yolanda buys two types of flowering plants. She buys 36 geraniums and 63 marigolds. She wants to plant an equal number of flowers in each row of her garden. Each row will contain only one type of flowering plant. 6.NS.4

Part A: Yolanda uses all the plants she bought in her garden. Determine the greatest number of flowering plants that could be in each row of the garden.

9 plants

Part B: How many rows of each type of flowering plant will be in Yolanda's garden?

4 rows of geraniums

7 rows of marigolds

NAME ______________ DATE ________ PERIOD ______ SCORE ______

Countdown: 19 Weeks

1. The distance between point (2, 2) and point (8, 2) is 6 units on a coordinate plane. Select all of the pairs of points that are 6 units apart. 6.NS.8

- [x] (1, 7) and (1, 1)
- [ ] (3, 3) and (–5, 3)
- [x] (–3, 4) and (–3, –2)
- [ ] (0, 0) and (–2, –4)
- [x] (–1, 5) and (5, 5)
- [x] (–8, 3) and (–2, 3)

2. During back-to-school week, all school supplies are tax-free. Rajiv took advantage of this sale and bought a ruler for \$0.79, three pens for \$1.49 each, and two notebooks for \$2.25 each. 6.NS.3

Part A: What is the total cost for Rajiv's purchases?

\$9.76

Part B: Rajiv paid using a \$10 bill. How much change did he receive?

\$0.24

3. A football field is 120 yards long. Sort the lengths into the appropriate bins by comparing them to the length of a football field. 6.RP.3

4 miles	400 feet	4,000 inches
1,760 inches	$\frac{1}{10}$ mile	120 feet

Longer than a Football Field	Shorter than a Football Field
4 miles	**4,000 inches**
400 feet	**1,760 inches**
$\frac{1}{10}$ mile	**120 feet**

Online Test Tip
On an online test, you might be asked to drag the lengths to a bin. In this book, you will be asked to write each length in the space provided.

4. Kelly keeps track of her test scores as shown in the table.

Test	Number of Items	Number Correct
1	50	35
2	40	27
3	60	48
4	100	75

Complete the table by ordering Kelly's test scores from least to greatest percent scored. 6.RP.3, 6.RP.3c

	Test	Test Score (%)
Least	**2**	**67.5**
	1	**70**
	4	**75**
Greatest	**3**	**80**

5. Makayla wants to buy a carton of juice. She could buy a 48-ounce container for \$2.88 or a 64-ounce container for \$3.52. 6.RP.2

Part A: What is the cost per ounce of the juice in the 48-ounce container?

\$0.06, or 6 cents, per ounce

Part B: What is the cost per ounce of the juice in the 64-ounce container?

\$0.055, or $5\frac{1}{2}$ cents, per ounce

Part C: Which container is the better buy? Justify your response.

The 64-ounce container is the better buy because the cost per ounce is less; 0.055 < 0.06.

Online Test Tip
On an online test, you might be asked to use a keypad with math symbols to enter your answers. In this book, you will be asked to write your answers in the spaces provided.

NAME ______________ DATE ________ PERIOD ______ SCORE ______

Countdown: 18 Weeks

1. A recipe for fruit salad calls for 2 strawberries for every 3 pieces of melon. 6.RP.3, 6.RP.3a

Part A: Complete the ratio table.

Number of Strawberries	2	4	6	8
Number of Melon Pieces	3	6	9	12

Part B: Graph the data on the coordinate plane.

Number of Melon Pieces

Number of Strawberries

Online Test Tip
On an online test, you might be asked to click the button to plot the points. In this book, you will be asked to draw the points on the graph.

2. A building blueprint has a scale of 2 inches equal to 25 feet. On the blueprint, the 10-story building has a height of 12 inches. What is the actual height of 1 story? 6.RP.3, 6.RP.3b

15 ft

3. Ronald picked many oranges from his trees. He squeezed out 256 fluid ounces of juice. How many half-gallon containers of juice was he able to fill? 6.RP.3, 6.RP.3d

4 containers

4. The table shows the temperatures at noon for the past five days.

Day	Temperature (°F)
Monday	−4
Tuesday	2
Wednesday	0
Thursday	−6
Friday	3

Complete the table to order the temperatures from least to greatest. 6.NS.7, 6.NS.7b

	Day	Temperature (°F)
Least	Thursday	−6
	Monday	−4
	Wednesday	0
	Tuesday	2
Greatest	Friday	3

5. Select whether each expression is equivalent to the sum 45 + 63. 6.NS.4

Yes	No	
☐	■	15(3 + 4)
■	☐	9(5 + 7)
☐	■	7(7 + 9)
■	☐	3(21 + 15)

NAME ____________ DATE ________ PERIOD ______ SCORE ______

Countdown: 17 Weeks

1. Li wants to buy a jacket that is originally priced at $65.00. Today the store is advertising the jacket for 40% off the original price. 6.RP.3, 6.RP.3c

Online Test Tip
On an online test, you might be asked to use a keypad with math symbols to enter dollar amounts. In this book, you will be asked to write the amount in the space provided.

Part A: What is the sale price of the jacket?

$39.00

Part B: Li has a coupon for an additional 10% off the sale price. What is the price of the jacket after the coupon?

$35.10

2. Students' bicycles are parked in the bicycle rack. There are 8 red, 10 blue, 3 black, and 4 other colors. Select whether each statement is true or false. 6.RP.1

True	False	
■	□	The ratio of red to blue bicycles is 4:5.
□	■	The ratio of black to red bicycles is 8:3.
■	□	The ratio of blue bicycles to all other colors is 2:3.
■	□	The ratio of black to the total number of bicycles is 3:25.

3. Kim needs to place 32 mystery books and 56 biography books on library shelves. She is to place the maximum number of books on each shelf so that all the shelves have the same number of books. Each shelf will contain only one type of book. 6.NS.4

Part A: Determine the number of books to be placed on each shelf.

8 books

Part B: How many shelves will Kim use for each type of book?

4 shelves for mysteries and 7 shelves for biographies

4. The table shows the elevations of several objects compared to sea level.

Object	Elevation (ft)
Scuba diver	–75
Light in a lighthouse	137
Shark	–48
Fish	–6
Top of weather buoy	10
Submarine	–182

Complete the table to order the objects from farthest away to closest to sea level. 6.NS.7, 6.NS.7b

	Object	Elevation (ft)
Farthest	Submarine	–182
	Light in a lighthouse	137
	Scuba diver	–75
	Shark	–48
	Top of weather buoy	10
Closest	Fish	–6

5. A carpenter has a board $18\frac{1}{2}$ feet long. He needs to cut as many $1\frac{3}{4}$-feet-long pieces as possible. How many pieces can the carpenter cut? Explain how you found your answer. 6.NS.1

10 pieces; Sample answer: I divided $18\frac{1}{2}$ by $1\frac{3}{4}$. The exact answer is $10\frac{4}{7}$. I rounded down to 10, because I needed to find the number of complete boards being cut.

NAME ________________ DATE ________ PERIOD ______ SCORE ______

Countdown: 16 Weeks

1. A theater received $8,917 in ticket sales for one performance of a play. Tickets for preferred seats cost $45 each and regular seats cost $34 each. All of the theater's 75 preferred seats were sold out that evening. How many tickets were sold? 6.NS.2

238 tickets

Online Test Tip
On an online test, you might be asked to use a keypad with math symbols to enter the number. In this book, you will be asked to write the number in the space provided.

2. The table shows the elevations of five objects as compared to sea level. 6.NS.7, 6.NS.7b

Object	Elevation (ft)
Duck	21
Swimmer	–1
Fish	–50
Goose	3
Submarine	–125

Complete the table to order the objects from closest to sea level to farthest from sea level.

	Object	Elevation (ft)	Distance from sea level (ft)
Closest	Swimmer	–1	1
	Goose	3	3
	Duck	21	21
	Fish	–50	50
Farthest	Submarine	–125	125

3. The length of a garden is $51\frac{1}{3}$ feet. One section of fencing is $3\frac{2}{3}$ feet long. 6.NS.1

Part A: How many sections of fencing are needed along the length of the garden?

14 sections

Part B: For each piece of fencing, 4 stakes are used to secure it in place. The stakes are equally spaced along the fencing piece, with one stake at each end. How far apart are the stakes on one piece of fencing?

$1\frac{2}{9}$ ft

4. Rosina finds a pair of shorts on the sale rack for $12.50. This price reflects a discount of 60%. What is the original price of the shorts? What is the amount of the discount? 6.RP.3, 6.RP.3c

5.00	7.50	12.50	17.50
18.75	20	20.83	31.25

Original price of shorts: $ 31.25

Amount of discount: $ 18.75

5. The ratio of boys to all students in a class is 2:5. Select whether each statement is true or false. 6.RP.3, 6.RP.3b

True	False	
☐	■	There could be 4 boys and 10 girls in the class.
■	☐	There could be 8 boys and 12 girls in the class.
■	☐	There could be 10 boys among the 25 students in the class.
☐	■	There could be 20 boys among the 30 students in the class.
■	☐	There could be 9 girls among the 15 students in the class.

NAME ______________ DATE ________ PERIOD ______ SCORE ______

Countdown: 15 Weeks

1. Select whether each statement shows an example of the Distributive Property. 6.EE.3

Yes	No	
☐	■	$4(2x + 5) = 8x + 5$
☐	■	$7(3x + 2) = 10x + 9$
■	☐	$15x + 25 = 5(3x + 5)$
■	☐	$6x + 300 = 6(x + 50)$

Online Test Tip
On an online test, you might be asked to click the appropriate box for each statement. In this book, you will be asked to shade in the boxes instead.

2. Praedup uses the inequality $r + 2 \geq 25$ to represent his rock and shell collection, where r is the number of rocks in his collection. Select all of the values that could be the number of rocks in Praedup's collection. 6.EE.5

- ☐ 15
- ■ 25
- ☐ 5
- ☐ −50
- ■ 82
- ■ 23
- ☐ 22

3. Nancy is running on a trail that is 5.3 miles long. After 20 minutes, she has run 1.45 miles. 6.EE.7

Part A: Write an addition equation to find how much farther Nancy has to run to complete the trail.

$n + 1.45 = 5.3$

Part B: Solve the equation to find the number of miles Nancy has to run to get to the end of the trail.

3.85 mi

4. A survey asked a group of students to name their favorite school subject. The results are shown in the table.

Favorite Subject	Portion of Student Responses
Math	0.4
History	$\frac{3}{25}$
Reading	28%
Science	$\frac{1}{5}$

Complete the table to order the school subjects from least to greatest percent of students who chose that subject as their favorite. 6.RP.3

	Favorite Subject	Percent of Students
Least	History	12
	Science	20
	Reading	28
Greatest	Math	40

5. Point (3, −4) is plotted on a coordinate plane. Select whether each statement is true or false about point (3, −4). 6.NS.6, 6.NS.6b

True	False	
■	☐	It is located in Quadrant IV.
☐	■	It is a reflection of point (−3, −4) over the x-axis.
☐	■	It has the same location as point (−4, 3).
☐	■	It is a reflection of point (3, 4) over the y-axis.
■	☐	It is a reflection of the point (−3, 4) over the x-axis and then over the y-axis.

NAME ____________ DATE ________ PERIOD ______ SCORE ______

Countdown: 14 Weeks

1. For the school bake sale, members of the cheerleading squad bake the number of muffins shown in the table. 6.EE.1

Name	Number of Muffins
Robert	4^3
Alicia	4×3
Joe	3^4
Melanie	8^2

Part A: Circle the names of the squad members who bake the same number of muffins.

(Robert) Alicia Joe (Melanie)

Part B: Another squad member, Miki, also bakes the same number of muffins as the members you circled in Part A. Miki represents the number as a power of 2. What must be the value of Miki's exponent? Justify your answer.

6; Because the number of muffins is 64, and $2^6 = 2 \times 2 \times 2 \times 2 \times 2 \times 2 = 64$, the exponent must be a 6.

2. A company manufactures small, solid, plastic cubes. They use the expression s^3, where s is the length of a side, to find the volume of plastic needed to make a cube. Luis claims that the volume of plastic needed to make a cube with side length 8 millimeters is 24 cubic millimeters. Do you agree with Luis's claim? Explain your reasoning. 6.EE.2, 6.EE.2c

No; Luis' claim is not accurate. The expression $s^3 = 8 \times 8 \times 8 = 512$ mm^3.

3. Soto designs and makes personal flags. The fabric he purchases is measured in feet. However, Soto needs to know the number of inches for each fabric because the dimensions of his flags are in inches. 6.RP.3, 6.RP.3d

Fabric Color	Length (ft)	Length (in.)
Blue	3	**36**
Red	**5**	60
Yellow	$2\frac{1}{2}$	**30**
Green	12	**144**
Purple	**20**	240

Part A: Complete the table.

Part B: Write an expression that Soto could use to convert $16\frac{3}{4}$ feet of white fabric to inches. Then find the number of inches, and show your work.

$16\frac{3}{4}$ ft $\times \frac{12 \text{ in.}}{1 \text{ ft}}$; 201 in.; $\frac{67}{4} \times \frac{12}{1} = \frac{67}{1} \times \frac{3}{1} = 201$

4. Justin bought a hat for \$36 and two admission tickets to a baseball game. Let t represent the cost of an admission ticket. Select whether each statement is true or false. 6.EE.2, 6.EE.2a, 6.EE.2c

True	False	
☐	■	The expression $2(t + 36)$ represents the total amount Justin spent.
■	☐	When each admission ticket costs \$5.50, Justin will spend \$47 in all.
■	☐	The expression $2t + 36$ represents the total amount Justin spent.
☐	■	When each admission ticket costs \$9.50, Justin will spend \$91 in all.

5. The table shows the distance of five divers from the surface of the water.

Diver	Distance from Water Surface (m)
A	−450
B	15
C	−230
D	−99
E	−100

Select all of the divers whose distance from the surface is less than Diver E's distance. 6.NS.7, 6.NS.7c

☐ Diver A
■ Diver B
☐ Diver C
■ Diver D

Online Test Tip
On an online test, you might be asked to click all of the correct answer choices. In this book, you will be asked to shade a box next to each correct answer choice.

NAME ______________ DATE ________ PERIOD ______ SCORE ______

Countdown: 13 Weeks

1. Write the appropriate number in each box to find the product. 6.NS.4

7	8	9	14	28
56	169	196	728	1,456

$7 \times 28 = 7(20 + \boxed{8}) = 140 + \boxed{56} = \boxed{196}$

2. Jessica wants to buy the items shown in the table for her aquarium. She has $40 to spend. She has a coupon for 20% off her total purchase. Determine the most items she can buy if she does not want to buy more than one of any item. Justify your answer. (Ignore sales tax.) 6.RP.3, 6.RP.3c

Item	Cost ($)
Artificial plant pack	13
Aquarium gravel	10
Coral bubbler	25
Driftwood	7
Eiffel Tower ornament	8

4 items; Sample answer: She can buy the Eiffel Tower ornament, the driftwood, coral bubbler, and the gravel. The total cost before the coupon is 8 + 7 + 25 + 10 = $50. When the coupon is applied, the total cost is 50 – (0.20)(50) = 50 – 10 = $40.

3. Cheryl sends the same number of e-mails each week as shown in the table. Let w represent the number of weeks that Cheryl sends e-mails. Let n represent the total number of e-mails sent. 6.EE.9

Week (w)	Total Number of E-mails (n)
1	7
2	14
3	21
4	28

Part A: Select whether each statement is true or false.

True	False	
☐	■	The equation $w = 7 + n$ represents the relationship between the number of weeks and the total number of e-mails.
■	☐	The total number of e-mails sent is 7 times the number of weeks.
■	☐	The number of e-mails Cheryl sends depends on the number of weeks.

Part B: Cheryl claims that based on the relationship shown in the table, in week 6 she will send over 40 e-mails. Do you agree with Cheryl's claim? Provide evidence to support your answer.

Yes; Sample answer: The equation $n = 7w$ represents the total number of e-mails. When $w = 6$, $n = 42$. Because 42 is greater than 40, Cheryl's claim is true.

4. Juanita purchased amusement park tickets for herself and her brothers. The cost of each ticket was x dollars. Juanita bought 3 tickets on Tuesday and 1 ticket on Wednesday. She paid $8 for herself and her brothers to ride the bus to the park. The expression $4x + 8$ represents the amount of money Juanita spent. Select all of the expressions that are equivalent to $4x + 8$. 6.EE.3, 6.EE.4

- ☐ $3x + 9$
- ■ $4(x + 2)$
- ☐ $2(x + 4)$
- ■ $2(2x + 4)$
- ■ $8 + 4x$
- ☐ $12x$
- ■ $\frac{1}{2}(8x + 16)$

5. Write the appropriate term in each box to create an expression equivalent to $7x + 2x + 6y$. 6.EE.3

3x	9x	15x	3y
2	3	2y	6y

$7x + 2x + 6y = \boxed{3}(\boxed{3x} + \boxed{2y})$

Online Test Tip
On an online test, you might be asked to drag the expressions into the spaces provided. In this book, you will be asked to write in the spaces.

NAME ________________ DATE ________ PERIOD ______ SCORE ______

Countdown: 12 Weeks

1. Members of a book club named their favorite genre of book. Circle the ratios that compare the number of members who did *not* choose mystery to the total number of responses. 6.RP.1

Genre	Number of Responses
Science Fiction	7
Mystery	8
History	6
Biographies	3

$\frac{1}{3}$	1 to 8	(2:3)	2:1
($\frac{2}{3}$)	8:24	(16 to 24)	3 to 2

2. Irfan is transferring the drawing of figure *ABCD* to a coordinate plane. He plots point *A* at (–2, –1), and point *B* at (1, 3) on a coordinate plane. Graph the ordered pairs that show points *C* and *D*, and then connect the points to form Irfan's figure. 6.NS.8

B, A, C, D, 3, 3, 4, 4

y, x, 10, –10, 10, –10, O, A, B, C, D

Online Test Tip

On an online test, you might be asked to click buttons to plot points and graph line segments. In this book, you will be asked to draw the points and lines.

3. Kwasi reads 30 minutes before school. He reads *x* more minutes after school. Write an equation to represent the total number of minutes *y* Kwasi reads. 6.EE.9

$30 + x = y$

4. Latoya has a 25-pound bag of potting soil. She puts 3 pounds of potting soil in each of *f* flowerpots. The amount of potting soil that remains can be represented by the expression 25 – 3*f*. 6.EE.2, 6.EE.2c

Part A: Latoya puts soil in 7 flowerpots. How much potting soil remains?

[4] pounds

Part B: Latoya realizes that she actually has two 25-pound bags of potting soil. Write the appropriate numbers and symbols in the spaces to represent the number of pounds of potting soil remaining after Latoya puts 3 pounds in each of *f* flowerpots.

2	3	4	5	6	+
25	27	28	50	54	–

[50] [–] [3] *f*

5. A fruit stand makes a profit when $p > 38$, where *p* is the number of pounds of fruit sold. Select all of the days that the fruit stand makes a profit. 6.EE.5

- ☐ Monday
- ■ Tuesday
- ■ Wednesday
- ■ Thursday
- ☐ Friday
- ■ Saturday

Day	Amount of Fruit Sold (lb)
Monday	32
Tuesday	45
Wednesday	39
Thursday	44
Friday	38
Saturday	56

Countdown

NAME ______________ DATE ________ PERIOD ______ SCORE ______

Countdown: 11 Weeks

1. Using the numbers, write two powers that have the same value. 6.EE.1

[2] [3] [6] [8]

$8^{2} = 2^{6}$

2. A rectangle has an area of $(24x + 30)$ square units. Select all of the dimensions that are possible for this rectangle. 6.EE.3

$24x + 30$

- [x] width 6 units; length $(4x + 5)$ units
- [ ] width 4 units; length $(6x + 7)$ units
- [ ] width 3 units; length $(21x + 27)$ units
- [ ] width 8 units; length $(3x + 4)$ units
- [x] width 2 units; length $(15 + 12x)$ units

3. In the last basketball game, Elena scored 2 more than one fourth of her team's total points. 6.EE.2, 6.EE.2a, 6.EE.6

Part A: Let n represent the number of points Elena's team scored. Write an expression for the number of points Elena scored.

$\frac{1}{4}n + 2$

Part B: The team scored 40 points. How many points did Elena score?

12 points

Online Test Tip
On an online test, you might be asked to use a keypad with math symbols to enter your expression. In this book, you will be asked to write your response in the space provided.

4. Joan runs at a constant rate for 2 hours. She takes 45 minutes to run 6 miles. De'Quan also runs at a constant rate. He runs $11\frac{1}{4}$ miles in 1 hour 15 minutes. 6.RP.3, 6.RP.3a, 6.RP.3d

Part A: Complete the table for Joan's running times and distances.

Joan's Running				
Distance (mi)	6	2	4	10
Time (min)	45	15	30	75

Part B: Does Joan or De'Quan run more miles in 75 minutes? Justify your response.

De'Quan; Sample answer: 1 hour 15 minutes = 75 minutes. De'Quan runs $11\frac{1}{4}$ mi, Joan runs 10 mi, and $11\frac{1}{4} > 10$.

5. The diagram shows the amount of fabric that Christine needs to make 1 tablecloth, including the fabric that will hang over the sides. The fabric costs $1.50 per square foot. Christine plans to make 1 tablecloth for each of the 4 seasons of the year. What is the total cost of the fabric that Christine needs for the tablecloths? 6.NS.3

$2\frac{1}{2}$ ft

6 ft

$90.00

NAME ________________ DATE ________ PERIOD ______ SCORE ______

Countdown: 10 Weeks

1. Steve surveyed the students in his class to find out their favorite sport. The table shows the results of the survey. What percent of Steve's classmates did *not* select soccer as their favorite sport? 6.RP.3, 6.RP.3c

Favorite Sport	
Sport	**Number of Students**
Basketball	8
Football	7
Soccer	12
Other	13

70%

2. Two-fifths of the girls in a school signed up to play softball. An equal number of girls signed up to play pitcher, infield, and outfield. What fraction of girls in the school signed up to play outfield? 6.NS.1

$\frac{2}{15}$

3. Select all of the equations for which the solution is 20. 6.EE.5

- ☐ $n - 4 = 24$
- ■ $10n = 200$
- ■ $\frac{n}{5} = 4$
- ☐ $7 + n = 13$

Online Test Tip
On an online test, you might be asked to click all of the correct answer choices. In this book, you will be asked to shade a box next to each correct answer choice.

4. A hiker walks at an average rate of 2 miles per hour. 6.EE.7

Part A: Write a multiplication equation to find how long it will take for the hiker to walk 11 miles. Let *n* represent the number of hours.

$2n = 11$

Part B: Solve the equation for *n*. How many hours does the hiker walk?

$n = 5.5$; The hiker walks 5.5 h.

5. Select whether each set of dimensions represents a triangle with an area of 24 square units. 6.G.1

Yes	No	
☐	■	base = 8 units, height = 12 units
■	☐	base = 6 units, height = 8 units
☐	■	base = 4 units, height = 6 units
☐	■	base = 3 units, height = 4 units
■	☐	base = 16 units, height = 3 units

NAME ______________ DATE ________ PERIOD ______ SCORE ______

Countdown: 9 Weeks

1. Lina stocked fruit to sell at a market. The ratio of apples to oranges is 1:4. Lina stocked no more than 200 of each type of fruit. 6.RP.3, 6.RP.3a

Part A: Complete the table to determine how many apples and oranges Lina may have stocked. Choose appropriate numbers for the last two columns.

Apples	2	3	8	12	15	10	20
Oranges	8	12	32	48	60	40	80

Sample answers are shown for the last two columns. Accept any pairs in the ratio 1:4.

Part B: How many apples would Lina stock if she has 104 oranges?

26 apples

2. William has 42 red tulip bulbs and 56 yellow tulip bulbs. He plans to use all the bulbs to make potted gifts for his teachers. William claims he can make 7 pots of tulips with an equal total number of red and yellow tulips in each pot. Do you agree with William's claim? Justify your reasoning. 6.NS.4

Yes; Sample answer: 7 is a factor of 42 and 56. For 7 pots, he must put 6 red tulips and 8 yellow tulips in each pot. 42 + 56 = 7(6 + 8).

3. Kimi has posted 3 × 3 × 3 × 3 puppy photos on a social network. 6.EE.1

Part A: Write the appropriate numbers in the boxes to represent 3 × 3 × 3 × 3 as a power.

2	3
4	12

The base is **3**. The exponent is **4**.

The power is 3^{4}.

Online Test Tip
On an online test, you might be asked to drag the numbers into the appropriate box. In this book, you will be asked to write the numbers instead.

Part B: How many puppy photos did Kimi post on the social network?

81 puppy photos

4. The diagram shows the coordinates of the vertices of a right trapezoid when it is drawn on a coordinate plane. Select whether each statement is true or false. 6.G.3

(3, 6) (a, 6) (3, −1) (r, s)

True	False	
■	☐	The length of the longest horizontal side is $r - 3$.
☐	■	The length of the vertical side is 5.
☐	■	$a = 3$
■	☐	$r > s$
☐	■	The length of the shortest horizontal side is $a - 6$.

5. The box-and-whisker plot displays the weights of 24 pets. Select all of the values that are quartiles of the data. 6.SP.5, 6.SP.5c

Pet Weights (lb)

0 2 4 6 8 10 12 14 16 18 20

- ☐ 2
- ☐ 10
- ■ 7
- ☐ 16
- ☐ 5
- ■ 12
- ☐ 14
- ☐ 9
- ☐ 8

NAME ______________ DATE ________ PERIOD ______ SCORE ______

Countdown: 8 Weeks

1. Benjamin needs to gather data about astronauts and space travel to write a report. Select whether each question can be classified as a statistical question. 6.SP.1

Online Test Tip
On an online test, you might be asked to click the appropriate box for each statement. In this book, you will be asked to shade in the boxes instead.

Yes	No	
☐	■	How many astronauts have walked on the moon?
■	☐	How many days did the missions stay on the moon?
☐	■	How many times did Neil Armstrong travel into space?
■	☐	How old were the astronauts when they traveled into space?

2. The raised vegetable garden in Susan's yard is in the shape of a rectangular prism with a volume of 48 cubic feet and a height of $\frac{3}{4}$ foot. 6.G.2

Part A: The base of the garden is not a square and the width is greater than 2 feet. What could be the length and width of the raised garden? Explain.

Sample answer: width: 4 ft, length: 16 ft; I used the formula $V = \ell wh$ and substituted to get $48 = \ell w\left(\frac{3}{4}\right)$ and then simplified to $\ell w = 64$. I chose two values other than 8 and greater than 2 that, when multiplied, resulted in 64.

Part B: The base of the garden is a square. What is the width and length of the raised garden?

width: 8 ft, length: 8 ft

3. Rey fenced off triangular areas *A* and *B* in his yard for his two pets. Rey claims that the combined area of these two triangles is equal to the area of triangle *C*. Is Rey's claim correct? Justify your answer. 6.G.1

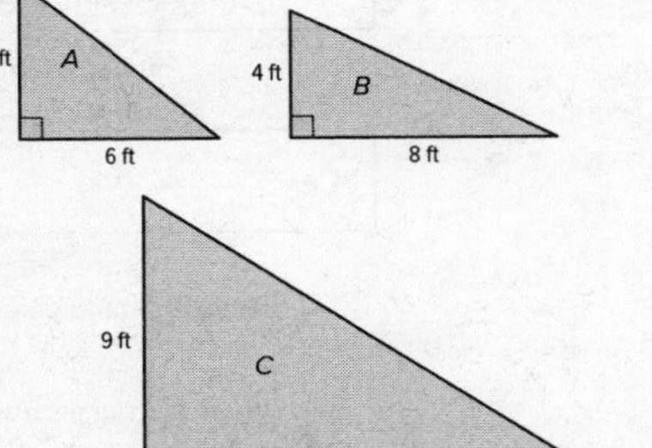

No; sample answer: The area of ΔA is 15 ft^2. The area of ΔB is 16 ft^2. The combined area is $15 + 16 = 31$ ft^2. The area of ΔC is 63 ft^2, and 31 ft^2 < 63 ft^2.

4. The table shows the average amount of money the boys and girls in Zina's class spent on their science fair projects. Zina spent at most $2 more than the average amount spent by the girls in her class. 6.EE.6

Average Amount Spent on Project	
Male	$15
Female	$16

Part A: Let *z* represent the amount of money Zina spent. Write the appropriate numbers and operations in the boxes to create an inequality of the situation.

+	–	×	÷	1
2	14	15	16	31

z [–] [2] ≤ [16]

Part B: What is the greatest amount that Zina could have spent?

$18

5. Select all of the products of 2.74 × 7.5. 6.NS.3

- ☐ 20.05
- ☐ 205.50
- ☐ 20.50
- ■ 20.55
- ☐ 20,550
- ☐ 205.5
- ■ 20.550
- ☐ 205.05

NAME ________________ DATE ________ PERIOD ______ SCORE ______

Countdown: 7 Weeks

1. Monique has five weeks to save at least $80 for a ski trip. Let *n* represent the amount she has to save each week. 6.EE.8

Part A: Write and solve an inequality to find the amount of money Monique needs to save each week.

$5n \geq 80$
$n \geq 16$

Part B: Interpret the solution in the context of the problem.

Monique needs to save at least $16 each week to have enough money for the ski trip.

2. Winifred has a college pennant on her wall. The pennant covers 54 square inches of wall space. Select all the possible values for *x* and *y*. 6.G.1

x in.
y in.

- ☐ $x = 6, y = 9$
- ☐ $x = 4, y = 13.5$
- ■ $x = 6, y = 18$
- ■ $x = 9, y = 12$

3. The diagram shows the dimensions of a school playground. What is the area of the playground? 6.G.1

40 yd
14 yd
8 yd
30 yd
60 yd

1,574 yd^2

4. In the last six basketball games, Russell averaged 20 points per game. The lists show the number of points per game for 4 other players. Select whether each set of numbers has the same average as Russell. 6.SP.3

Yes	No	
☐	■	20, 20, 20, 20, 20, 23
■	☐	15, 16, 17, 18, 19, 35
☐	■	16, 17, 20, 20, 21, 22
■	☐	15, 17, 19, 21, 22, 26

5. The list shows Moira's quiz scores: 6, 4, 10, 7, 10, 8, 9, 6. Select whether each statement is true or false in representing the quiz scores. 6.SP.3

True	False	
■	☐	6 is a mode of the quiz scores.
☐	■	8.5 is the median quiz score.
■	☐	10 is a mode of the quiz scores.
■	☐	7.5 is the median quiz score.
☐	■	4 is the range of the quiz scores.

Online Test Tip
On an online test, you might be asked to click the appropriate box for each statement. In this book, you will be asked to shade in the boxes.

NAME ______________ DATE ________ PERIOD ______ SCORE ______

Countdown: 6 Weeks

1. The ratio of the areas of two parallelograms is 4:9. The perimeter of the smaller parallelogram is 20 units. What is the perimeter of the larger parallelogram? 6.G.1

30 units

2. The box plot shows some student test scores. 6.SP.4

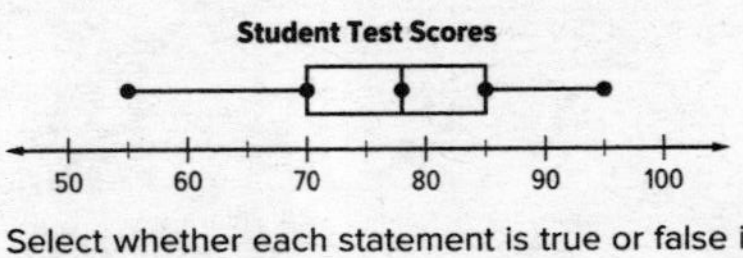

Select whether each statement is true or false in representing the student test scores.

True	False	
■	□	Half of the test scores are between 70 and 85.
□	■	The lowest test score is 60.
□	■	The mean of the test scores is 78.
■	□	The median test score is 78.
□	■	The mode of the test scores is 85.
□	■	More than 25% of the test scores are between 55 and 70.

3. The diagram shows the dimensions of a gift box that Andrea needs to wrap. What is the least amount of wrapping paper needed to completely cover the box? 6.G.4

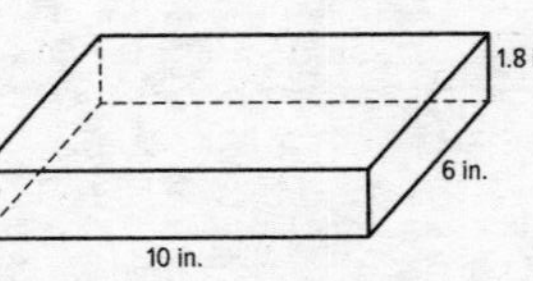

177.6 in^2

4. A rectangular bathtub is $5\frac{1}{2}$ feet long, $1\frac{1}{2}$ feet wide, and 3 feet high. Daniel fills the tub to a depth of 2 feet. What is the volume of the water in the tub? 6.G.2

$16\frac{1}{2}$ ft^3

Online Test Tip
On an online test, you might be asked to use a keypad with math symbols to enter the expression. In this book, you will be asked to write the expression in the space provided.

5. At a fabrication plant, 9 of the employees each earn $10,000 per quarter and 1 employee earns $70,000 per quarter. 6.SP.5, 6.SP.5c

Part A: Find the median and mean salary per quarter.

median: $10,000; mean: $16,000

Part B: The industry employee average salary for fabrication plants is $13,000 per quarter. Mr. Gomez is trying to recruit people to work for the plant. How might he advertise the position using the mean salary?

Sample answer: He might say the company pays more than the average industry salary, because 16,000 > 13,000.

Part C: Evaluate the advertisement in Part B. Do you agree with the claim made in the advertisement? Explain.

Sample answer: No, the median represents the salaries better than the mean, because 9 of the employees earn the median salary, $10,000.

Copyright © McGraw-Hill Education. Permission is granted to reproduce for classroom use.

Countdown

NAME ______________ DATE ______ PERIOD ______ SCORE ______

Countdown: 5 Weeks

1. The figure shows a trapezoid with a height of 4 units. The area of the trapezoid is 20 square units. Select all of the dimensions for *a* and *b* that would represent the trapezoid. 6.G.1

- [ ] $a = 3$ units, $b = 2$ units
- [x] $a = 6$ units, $b = 4$ units
- [ ] $a = 12$ units, $b = 8$ units
- [x] $a = 7.5$ units, $b = 2.5$ units
- [ ] $a = 4$ units, $b = 1$ units
- [ ] $a = 23$ units, $b = 17$ units

2. A homeowner has two rectangular structures in her backyard. The dimensions of the hot tub are 6 feet by 8 feet. The dimensions of the fire pit are 7 feet by 9 feet. The length of the square backyard is 20 feet. What area of the yard is not covered by the hot tub and the fire pit? 6.G.1

289 ft²

3. The diagram shows the dimensions of a wooden toy chest. One can of wood stain covers 12 square feet. How many cans are needed to stain all 6 outside surfaces of the toy chest? 6.G.4

5 cans

4. The list shows Jim's recent golf scores. 6.SP.5, 6.SP.5c

72, 78, 81, 77, 92, 80, 78, 84, 75

Part A: What is the range of the scores?

20

Part B: What is the interquartile range? Justify your answer.

6.5; first quartile = 76, third quartile = 82.5, IQR = 82.5 − 76 = 6.5

5. Ryne is collecting some data about his favorite minor league baseball team. He finds information about the players' salaries, years of experience, and favorite uniform numbers. Write the measure that best represents each set of data. 6.SP.5, 6.SP.5c

Online Test Tip
On an online test, you might be asked to drag the words into the space provided. In this book, you will be asked to write the words instead.

mode median mean

median — Favorite uniform number: 7, 14, 11, 22, 3, 1, 99, 30, 27, 12, 19

mode — Years of experience: 3, 1, 6, 3, 2, 3, 3, 3, 1, 4, 3

mean — Salary: \$10,750, \$13,500, \$11,750, \$13,000, \$14,500, \$12,000, \$13,750, \$15,500, \$14,000, \$15,750, \$14,750

NAME ________________ DATE ________ PERIOD ______ SCORE ______

Countdown: 4 Weeks

1. The original dimensions of a rectangular garden that Emma designs is 10 feet long and 6 feet wide. She now plans to double the area of the garden by changing one or both of the dimensions. She wants the area of the garden to be 120 square feet, but neither the length nor the width can be greater than 25 feet. 6.G.1

Part A: Complete the table to find the measures in Emma's options.

	Length (ft)	Width (ft)	Area (ft²)	Perimeter (ft)
Original Design	10	6	60	32
Option 1	10	12	120	44
Option 2	15	8	120	46
Option 3	20	6	120	52
Option 4	5	24	120	58

Part B: Emma has 50 feet of garden fencing. Which option will let Emma surround the garden completely with the greatest amount of fencing?

Option 2

Part C: For Option 5, Emma multiplies the width in her original plan by $\frac{1}{2}$. Does this option meet the requirements for her garden? Explain.

no; A width of 3 ft would result in a length of 40 ft, and 40 > 25. Also, the perimeter would be 86 ft, which is much greater than her 50 ft of fencing.

2. The diagram shows a placemat made with white fabric and gray fabric. Select whether each statement is true or false in representing the diagram. 6.G.1

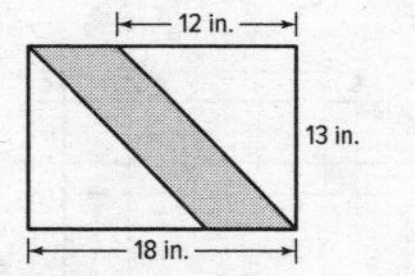

True	False	
☐	■	The length of the placemat is 12 in.
■	☐	The area of the gray fabric is 78 in².
☐	■	The area of the placemat is 2,808 in².
■	☐	The area of the white fabric is 156 in².

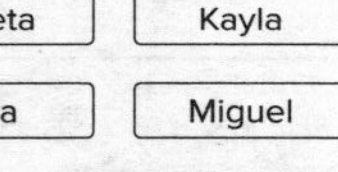

Online Test Tip
On an online test, you might be asked to click the appropriate box for each statement. In this book, you will be asked to shade in the boxes instead.

3. A trapezoid has an area of 33.6 square centimeters and a height of 4 centimeters. 6.G.1

Part A: What is the sum of the base lengths of the trapezoid?

16.8 cm

Part B: The length of one of the bases of the trapezoid is three times the length of the other base. What are the lengths of the bases?

4.2 cm and 12.6 cm

4. The table shows the number of miles Jayden cycled each week for 5 weeks. Write the appropriate numbers to find the mean number of miles Jayden cycled per week. 6.SP.3

Week	Number of Miles
1	16
2	19
3	20
4	18
5	22

1	2	3	4	5	6	16
17	18	19	20	21	22	38

$$\frac{16 + 19 + 20 + 18 + 22}{5} = 19$$

Mean: 19 miles

5. Six students kept track of the numbers of hours they spent on their science projects each week. Sort the names of the students into the appropriate bins based on a comparison of the median and mode of his or her data set. 6.SP.3, 6.SP.5, 6.SP.5c

Student	Number of Hours Spent on Science Project
Julieta	4, 6, 4, 5, 4, 5
Kayla	5, 5, 5, 5, 5, 5
Fina	3, 6, 3, 4, 2, 3
Miguel	4, 1, 5, 5, 3, 2
Shane	4, 6, 2, 2, 6, 2
William	3, 1, 6, 4, 4, 5

Julieta | Kayla
Fina | Miguel
Shane | William

Median Greater than Mode	Median Equal to Mode	Median Less Than Mode
Julieta Shane	Kayla Fina William	Miguel

Countdown

NAME ______________ DATE __________ PERIOD ________ SCORE ________

Countdown: 3 Weeks

1. Figure *RSTV* has vertices located at *R*(3, 2), *S*(7, 2), *T*(7, 8), and *V*(3, 8). 6.G.3, 6.NS.8

Part A: Graph the figure *RSTV* on the coordinate plane.

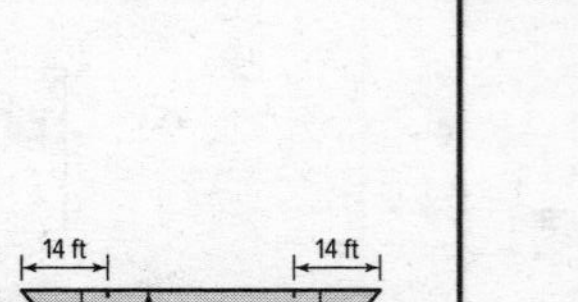

Part B: Select whether each statement is true or false about figure *RSTV*.

True	False	
■	☐	Figure *RSTV* is a rectangle.
■	☐	The length of $\overline{TV}$ is 4 units.
☐	■	The length of $\overline{TV}$ is greater than the length of $\overline{TS}$.
☐	■	The expression 2 × 4 + 6 represents the perimeter of figure *RSTV*.
■	☐	The area of figure *RSTV* is 24 square units.

2. The diagram shows the dimensions of an outdoor patio. Select all of the expressions that represent the area of the patio in square feet. 6.G.1

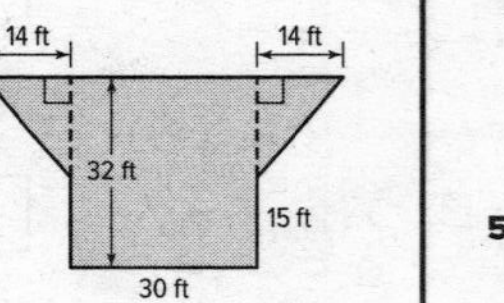

- ■ (14 × 17) + (30 × 32)
- ☐ 119 + 960
- ☐ 14 + 32 + 14 + 15 + 30
- ■ $(2 \times \frac{1}{2} \times 14 \times 17) + (32 \times 30)$
- ■ 960 + 119 + 119
- ■ $(30 \times 15) + \left(\frac{1}{2}\right)(17)(30 + 58)$

3. The table shows Mateo's scores on some math quizzes. Compare and contrast the measures of variation for both weeks. 6.SP.5, 6.SP.5c

Month	Mateo's Math Quiz Scores
March	75, 70, 80, 90, 85, 75, 80, 90
April	85, 80, 72, 80, 90, 80, 85, 95

March: range: 20; median 80; Q1: 75; Q3: 87.5; IQR: 12.5
April: range: 23; median 82.5; Q1: 80; Q3: 87.5; IQR: 7.5
The ranges are close in value; the scores in March have a greater spread.

4. The list shows the number of hours Rachael volunteered at six events: 15, 18, 5, 20, 17, and 21. Identify the outlier in the data set. Then describe how the outlier affects the mean. 6.SP.5, 6.SP.5c

outlier: **5** hours

The mean with the outlier is 16 hours, and the mean without the outlier is 18.2 hours. So the outlier decreases the mean.

5. The table shows the ages of the members of a swim club. Paco draws a histogram and uses it to conclude that 12 members are over the age of 39. 6.SP.4, 6.SP.5a

Ages of Swim Club Members									
11	18	25	32	39	47	57	59	40	35
41	26	28	15	20	38	42	12	12	20
18	45	19	41	21	50	28	16	35	24
20	40	14	18	31	19	58	17	27	30

Part A: Complete the histogram to represent the data.

Ages of Swim Club Members

Frequency: 0, 2, 4, 6, 8, 10, 12, 14

Age: 11–17, 18–24, 25–31, 32–38, 39–45, 46–52, 53–59

Online Test Tip
On an online test, you might be asked to click in the graph to shade the appropriate sections. In this book, you will be asked to draw the shading in the graph.

Part B: Is Paco's statement valid? Explain your reasoning.

no; Sample answer: The graph shows 12 people are over the age of 38. It cannot be determined from the histogram how many of the 7 people in the interval 39–45 are older than 39 years.

NAME ______________ DATE ________ PERIOD ______ SCORE ______

Countdown: 2 Weeks

1. The diagram shows the dimensions of two boxes of macaroni. 6.G.2

Box A: Macaroni, $4\frac{1}{2}$ in., 2 in., $7\frac{1}{4}$ in.

Box B: Macaroni, $4\frac{1}{2}$ in., ?, $7\frac{1}{4}$ in.

Part A: Find the volume of Box A.

$65\frac{1}{4}$ in³

Part B: The volume of Box B is $97\frac{7}{8}$ cubic inches greater than the volume of Box A. Explain a method you could use to find the width of Box B. Then find the width of Box B.

5 in.; Sample answer: Find volume of Box B by adding $97\frac{7}{8}$ in³ to the volume of Box A. Then substitute $163\frac{1}{8}$, $4\frac{1}{2}$, and $7\frac{1}{4}$ into the formula *Volume of Box B* = ℓwh, and solve for w: $163\frac{1}{8} = \left(4\frac{1}{2}\right)(w)\left(7\frac{1}{4}\right)$, and $w = 5$.

2. A rectangular prism has a length of 6.2 centimeters, a width of 2.4 centimeters, and a height of 3 centimeters. Select all of the expressions that are equivalent to the surface area, in square centimeters, of the rectangular prism. 6.G.4

- ☐ (6.2)(2.4)(3)
- ☐ 2(6.2) + 2(3) + 2(2.4)
- ■ 37.2 + 29.76 + 14.4
- ■ 2(6.2)(3) + 2(6.2)(2.4) + 2(3)(2.4)
- ■ 2(18.6 + 14.88 + 7.2)

Online Test Tip

On an online test, you might be asked to click all of the correct answer choices. In this book, you will be asked to shade a box next to each correct answer choice.

3. Sofia asked a group of middle school students how many hours a week they spend playing video games. The table shows the results of her survey. 6.SP.4, 6.SP.5, 6.SP.5c

Hours Spent Playing Video Games Each Week					
10	8	6	7	3	12
15	6	2	6	9	11
12	6	13	9	1	7
5	8	2	10	6	9

Part A: Complete the line plot to represent the data.

Hours Spent Playing Video Games Each Week

0 1 2 3 4 5 6 7 8 9 10 11 12 13 14 15

Part B: Find and interpret the median and mode of the data.

median: 7.5, mode: 6; Sample answer: One-half of the students play video games less than 7.5 h each week, and one-half play more than 7.5 h each week. More students play 6 h each week than any other number of hours.

4. The histogram shows the number of minutes students spend on chores each day. Select whether each statement is true or false. 6.SP.5, 6.SP.5a, 6.SP.5c

Minutes Spent on Chores Each Day

Frequency: 0 4 8 12 16 20 24

10–19 20–29 30–39 40–49 50–59

Number of Minutes

True	False	
■	☐	The data represent the responses of 60 students.
☐	■	The interval 30–39 represents the greatest number of students.
■	☐	More students spend at most 39 minutes on chores than spend more than 39 minutes on them.
■	☐	The greatest amount of time a student spends on chores could be 59 minutes.

5. The box-and-whisker plot shows the hours spent on a project by students in an art class. Find the median and the measures of variability. Then describe the data. 6.SP.4, 6.SP.5, 6.SP.5c

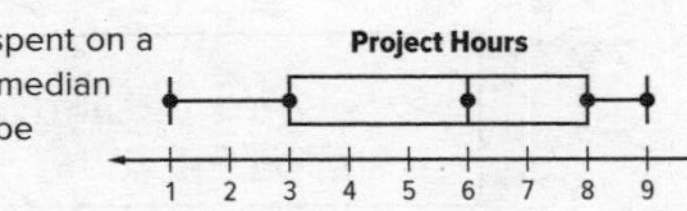

median: 6; Q_1: 3; Q_3: 8; range: 8; IQR: 5; no outliers; Sample answer: The left half of the data is more spread out than the right half. The median is slightly closer to Q_3 than to Q_1.

NAME ______ DATE ______ PERIOD ______ SCORE ______

Countdown: 1 Week

1. Evan fills the prism shown with $148\frac{1}{2}$ cubic inches of sand. Shade the height of the sand in the prism. 6.G.2

10 in. | 6 in. | $5\frac{1}{2}$ in.

2. The table shows the scores Maliah earned on her first five history tests. 6.SP.5, 6.SP.5b, 6.SP.5c

History Test Scores				
80	75	90	75	95

Part A: Sort the score she earned on her sixth test into the appropriate bin based on the measure of center for 6 test scores.

70 | 75 | 80 | 85 | 90 | 95 | 100

Mean is 85.	Median is 82.5.	Mode is 90.
95	85	90

Part B: The range of scores on the sixth test is 0–100. Is it possible for Maliah to get a test score that will change her mean score to 90? Explain your reasoning.

no; To have a mean of 90, the sum of the 6 test scores has to be 6 × 90, or 540. The sum of the first five test scores is 415, and 540 – 415 = 125. Maliah would have to get a score of 125 on the sixth test, which is not in the range of possible scores.

Online Test Tip
On an online test, you might be asked to use a keypad with math symbols to enter the answer. In this book, you will be asked to write the answer in the space provided.

3. Write a set of data that contains ten values and can be represented by the box-and-whisker plot shown. State the median, first and third quartiles, and lower and upper extremes. 6.SP.4, 6.SP.5, 6.SP.5c

9 10 11 12 13 14 15 16 17 18 19

Sample answer: {10, 10, 11, 12, 12, 14, 15, 16, 17, 18}; median: 13; Q_1: 11; Q_3: 16; lower extreme: 10; upper extreme: 18

4. The line plot represents the number of concert tickets sold by band members. Susan gave several interpretations of the data. Select whether each of her statements is true or false in interpreting the data. 6.SP.2, 6.SP.5, 6.SP.5d

Number of Concert Tickets Sold

0 1 2 3 4 5 6 7 8 9 10 11 12 13 14 15

True	False	
☐	■	The shape of the data is symmetric.
■	☐	The data value 1 is an outlier.
■	☐	The median is the appropriate measure to use to describe the center.
■	☐	The spread of the data around the center is about 2.3 tickets, which is the mean absolute deviation.

5. The high temperatures over the past six days were 82°, 78°, 70°, 72°, 71°, and 67°. Find the measure of center that best describes the data. Explain why you think it is the best measure for this data. 6.SP.5, 6.SP.5c, 6.SP.5d

mean: ≈ 73.3°; The set of data has no extreme values or numbers that are repeated, so the mean is the best representation.

NAME ______________ DATE ________ PERIOD ______ SCORE ______

Chapter 1 Test

1. Miriam buys 24 petunia plants and 40 azalea plants. She wants to plant an equal number of flowers in each row of her garden. Each row will contain only one type of flowering plant. 6.NS.4

Part A: Determine the greatest number of plants that could be in each row of the garden.

8

Part B: Miriam plants the greatest number of flowering plants possible in each row. How many rows of each type of flower will be in Miriam's garden?

3 rows of petunias and 5 rows of azaleas

2. For a family picnic, Akeela wants to buy the same number of bratwurst and buns. The bratwurst come in packages of 6, and the buns are sold in packages of 8. 6.NS.4

Part A: What is the least number of bratwurst and buns that Akeela could buy?

24

Part B: How many packages of each should Akeela buy to have the least number of total packages?

4 packages of bratwurst and 3 packages of buns

3. Billy has both baseball and football card collections. He arranges his cards in equal rows. Using his current card collection, Billy is able to make rows of 9 cards, with each row containing only one type of card. Select all the ways that Billy can have each type of card in his collection. 6.NS.4

- [x] 27 baseball cards and 45 football cards
- [ ] 18 baseball cards and 24 football cards
- [x] 36 baseball cards and 72 football cards
- [ ] 15 baseball cards and 63 football cards
- [x] 27 baseball cards and 81 football cards

4. Thulani goes to the library every 7 days. He goes to the market every 4 days. Today, August 1, Thulani goes to both the library and the market. How many more times will he go to both places on the same day for the remainder of the year? 6.NS.4

5 times

5. Alicia took a poll to determine her classmates' favorite pets. She wrote the results on the board: Dog, 8; Cat, 5; Bird, 2; and Fish, 3. Select whether each statement is true or false. 6.RP.1

True	False	
[ ]	[x]	The ratio of birds to dogs is 4:1.
[x]	[ ]	The ratio of fish to cats is 3 to 5.
[x]	[ ]	The ratio of dogs to the other pets is 4:5.
[ ]	[x]	The ratio of birds to the total number of pets is 9 to 1.

6. Jillian has 3 pencils and 4 pens. Select all of the ways to write the ratio of pens to pencils. 6.RP.1

- [ ] 4 + 3
- [x] 4 to 3
- [x] $\frac{4}{3}$
- [ ] 3:4
- [x] 4:3
- [ ] 4 – 3

7. George surveyed his friends about recent driving trips their families took for vacation. Write the appropriate unit rate for each distance traveled. 6.RP.2

200 miles in 4 hours	$\frac{50 \text{ miles}}{1 \text{ hour}}$
270 miles in 6 hours	$\frac{45 \text{ miles}}{1 \text{ hour}}$
1,440 miles in 30 hours	$\frac{48 \text{ miles}}{1 \text{ hour}}$

$\frac{1 \text{ hour}}{50 \text{ miles}}$	$\frac{144 \text{ miles}}{3 \text{ hours}}$	$\frac{45 \text{ miles}}{1 \text{ hour}}$
$\frac{48 \text{ miles}}{1 \text{ hour}}$	$\frac{1 \text{ hour}}{45 \text{ miles}}$	$\frac{100 \text{ miles}}{2 \text{ hours}}$
$\frac{90 \text{ miles}}{2 \text{ hours}}$	$\frac{50 \text{ miles}}{1 \text{ hour}}$	$\frac{1 \text{ hour}}{48 \text{ miles}}$

8. The table shows the cost of the fruit that Nadine bought at the market. 6.RP.2

Fruit	Amount (lb)	Cost ($)
Lemons	2	0.84
Oranges	5	2.25
Bananas	3	1.17

Part A: Complete the table to order the unit prices of the fruit from least to greatest.

	Fruit	Unit Price ($ per lb)
Least	Bananas	0.39
	Lemons	0.42
Greatest	Oranges	0.45

Part B: How much more do 10 pounds of oranges cost than 10 pounds of bananas? Justify your response.

$0.60; 10 pounds of oranges cost $4.50, and 10 pounds of bananas cost $3.90; the difference is 4.50 – 3.90 = $0.60.

9. A recipe calls for 3 eggs for every batch. Write the appropriate numbers in the table to show the eggs needed for different batches. 6.RP.3, 6.RP.3a, 6.RP.3b

$\frac{2}{3}$	1	$\frac{4}{3}$	3
4	6	7	12
15	36	63	135

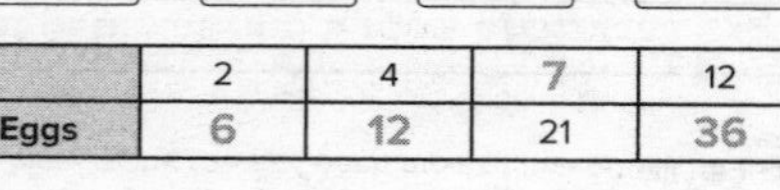

Batches	2	4	7	12	15
Number of Eggs	6	12	21	36	45

10. Victoria reads at a constant rate of 10 pages in 16 minutes. 6.RP.3, 6.RP.3a

Part A: Use Victoria's reading rate to complete the table.

Number of Pages	5	25	35	40
Time (min)	8	40	56	64

Part B: How many minutes will Victoria take to read 100 pages?

160 min

11. Antoine and Angela both like to walk for exercise. Today they are walking together. Antoine walks every 3 days, and Angela walks every 5 days. Circle all the days on which they will walk together again. 6.NS.4

8 days 12 days (15 days) 25 days (45 days)

12. Ciara takes 6 minutes to make 1 bracelet. 6.RP.3, 6.RP.3a, 6.RP.3b

Part A: Use Ciara's rate to complete the ratio table.

Number of Bracelets	1	2	3	5
Time (min)	6	12	18	30

Part B: Write the values in the table as ordered pairs (bracelets, minutes).

(1, 6), (2, 12), (3, 18), (5, 30)

Part C: Graph the ordered pairs on the coordinate plane.

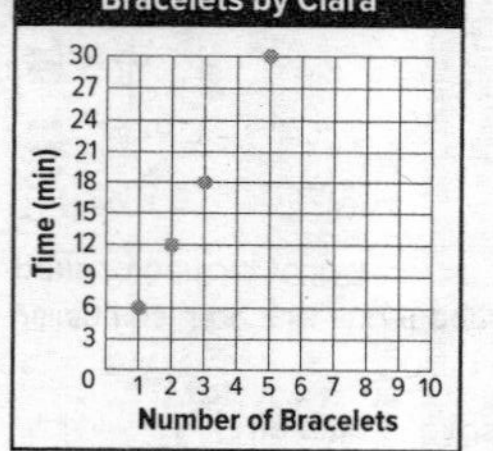

13. The graph shows the distance Melvyn can ride his bike for different periods of time. He rides his bike at a constant rate of speed. On Tuesday, Melvyn rode his bike for one hour. How many miles did he travel? Explain how you solved the problem. 6.RP.3, 6.RP.3b

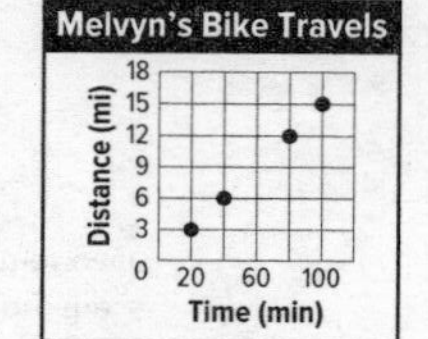

9 mi; Sample answer: 1 hour = 60 minutes. Using the pattern of the points, I find the point with an x value of 60. The point is (60, 9). So Melvyn travels 9 miles in 60 minutes, or 1 hour.

14. Rosario paid $2.50 for 3 pounds of apples. Select all of the rates that are equivalent to the rate Rosario paid. 6.RP.3, 6.RP.3b

- ☐ $0.80 for 1 pound
- ☐ $4.50 for 5 pounds
- ■ $7.50 for 9 pounds
- ☐ $9.60 for 11 pounds
- ■ $10.00 for 12 pounds

15. On a map, 2 inches represents 75 miles of actual distance. 6.RP.3

Part A: Two towns are 6 inches apart on the map. How many miles apart are the two towns?

225 mi

Part B: Two cities are 600 miles apart. How many inches apart on the map are the two cities?

16 in.

16. A 6-ounce drink costs $2.16, and a 10-ounce drink costs $3.25. Which drink is the better buy? Justify your answer. 6.RP.3

10-oz drink; $2.16 for 6 oz is $0.36 per oz; $3.25 for 10 oz is $0.325 per oz. Because 0.325 < 0.36, the 10-oz drink is the better buy.

17. Jen wrote the ratio $\frac{2}{3}$. Select whether each action will result in an equivalent ratio. 6.RP.3, 6.RP.3a

Yes	No	
☐	■	Multiply the numerator by 3 and the denominator by 2.
☐	■	Multiply the numerator by 2 and the denominator by 3.
☐	■	Add 6 to the numerator, and add 6 to the denominator.
■	☐	Multiply the numerator by 7 and the denominator by 7.

18. Sally earns $37.00 for 4 hours of babysitting. At this rate, how much more would she earn for 9 hours of babysitting? 6.RP.3

$46.25

19. The table shows the rate at which four people walk. 6.RP.3, 6.RP.3a, 6.RP.3b

Person	Distance (mi)	Time (h)
Aisha	5.0	2.0
Bob	7.5	5.0
Cora	9.0	3.6
Dylan	3.75	2.5

Part A: Select whether each statement is true or false.

True	False	
☐	■	Aisha and Bob walk at the same rate.
■	☐	Bob and Dylan walk at the same rate.
☐	■	Cora and Dylan walk at the same rate.
■	☐	Aisha and Cora walk at the same rate.

Part B: Emilio walks 19.2 miles in 6.0 hours. Fala walks 10.5 miles in 3.0 hours. Compare the unit rates of the 6 people. Graph the walking rates in miles per hour on the number line. Label each point with the first initial of the person's name.

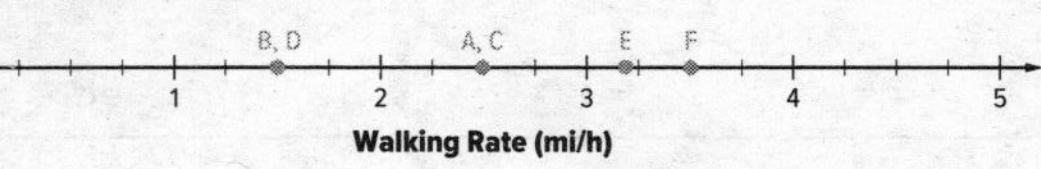

20. A manufacturer of rubber balls estimates that 3 out of every 500 balls produced are defective. The manufacturer produces 100,000 balls each week. Predict the number of rubber balls that are not defective each week. 6.RP.3

99,400 balls

NAME ______________ DATE ________ PERIOD ______ SCORE ______

Chapter 2 Test

1. After 20 minutes Juan had completed 14 questions, which is 0.7 of his assignment. What percent of the assignment had Juan *not* completed? 6.RP.3

30%

2. Sort the decimals into the appropriate bins by how they compare to 100%. 6.RP.3

0.01	0.953	1.32	2.002
0.86	1	12.5	1.015

Greater than 100%	Equal to 100%	Less than 100%
1.32 2.002 12.5 1.015	1	0.01 0.953 0.86

3. Stephanie surveyed the students in her class to find out their favorite color. Her results are in the table. What percent of Stephanie's classmates did *not* choose blue as their favorite color? 6.RP.3

Stephanie's Results	
Color	**Number**
Red	6
Blue	9
Other	10

64%

4. A principal states that 50% of the students in the school are girls. The fractions of girls in several classrooms at the school are listed. Select whether 50% could be used as an estimate to represent each fraction. 6.RP.3

Yes	No	
■	□	$\frac{4}{9}$
□	■	$\frac{1}{8}$
■	□	$\frac{7}{12}$
□	■	$\frac{5}{6}$
■	□	$\frac{9}{20}$

5. Ralph made the pattern shown on the grid. 6.RP.3

Part A: Select all of the expressions that represent the portion of the model that Ralph shaded.

- □ 64%
- ■ 0.36
- □ 0.25
- ■ $\frac{9}{25}$
- ■ 36%
- □ $\frac{1}{2}$

Part B: Ralph wants to show $\frac{13}{20}$ on another grid of the same size. How many squares must he shade?

65 squares

6. Sort the fractions into the appropriate bins by their decimal equivalents. 6.RP.3

$\frac{36}{48}$	$\frac{15}{24}$	$\frac{75}{120}$
$\frac{65}{130}$	$\frac{10}{16}$	$\frac{18}{24}$

Equal to 0.5	Equal to 0.625	Equal to 0.75
$\frac{65}{130}$	$\frac{15}{24}$ $\frac{75}{120}$ $\frac{10}{16}$	$\frac{36}{48}$ $\frac{18}{24}$

7. Regina scored 84% on a test. She answered 63 items correctly. How many items did Regina answer incorrectly? 6.RP.3, 6.RP.3c

12 items

8. The Wilson family had a celebration dinner at a local restaurant. The cost of the dinner was $80.00. 6.RP.3, 6.RP.3c

Part A: The Wilsons plan to leave an 18% tip for the server. How much money would the tip be?

$14.40

Part B: The sales tax rate is 7.5%. How much money do the Wilsons have to pay for the sales tax on the dinner?

$6.00

Part C: What is the total amount that the Wilsons pay?

$100.40

9. A student conducted a survey of sixth-grade students to determine the number of movies they watch each month. Complete the table to order the responses from least to greatest percent of students. 6.RP.3

Movies Watched per Month				
Number of Movies	0–4	5–6	7–8	9+
Portion of Student Responses	27%	0.2	$\frac{1}{4}$	$\frac{7}{25}$

	Number of Movies Watched	Percent of Students
Least	5–6	20%
	7–8	25%
	0–4	27%
Greatest	9+	28%

10. Parminder estimated that between 25% and 50% of students walk to school. Circle each fraction that could represent the percent of students who walk to school. 6.RP.3

($\frac{3}{10}$) ($\frac{2}{5}$) $\frac{2}{3}$ ($\frac{3}{8}$) $\frac{2}{9}$ ($\frac{7}{20}$) $\frac{6}{11}$

11. Josie made a pattern using red and blue tiles. Three fourths of the tiles were blue. Select all of the ways Josie could write the fraction of blue tiles as a decimal. 6.RP.3

- ☐ Divide 4 by 3.
- ■ Divide 3 by 4.
- ☐ Divide 1 by 4.
- ☐ Multiply the numerator by 10. Then use place value.
- ■ Multiply the numerator and the denominator by 25. Then use place value.
- ☐ Multiply the denominator by 2.5. Then use place value.
- ☐ Multiply the numerator and denominator by $3\frac{1}{3}$. Then use place value.

12. To celebrate the 6th anniversary of a store opening, the manager has a sale of "$6.00 off every item in the store." What percent of the different prices would equal $6 off? Write a number so that each statement represents a $6.00 discount. 6.RP.3, 6.RP.3c

120	16	30	50	60	6	24	10	15

10% off of $ 60

15 % off of $40

20% off of $ 30

25% off of $ 24

50 % off of $12

13. Carmen has $100 to spend. Sales tax in her city is 10%. Which 3 different items can Carmen buy to spend as much of her $100 as possible? Explain your answer. 6.RP.3, 6.RP.3c

Item	Price ($)
Jeans	25.00
Belt	23.50
Shoes	35.00
Skirt	30.00
Purse	31.00

Jeans, shoes, and skirt; 25.00 + 35.00 + 30.00 = $90.00; sales tax is 10% of $90 = 0.1(90) = $9.00. Carmen would spend 90.00 + 9.00 = $99.00 for her purchases.

14. A light bulb manufacturer estimates that $\frac{1}{4}$% of light bulbs produced will be defective. The manufacturer produces 200,000 light bulbs in one month. About how many bulbs can they expect to be defective? 6.RP.3, 6.RP.3c

500 light bulbs

15. Marie scored a 75% on her last test. Select all of the statements that could be true. 6.RP.3, 6.RP.3c

- [x] Marie answered 1 item incorrectly out of 4 items.
- [ ] Marie answered 40 items correctly out of 50 items.
- [x] Marie answered 15 items incorrectly out of 60 items.
- [ ] Marie answered 18 items incorrectly out of 24 items.
- [x] Marie answered 42 items correctly out of 56 items.

16. An electronics store buys a television at a wholesale price of $120. The store then sells the television to its customers for $300. What percent of the wholesale price is the selling price? 6.RP.3, 6.RP.3c

250%

17. At basketball practice, Derrick tossed a basketball from the free-throw line to the basket 80 times. Of his 80 attempts, he made 66 baskets. 6.RP.3, 6.RP.3c

Part A: What percent of throws did Derrick make?

82.5%

Part B: At practice the next day, Derrick made 54 baskets out of 70 attempts. Describe how Derrick's overall percentage for the two days compares to his percentage for the previous day. Justify your answer.

Derrick's overall percentage decreased. For the two days, Derrick made 54 + 66 = 120 baskets out of 80 + 70 = 150 throws. He made $\frac{120}{150}$ = 80% of his throws. The previous day, Derrick made 82.5%, so his percentage decreased.

18. Mr. Allen estimated that 50 people at a basketball game were cheering for the visiting team. Select all of the statements that could represent this estimate. 6.RP.3, 6.RP.3c

- [x] 24% of 195 people
- [ ] 18% of 487 people
- [ ] 62% of 148 people
- [x] 67% of 77 people
- [x] 11% of 512 people

19. Fifteen hundredths of the students in the sixth grade wore a blue shirt yesterday. Sort the expressions into the bin that describes whether or not the expression represents the numeral. 6.RP.3

0.015	15%
0.15	1,500
$\frac{100}{15}$	$\frac{15}{100}$
1.5	0.15%

Represents fifteen hundredths	Does not represent fifteen hundredths
15%	0.015
0.15	1,500
$\frac{15}{100}$	$\frac{100}{15}$
	1.5
	0.15%

20. Alphonse did enough sit-ups to rank in the 99th percentile for boys his age. This means that less than 1% of all the boys did more sit-ups than Alphonse. Select whether each decimal could represent the fraction of boys who did more sit-ups than Alphonse. 6.RP.3

Yes	No	
☐	■	0.01
■	☐	0.002
☐	■	0.95
☐	■	0.04
☐	■	0.103
■	☐	0.0056

NAME ______________ DATE ________ PERIOD ______ SCORE ______

Chapter 3 Test

1. Roberta buys a sweater and a scarf. The sweater costs $24.79 and the scarf costs $8.89. 6.NS.3

Part A: What is the total cost of the two items?

$33.68

Part B: Roberta has a $50 gift card. How much is left on the card after she pays for the two items?

$16.32

2. Greg found $0.72 on the floorboard of his car. Select all of the expressions that are equivalent to 0.72. 6.NS.3

- [ ] 0.2 – 0.92
- [ ] 0.82 – 0.01
- [x] 0.9 – 0.18
- [x] 0.3 + 0.42
- [ ] 0.7 + 0.2
- [x] 0.05 + 0.67

3. LaToya's mother uses 5.84 pounds of apples to make applesauce. She got them from a bag of apples that weighs 16.3 pounds. How many pounds of apples are left in the bag? 6.NS.3

10.46 lb

4. A runner estimated that he ran about 12 miles. Select all of the rates and times that the runner could have run. 6.NS.3

- [x] 3.3 miles per hour for 3.8 hours
- [x] 6.1 miles per hour for 1.9 hours
- [x] 5.8 miles per hour for 2.3 hours
- [ ] 6.75 miles per hour for 3.4 hours

5. A bus travels about 400 miles between cities. Select whether the rates and times could represent the estimated distance the bus traveled. 6.NS.3

Yes	No	
■	☐	53.2 miles per hour for 7.74 hours
■	☐	39.8 miles per hour for 10.15 hours
☐	■	47.6 miles per hour for 9.8 hours
■	☐	76.3 miles per hour for 5.24 hours

6. The table shows the cost of several items, including tax. Suzanne needs to buy school supplies. She has $5.25 to spend. Select all of the items that Suzanne can buy. 6.NS.3

Item	Cost ($)
Pencil	0.75
Notebook	1.50
Marker	1.05
Pen	1.55

- [x] 3 notebooks
- [ ] 4 pens
- [x] 4 markers
- [x] 6 pencils
- [ ] 3 markers and 2 pens
- [x] 2 notebooks and 3 pencils

7. Katrina runs 4.23 miles each day. How many miles does she run in 2 weeks? 6.NS.3

59.22 mi

8. Kami bought some material to make a blanket in the shape of a rectangle. The material costs $12.00 per square yard. How much did Kami pay for the material? 6.NS.3

1.35 yd

2 yd

$32.40

9. Write the appropriate number of decimal places in each sum, difference, product, or quotient. Do not count a zero in the final decimal place. 6.NS.3

0 1 2 3 4 5

12.59 – 6.09	1	decimal places
0.75 × 0.9	3	decimal places
15.25 ÷ 0.25	0	decimal places
18 + 3.4 + 22.15	2	decimal places
1.945 × 3.8	3	decimal places

10. Manuel was examining the product of 48 × 0.73. He realized that he could create other multiplication problems that have the same product. Select whether each expression has the same product as 48 × 0.73. 6.NS.3

Yes	No	
☐	■	43 × 0.78
■	☐	4.8 × 7.3
■	☐	0.48 × 73
☐	■	7.8 × 4.3
■	☐	480 × 0.073

11. Zach walks at a rate of 2.83 miles per hour. Nora walks at a rate of 2.18 miles per hour. How many miles farther will Zach have walked after they each walk for 1.5 hours? 6.NS.3

0.975 mi

12. A football stadium holds 55,296 people. The seating is divided into 36 sections. 6.NS.2

Part A: There is an equal number of seats in each section. How many seats are in each section?

1,536 seats

Part B: The seats in each section are in 32 rows. There is an equal number of seats in each row. How many seats are in each row?

48 seats

13. A principal paid $5.74 for one school shirt that displays the school mascot. 6.NS.3

Part A: Select all of the numbers of shirts that he could have purchased at that price.

- ■ 12 shirts for $68.88
- ☐ 84 shirts for $493.64
- ■ 125 shirts for $717.50
- ☐ 392 shirts for $2,284.52

Part B: During the first month on sale, the school store sold 186 shirts for $6.50 each. How much profit did the school make on these shirts?

$141.36

14. Sort each number of miles and number of hours traveled into the appropriate bin to identify the rate in miles per hour. 6.NS.2

718 miles in 5.95 hours | 45.8 miles in 4 hours | 2,865 miles in 24.8 hours | 419.72 miles in 80.6 hours | 935.47 miles in 22.75 hours

Less Than 10 Miles per Hour	Between 10 and 99 Miles per Hour	Greater Than 100 Miles per Hour
419.72 miles in 80.6 hours	45.8 miles in 4 hours 935.47 miles in 22.75 hours	718 miles in 5.95 hours 2,865 miles in 24.8 hours

15. Althea wants to save $286.15 in a year to buy a new bicycle. She estimates that she needs to save $4.50 each week to reach her goal. Is Althea's estimate reasonable? Justify your answer. 6.NS.2

No; Sample answer: Estimate 286.15 as 300 and 52 weeks as 50, and divide: 300 ÷ 50 = 6. She needs about $6 per week and will not reach her goal saving only $4.50 each week.

16. A garden is 22.5 feet wide and 58.1 feet long. 6.NS.3

Part A: About how many square feet is the garden? Write the appropriate numbers to estimate the area.

1 2 3 4 5
6 7 8 9 0

$$\begin{array}{r} 20 \\ \times\ 60 \\ \hline 1200 \end{array}$$

Part B: A 3.8-pound bag of fertilizer covers 1,000 square feet. Each bag costs $9.95. How many bags are needed to cover the garden? About how much will it cost to buy the bags of fertilizer?

Bags: **2 bags**

Cost estimate: **about $20**

Part C: Were your estimates in Parts A and B reasonable? Explain. Use the actual square footage and cost of the bags in your explanation.

Area: **22.5 × 58.1 = 1,307.25. The estimate of 1,200 is close to 1,307.25, so it is reasonable.**

Cost: **2 × 9.95 = 19.90. The estimate of $20 is close to $19.90, so it is reasonable.**

17. A manufacturer makes paper clips that are shipped in boxes of 100. One day 4,725 paper clips were made and were packaged in 47 boxes with 25 clips left over. Select all of the division problems that have the same quotient of 47 R 25. 6.NS.2

- [x] 1,811 ÷ 38
- [ ] 4,069 ÷ 86
- [ ] 5,052 ÷ 107
- [x] 18,308 ÷ 389

18. The table shows the workout results of four joggers. 6.NS.3

Jogger	Distance (mi)	Time (h)
Wesley	7.7	3.50
Xavier	3.5	1.25
Yvette	4.224	1.76
Zubin	5.175	2.25

Complete the table to order the joggers from the slowest to fastest rate.

	Jogger	Rate (mph)
Slowest	**Wesley**	**2.2**
	Zubin	**2.3**
	Yvette	**2.4**
Fastest	**Xavier**	**2.8**

19. Joshua was experimenting with the division problem 0.72 ÷ 0.8 and noticed that he could create other division problems with the same quotient. Select all of the division problems that have the same quotient. 6.NS.3

- [ ] 72 ÷ 8
- [x] 7.2 ÷ 8
- [ ] 0.072 ÷ 0.008
- [x] 72 ÷ 80

20. The two rectangles have the same area. What is the perimeter of rectangle A? 6.NS.3

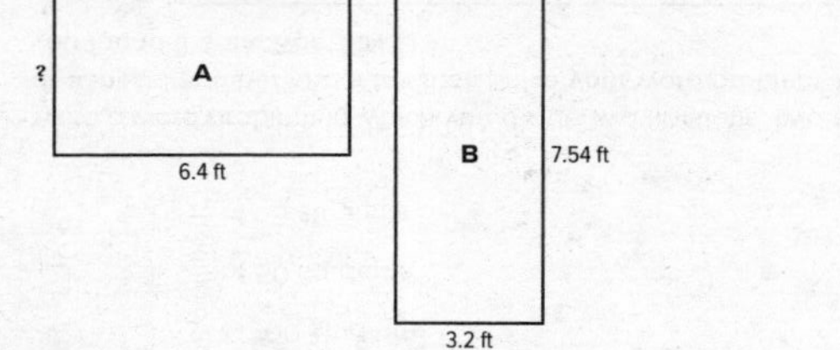

20.34 ft

NAME ______________ DATE ________ PERIOD ______ SCORE ______

Chapter 4 Test

1. Henry is designing a rectangular flower garden and says the area is about 36 square feet. Select whether each set of dimensions could be the approximate dimensions of Henry's garden. 6.NS.1

Yes	No	
■	□	$3\frac{3}{4}$ feet wide by $8\frac{7}{8}$ feet long
■	□	$5\frac{5}{6}$ feet wide by $6\frac{1}{5}$ feet long
□	■	$2\frac{7}{8}$ feet wide by $7\frac{4}{5}$ feet long
■	□	$10\frac{2}{5}$ feet wide by $3\frac{4}{7}$ feet long

2. A farmer harvested 35 acres of corn and 20 acres of beans. Animals ate $\frac{1}{8}$ of the corn he originally planted. How many acres of corn did the farmer plant? 6.NS.1

40 acres

3. Sort the fractions into the appropriate bins by their estimates. 6.NS.1

$\frac{5}{9}$ $\frac{1}{8}$ $\frac{2}{5}$ $\frac{3}{19}$ $\frac{3}{7}$

$\frac{7}{8}$ $\frac{6}{14}$ $\frac{9}{11}$ $\frac{2}{13}$ $\frac{10}{12}$

Estimate of 0	Estimate of $\frac{1}{2}$	Estimate of 1
$\frac{1}{8}$	$\frac{5}{9}$	$\frac{7}{8}$
$\frac{3}{19}$	$\frac{2}{5}$	$\frac{9}{11}$
$\frac{2}{13}$	$\frac{3}{7}$	$\frac{10}{12}$
	$\frac{6}{14}$	

4. Of all the sixth grade students in the school, 40 students wear glasses. Select whether each expression could represent the number of sixth grade students who wear glasses. 6.NS.1

Yes	No	
□	■	$\frac{1}{3}$ of 60 students
■	□	$\frac{2}{5}$ of 100 students
□	■	$\frac{3}{5}$ of 50 students
■	□	$\frac{8}{9}$ of 45 students

5. Write a word problem in which you divide two fractions, two mixed numbers, or a mixed number and a fraction. Solve your word problem and show how you found the answer. 6.NS.1

Problem: **Sample answer: Jen bought $15\frac{1}{2}$ feet of ribbon to make bows. Each bow needs $\frac{3}{4}$ foot of ribbon. How many bows can Jen make?**

Solution: **20 bows; $15\frac{1}{2} \div \frac{3}{4} = \frac{31}{2} \times \frac{4}{3} = \frac{62}{3} = 20\frac{2}{3}$**

6. The answer to a multiplication problem is $\frac{3}{5}$. 6.NS.1

Part A: Select whether each statement is true or false.

True	False	
□	■	Both factors are less than $\frac{3}{5}$.
■	□	One factor is less than $\frac{3}{5}$; the other factor is greater than $\frac{3}{5}$.
■	□	Both factors are greater than $\frac{3}{5}$.

Part B: Write an example to support one of the true statements.

Sample answer: $\frac{3}{4} \times \frac{4}{5} = \frac{3}{5}$; both fractions are greater than $\frac{3}{5}$.

7. On a grid, $\frac{2}{3}$ of the squares are shaded with a color. One fourth of all the squares on the grid are shaded blue. What fraction of the shaded squares are blue squares? 6.NS.1

$\frac{3}{8}$

8. Write the appropriate number for each product or quotient. 6.NS.1

Answer choices: $\frac{1}{6}$, $\frac{6}{25}$, $\frac{8}{75}$, $4\frac{1}{6}$, 6, $9\frac{3}{8}$

$1\frac{1}{4} \div 7\frac{1}{2} =$ $\frac{1}{6}$

$\frac{2}{3} \div 6\frac{1}{4} =$ $\frac{8}{75}$

$\frac{4}{5} \div \frac{2}{15} =$ 6

$1\frac{1}{4} \times 7\frac{1}{2} =$ $9\frac{3}{8}$

$6\frac{1}{4} \times \frac{2}{3} =$ $4\frac{1}{6}$

$1\frac{1}{2} \div 6\frac{1}{4} =$ $\frac{6}{25}$

$1\frac{1}{2} \div \frac{4}{25} =$ $9\frac{3}{8}$

$\frac{4}{5} \times \frac{2}{15} =$ $\frac{8}{75}$

9. A survey asked 200 students to name their favorite fruit. The table shows the results of the survey. 6.NS.1

Fruit	Fraction of Students
Banana	$\frac{1}{8}$
Peach	$\frac{2}{5}$
Plum	$\frac{1}{10}$
Orange	$\frac{3}{8}$

Part A: How many students named a peach as their favorite fruit?

80 students

Part B: How many more students chose an orange rather than a plum? Justify your answer.

55 students; Multiply: $\frac{3}{8} \times 200 = 75$ and $\frac{1}{10} \times 200 = 20$. Subtract: $75 - 20 = 55$ more chose orange.

10. At an apple orchard, Margaret picked $19\frac{1}{2}$ pounds of apples. The cashier put the apples into 3 bags with the same weight. How many pounds of apples are in each bag? 6.NS.1

$6\frac{1}{2}$ lb

11. A bookcase has four identical, rectangular shelves. One shelf is shown. 6.NS.1

$2\frac{1}{2}$ in.

$8\frac{3}{4}$ in.

Part A: What is the total area of the four shelves?

$87\frac{1}{2}$ in^2

Part B: How many books with spines that are $1\frac{1}{4}$ inches wide can fit on each shelf?

7 books

12. Two mixed numbers are divided. The quotient is $5\frac{1}{2}$. Select whether each statement is true or false. 6.NS.1

True	False	
■	□	Both the dividend and the divisor are less than $5\frac{1}{2}$.
■	□	The divisor is less than $5\frac{1}{2}$; the dividend is greater than $5\frac{1}{2}$.
■	□	Both the dividend and the divisor are greater than $5\frac{1}{2}$.
□	■	The dividend is less than $5\frac{1}{2}$; the divisor is greater than $5\frac{1}{2}$.

13. The length of a basketball court is 94 feet. 6.RP.3, 6.RP.3d

Part A: Sort the lengths into the appropriate bins by how each length compares to the length of a basketball court.

$\frac{1}{40}$ mi | 30 yd | $\frac{1}{20}$ mi | 1,128 in. | $102\frac{3}{5}$ ft

Less than 94 ft	Equal to 94 ft	Greater than 94 ft
30 yd	1,128 in.	$\frac{1}{20}$ mi
		$102\frac{3}{5}$ ft
		$\frac{1}{40}$ mi

Part B: What is the length of the basketball court in yards? Justify your answer.

$31\frac{1}{3}$ yd; 94 feet $\times \frac{1 \text{ yard}}{3 \text{ feet}} = \frac{94}{3} = 31\frac{1}{3}$

Copyright © McGraw-Hill Education. Permission is granted to reproduce for classroom use.

14. A group orders 3 large veggie pizzas. Each slice represents $\frac{1}{8}$ of the entire pizza. The group eats $\frac{3}{4}$ of the pizza. How many slices of pizza are left? Justify your answer. 6.NS.1

6 slices; Sample answer: Divide $3 \div \frac{1}{8} = 24$ slices in all. Then multiply $\frac{3}{4} \times 24 = 18$ slices that were eaten. Subtract $24 - 18 = 6$ slices left.

15. Mrs. Benitez slices some oranges so that each wedge is $\frac{1}{4}$ of the orange. Then she cuts the same number of apples into pieces so that each piece is $\frac{1}{6}$ of the apple. Let n represent the number of each type of fruit. Select whether each statement is true or false. 6.NS.1

True	False	
■	□	There are $2n$ more pieces of apple than wedges of orange.
□	■	There are $n + 2$ more pieces of apple than wedges of orange.
□	■	There are $2n$ more wedges of orange than pieces of apple.
□	■	There are $n + 2$ more wedges of orange than pieces of apple.
□	■	The number of orange wedges can be represented by $n \div 4$.
■	□	The number of apple pieces can be represented by $n \div \frac{1}{6}$.

16. A tile pattern uses $\frac{1}{4}$ white tile, and the rest are colored tiles. Five colors are used equally. What fraction of the tile pattern is each color? 6.NS.1

$\frac{3}{20}$

17. A carpenter wants to cut a board $16\frac{1}{2}$ feet in length into $1\frac{7}{8}$ feet pieces. 6.NS.1

Part A: How many pieces can be cut from the board?

8 pieces

Part B: The carpenter cuts the leftover piece into four equal-length pieces. How long is each piece?

$\frac{3}{8}$ ft

18. An adult elephant weighs 5,000 pounds. 6.RP.3, 6.RP.3d

Part A: Write the correct measurements in the boxes to show how to convert that weight to tons.

1 T	1 lb	1 oz	1 fl oz	16 oz	5,000 lb	8 fl oz
$2\frac{1}{2}$ T	$312\frac{1}{2}$ T	$\frac{2}{5}$ T	625 T	$\frac{2}{625}$ T	2,000 lb	1

$\frac{5{,}000 \text{ lb}}{1} \cdot \frac{1 \text{ T}}{2{,}000 \text{ lb}} = 2\frac{1}{2} \text{ T}$

Part B: A baby elephant weighs 260 pounds. How many ounces do the adult and baby elephants weigh together?

84, 160 oz

19. A brick of cheese is $\frac{3}{4}$ inch thick. A deli cuts the brick of cheese into slices that are $\frac{1}{10}$ inch thick. 6.NS.1

Part A: How many $\frac{1}{10}$-inch slices can be cut from the brick of cheese?

7 slices

Part B: What is the thickness of the leftover piece of cheese?

$\frac{1}{20}$ in.

20. A bag of dog food weighs $31\frac{1}{4}$ pounds. After one week, $3\frac{1}{8}$ pounds of dog food was used. What fraction of the bag of dog food remains? 6.NS.1

$\frac{9}{10}$ bag

NAME ______________ DATE ________ PERIOD ______ SCORE ______

Chapter 5 Test

1. The eight values in the boxes show how much the price of one share of a stock has changed. Sort the amounts into the appropriate bins based on whether the stock is gaining value, losing value, or neither. 6.NS.5

\$3	\$25	–\$6	\$47
–\$20	–\$35	\$0	–\$1

Gaining Value	Losing Value	Neither
\$3 \$25 \$47	–\$6 –\$20 –\$35 –\$1	\$0

2. Write the point on the number line that represents the integer described by each statement. 6.NS.6, 6.NS.6a

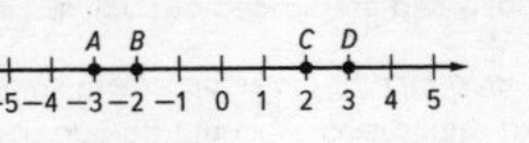

A B C D

Point D: the opposite of –3

Point C: the opposite of –2

Point A: the opposite of 3

Point B: the opposite of 2

3. Two points are graphed on a coordinate plane. Graph and label the four ordered pairs on the coordinate plane. 6.NS.6, 6.NS.6b

(–c, d) (–e, –f) (c, –d) (–e, f)

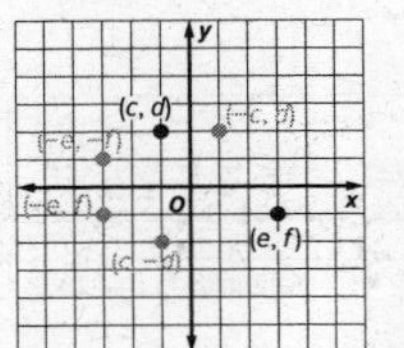

4. A paleontologist uncovered a bone in a hole that is 4.5 feet deep. A bird was in a tree at a height of 10.5 feet. A catfish lay at the bottom of a lake at a depth of 12.5 feet. 6.NS.6, 6.NS.6c

Part A: Graph the values given in the problem on the number line.

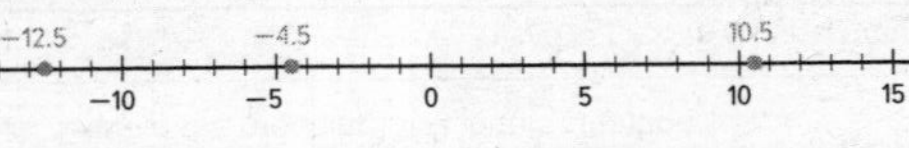

Part B: Nate claims that the catfish is closer to the surface of the water than either the bird or the bone is to ground level. Do you agree with his claim? Explain your reasoning.

No; sample answer: Ground level and the water surface are represented by 0 on the number line. Both 10.5 and –4.5 are closer to 0 than –12.5.

5. The freezing point of water is 0°C. The table shows the temperature of a water sample that each student recorded during a science lab. 6.NS.7, 6.NS.7b

Student	Sample Temperature (°C)
Karen	–23.4
Claudia	37
Jamal	99.9
Mateo	–3.89

Part A: Write the temperatures in order from coldest to hottest.

Coldest → Hottest: –23.4, –3.89, 37, 99.9

Part B: Mateo realizes he made an error in recording the temperature of his water sample. He should have recorded the temperature as –38.9°C. How does this new information change your answer to Part A?

The order changes; –38.9 is now the coldest temperature. The new order is –38.9, –23.4, 37, and 99.9.

6. Select whether each inequality about the coordinates of the points on the number line is true or false. 6.NS.6, 6.NS.6a, 6.NS.7, 6.NS.7a

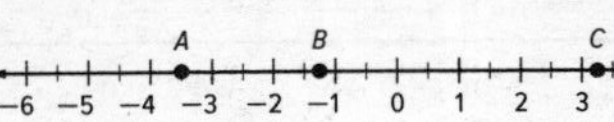

True	False	
☐	■	$A > B$
■	☐	$C > B$
☐	■	$C < A$
■	☐	$A < 0$

7. Identify the phrase that *cannot* be described by the same absolute value expression as the other three. Explain your reasoning. 6.NS.7, 6.NS.7c

winning 6 marbles | owing $3 | 6° below normal | account balance of –$6

Owing $3; the other phrases each have an absolute value of 6.

8. Lucia has a checking account. Her bank will not honor any check she writes that will make her account balance less than –$20. Lucia wrote her landlord a check. When the check is cashed, her checking account will have a balance of –$10. Explain whether or not the bank will honor the check Lucia wrote to her landlord. 6.NS.7, 6.NS.7d

Sample answer: An account with a balance less than –$20 means the debt is greater than $20. Although –10 is greater than –20, a debt of $10 is not as great as a debt of $20, so the check will be honored.

9. The coordinate plane represents a city, with (0, 0) as the city's center. Each unit on the city's coordinate plane represents 1 mile. The table shows the location of four city-owned buildings. 6.NS.8

Building	Location
A	(1, 0)
B	(–2, 3)
C	(–2, –4)
D	(3, –4)

Part A: On the coordinate plane, graph and label the ordered pairs that show the locations of Buildings *A*, *B*, *C*, and *D*.

B(–2, 3) A(1, 0) C(–2, –4) D(3, –4)

Part B: Find the distance between buildings *C* and *D*: 5 miles

10. Let *s* be an integer. Alonso claims that –*s* must always be less than 0. Iliana claims that –*s* is only sometimes less than 0. Whose statement is correct? Explain. Support your reasoning with an example. 6.NS.6, 6.NS.6a

Iliana; sample answer: When s is negative, –s, which means "the opposite of s," is greater than 0. For example, when s = –2, –s = –(–2) = 2, so –s > 0.

11. Omar divided a circular pizza into 8 equal sections. He gave his friend 3 sections. Explain why the amount he gave to his friend can be represented by a point plotted to the right of 0 on a number line. Then write the amount he gave to his friend as a decimal. 6.NS.6

Sample answer: The pizza represents 1 whole. On a number line, 1 is to the right of 0. Any fraction of 1 is greater than 0, so the amount Omar gave to his friend is to the right of 0. $\frac{3}{8} = 0.375$.

12. Michael models the landscaping features in a yard on a coordinate plane. A patio is represented by figure *ABCD*. The pond is located at (4, –1). A bench is located at (–4, 3). A clock is located at (–1, –1). A water feature is located at (1, –3). Select whether each statement is true or false in representing the points. 6.NS.6, 6.NS.6b

True	False	
■	☐	The pond is located at the reflection of point *C* across the *x*-axis.
■	☐	A bench is located at the reflection of point *B* across the *y*-axis.
☐	■	A clock is located at the reflection of point *D* across the *x*-axis.
☐	■	A water feature is located at the reflection of point *A* across the *y*-axis.

13. Mrs. Ortiz measured the outside temperature at noon as –2°F. Later that day, she measured the temperature as –5°F. Write an inequality that correctly compares –2 and –5. Then explain the meaning of the inequality for the situation. 6.NS.7, 6.NS.7b

Sample answer: –2 > –5; The temperature was warmer at noon than later in the day. That is, –2°F > –5°F because –2 is to the right of –5 on a number line.

14. Katie owes Mathias $10 and Cabrini $5. Katie has $3 in her pocket. 6.NS.5

Part A: Explain the meaning of 0 in this situation.

The integer 0 represents neither owing money nor having money.

Part B: Graph the integers given in the problem on the number line.

15. Afia's school is plotted at (–8, –3) on a coordinate plane. Her babysitter's house is located at (8, –3). What is the distance between Afia's school and her babysitter's house? Explain how you solved the problem. 6.NS.8

16 units; Sample answer: Both *y*-coordinates are the same. So I looked at the *x*-coordinates. I found the absolute value of each *x*-coordinate: |–8| = 8 and |8| = 8. Then I added the absolute values: 8 + 8 = 16.

16. The table indicates Imamu's data usage over the last four months. Positive values indicate the amount of data that went over his data package plan, and negative values indicate the amount of data that was under the plan. Identify the month that Imamu used the least amount of data. Justify your response. 6.NS.7, 6.NS.7d

Month	Data (GB)
January	0.75
February	–2.25
March	1
April	–1.5

February; sample answer: 0 GB represents using all the data in his data package plan. The month with the greater absolute value of the negative amounts is the month in which Imamu used the least amount of data in his plan. Because |–2.25| > |–1.5|, the least amount of data used was in February.

17. The average amount of time customers waited to get their food at a restaurant was 25 minutes. The table shows the difference between the average times and the actual times customers at four tables waited to get their food. Select whether each statement is true or false about the time spent waiting. 6.NS.7, 6.NS.7b

Table	Average Time – Actual Time Waiting (min)
A	$2\frac{1}{2}$
B	$-3\frac{1}{2}$
C	4.5
D	–5.75

True	False	
■	☐	The time spent waiting at Table A is greater than the time spent waiting at Table B.
☐	■	The time spent waiting at Table C is farther from 0 on a number line than the time spent waiting at Table D.
☐	■	The time spent waiting at Table A is greater than the time spent waiting at Table C.
■	☐	The customers at Table D spent the least time waiting.

18. The temperature in a freezer is set at –18°C. The temperature in a refrigerator is 21° warmer. Should the temperature of the refrigerator be represented by a positive integer or negative integer? Explain your reasoning. 6.NS.6, 6.NS.6a

Positive integer; sample answer: A rise of 18° would result in a temperature of 0°C. Since the rise is greater than 18°, the temperature is greater than 0 and should be represented by a positive integer.

19. Robert's house is represented by (0, 0) on the coordinate plane. A landscape planner suggested Robert plant trees at $\left(-3\frac{1}{2}, 4\right)$, $\left(2\frac{1}{2}, -2\frac{1}{2}\right)$, $\left(-4\frac{1}{2}, -4\right)$, and (3, 2). Did Robert correctly plot the location of the four trees? Justify your answer. 6.NS.6, 6.NS.6c

No; sample answer: For each ordered pair that includes an *x*- or *y*-coordinate with a $-\frac{1}{2}$, Robert plotted the ordered pair 1 unit from where it should be plotted. For example, he plotted $\left(-3\frac{1}{2}, 4\right)$ at $\left(-2\frac{1}{2}, 4\right)$.

20. Consider this set of expressions. 6.NS.7, 6.NS.7c

|3| –|4| |–2| + |–3| |–5| – |4|

Part A: Simplify each expression.

A: |3| = **3**

B: –|4| = **–4**

C: |–2| + |–3| = **5**

D: |–5| – |4| = **1**

Part B: Graph each value on the number line. Label the points.

NAME ________________ DATE ________ PERIOD ______ SCORE ______

Chapter 6 Test

1. A teacher wrote the expression 4^5 on the board. Select all of the expressions that are equivalent to 4^5. 6.EE.1

- ☐ 4 × 5
- ☐ 4 + 4 + 4 + 4 + 4
- ■ 4 × 4 × 4 × 4 × 4
- ☐ 5 × 5 × 5 × 5

2. A farmer has a square-shaped pen for his chickens. 6.EE.1

25 yd

Part A: Write a power that represents the enclosed area. What is the area of the chicken pen?

Power: 25^2

Square yards: 625

Part B: The farmer needs to know the size of the chicken pen in square feet. Write a power that represents the enclosed area using feet, not yards. What is the area of the pen?

Power: 75^2

Square feet: 5,625

3. Using the numbers, write two powers that have the same value. 6.EE.1

2 3 4 9

Using each number only once: $9^{2} = 3^{4}$

Using the numbers more than once: $4^{2} = 2^{4}$

4. Select whether each expression simplifies to a value of 4. 6.EE.1

Yes	No	
☐	■	3 + 8 ÷ 2 × 4
☐	■	2 × 5 − 4 + 1
■	☐	12 ÷ (8 − 6 + 1)
☐	■	9 ÷ 3 × 3 + 3

5. Hanako is curious to know how easy it is to write a power that has a value greater than 100. 6.EE.1

Part A: Sort the powers into their appropriate bins by how each compares to 100.

10^2 5^3 2^5 $\left(\frac{3}{4}\right)^8$ $(7.5)^4$ $(9.93)^2$

Less than 100	Equal to 100	Greater than 100
2^5 $\left(\frac{3}{4}\right)^8$ $(9.93)^2$	10^2	5^3 $(7.5)^4$

Part B: Between what two consecutive powers of 3 does 100 lie?

3^4 and 3^5

6. The expression $4(n + 8)$ represents the cost of 4 friends going to a ball game. Each person pays $\$n$ admission plus \$8 for a team towel to wave. Select all the phrases that describe the expression $(n + 8)$. 6.EE.2, 6.EE.2b

- ☐ a product of two factors
- ☐ a constant
- ☐ a coefficient
- ■ a factor
- ☐ like terms
- ■ a sum of two terms
- ☐ a quotient

7. The width of a rectangle is x. The length is 5 times the width. 6.EE.2

Part A: Select all of the expressions that represent the length of the rectangle.

- ■ $5x$
- □ $x + 5$
- ■ $5 \cdot x$
- ■ $5(x)$
- □ $\frac{5}{x}$

Part B: The width of the rectangle is 4 units. How many units is the perimeter?

48 units

8. The side lengths of a triangle are shown. Let x be 4 units. How many units is the perimeter of the triangle? Justify your answer. 6.EE.2, 6.EE.2c

$x + 5$ | $4x - 1$ | $3x$

36 units; For $x = 4$ units, the side lengths are 9, 12, and 15 units; $9 + 12 + 15 = 36$ units.

9. Juan has 3 more marbles than Ed. Let n represent the number of Ed's marbles. 6.EE.2, 6.EE.2c

Part A: Circle all of the expressions that represent the number of Juan's marbles.

$3n$	$3 - n$	$3 \div n$	($n + 3$)
($3 + n$)	$n \div 3$	$n - 3$	$3 \cdot n$

Part B: Ed has 11 marbles. How many marbles does Juan have?

14

10. A fitness club charges its members a one-time fee of $40 and a monthly rate of $25. Let m represent the number of months. Write an expression for the total amount paid after m months. Then find how much a customer will have paid after 5 months. 6.EE.2, 6.EE.2a, 6.EE.6

Expression: $40 + 25m$

Cost: $165

11. In the last basketball game, Kevin scored 2 less than a third of his team's points. 6.EE.2, 6.EE.2a, 6.EE.6

Part A: Let n represent the number of points Kevin's team scored. Write an expression for the number of points Kevin scored.

$\frac{1}{3}n - 2$

Part B: Kevin scored 14 points. How many points did the team score?

48 points

12. The Commutative Property states that the order of terms in an expression does not affect the outcome. 6.EE.3

Part A: Select whether each operation is true or false under the Commutative Property.

True	False	
■	□	addition
□	■	subtraction
■	□	multiplication
□	■	division

Part B: For a statement you marked as true in Part A, give an example that shows the Commutative Property applies.

Sample answer: $3 + 5 = 5 + 3$ because $8 = 8$.

Part C: For a statement you marked as false in Part A, give an example that shows that the Commutative Property does not apply.

Sample answer: $8 \div 4$ does not equal $4 \div 8$, because $2 \neq \frac{1}{2}$.

13. Select all of the statements that are an example of an Identity Property. 6.EE.3

- ☐ $n - n = 0$
- ■ $n + 0 = n$
- ■ $n \cdot 1 = n$
- ☐ $n \div n = 1$

14. Antonio was trying to find 6 × 82 when his calculator stopped working. Show how he could use the Distributive Property to mentally find the product. 6.EE.3, 6.NS.4

Sample answer: $6 \times 82 = 6(80 + 2) = 6(80) + 6(2) = 480 + 12 = 492$

15. The area of the rectangle is $42x + 14$. Select whether each set of dimensions could be the width and length of the rectangle. 6.EE.3, 6.NS.4

$42x + 14$

Yes	No	
■	☐	width 7; length $6x + 2$
☐	■	width 21; length $2x + 0.5$
■	☐	width 2; length $7 + 21x$
■	☐	width $3x + 1$; length 14
☐	■	width 6; length $7x + 8$

16. The table shows the cost of some school supplies. Migina wants to buy 3 pencils, 4 pens, and 2 notebooks. 6.EE.1, 6.NS.3

Item	Cost
Pencils	\$0.29
Pens	\$1.45
Notebooks	\$2.25

Part A: Write an expression to find the total cost of the items she wants to buy.

$(3 \times 0.29) + (4 \times 1.45) + (2 \times 2.25)$

Part B: Migina has a \$20 bill. Does she have enough money to buy the items she wants? Explain how you solved the problem.

Yes; Sample answer: $(3 \times 0.29) + (4 \times 1.45) + (2 \times 2.25) = 0.87 + 5.80 + 4.50 = \$11.17$, and $11.17 < 20$.

17. A rectangular vegetable garden is $(x + 3)$ feet wide and $(2x + 7)$ feet long. 6.EE.3

Part A: Write an expression for the number of feet of fencing that is needed to completely enclose the garden. Justify your answer.

$(6x + 20)$ ft; $2(x + 3) + 2(2x + 7) = 2x + 6 + 4x + 14 = 2x + 4x + 6 + 14 = 6x + 20$

Part B: Let $x = 5$. How many feet of fencing are needed?

50 ft

18. A square has a perimeter given by the expression $20x + 24y$. Write an expression for the length of one side of the square. 6.EE.3

$5x + 6y$

19. Select all of the expressions that simplify to $11x + 10$. 6.EE.4

- ■ $3(3x + 2) + 4 + 2x$
- ■ $2(5x + 4) + x + 2$
- ☐ $3x + 2(3x + 5)$
- ☐ $x + 3(3x + 1) + x + 9$
- ☐ $3(x + 3) + x + 2(3x + 1)$

20. Select all of the expressions that have $3x + 2y$ as one of their factors. 6.EE.4

- ■ $18x + 12y$
- ☐ $3x + 4y + 4x + 2y$
- ■ $4x + y + 2x + 3y$
- ☐ $6x + 9y$

NAME ________________ DATE ________ PERIOD ______ SCORE ______

Chapter 7 Test

1. Select all of the equations for which the solution is 4. 6.EE.5

- ■ $5x = 20$
- ■ $13 - n = 9$
- ■ $22 \div n = 5.5$
- ■ $x + 13 = 17$

2. Loviano bought an apple and an orange. He paid a total of $1.84. The apple cost $0.78. 6.EE.7

Part A: Let *n* represent the cost of the orange. Write an addition equation to find the cost of the orange.

$n + 0.78 = 1.84$

Part B: Solve the equation. How much did Loviano pay for the orange?

$n = 1.06$; He paid $1.06.

3. The number line shows the distances between three towns: *A*, *B*, and *C*. 6.EE.7

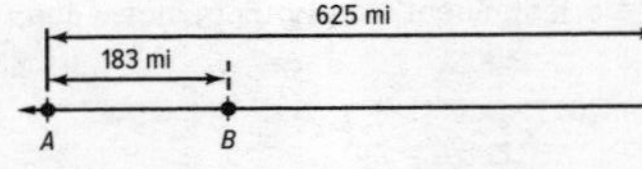

Part A: Write an addition equation to represent the number of miles *n* from Town B to Town C.

$183 + n = 625$

Part B: Solve the equation to find the number of miles from Town B to Town C.

442 mi

4. The table shows the distances some landmarks are from the Nature Center. The eagle's nest is 1.6 kilometers farther from the Nature Center than the waterfall. Write and solve an addition equation to find how far the Nature Center is from the waterfall. 6.EE.7

Landmark	Distance to Nature Center (km)
Big rock	0.85
Waterfall	*x*
Eagle's nest	3.25

$x + 1.6 = 3.25$; 1.65 km

5. Joey and Armando live on the same street as a city park. The park is $\frac{9}{10}$ mile from Joey's home. Joey leaves home and walks to Armando's home. Then he and Armando walk $\frac{3}{5}$ mile to the park. Write and solve an equation to find how far Joey walked to get to Armando's home. 6.EE.7

$n + \frac{3}{5} = \frac{9}{10}$; $\frac{3}{10}$ mi

6. Select whether each equation is an example of the Addition Property of Equality. 6.EE.7

Yes	No	Equation
☐	■	$x + 3 = 7$ $x + 3 - 3 = 7 - 3$
☐	■	$x - 7 = 10$ $x - 7 + 7 = 10$
■	☐	$x - 1.5 = 4.5$ $x - 1.5 + 1.5 = 4.5 + 1.5$
☐	■	$x - \frac{2}{3} = \frac{4}{5}$ $x - \frac{2}{3} + \frac{2}{3} = \frac{4}{5} + \frac{4}{5}$

7. Peter is 12 years old. Peter is 5 years younger than his brother. 6.EE.7

Part A: Let *n* represent the age of Peter's brother. Write a subtraction equation to find the age of Peter's brother.

12 | 5 | *n* | + | − | × | ÷ | =

$n - 5 = 12$

Part B: Solve the equation to find the age of Peter's brother.

17 years old

8. Martha bought a shirt for $12.64. 6.EE.7

Part A: The shirt was discounted $8.75. Write a subtraction equation to find the original cost of the shirt n.

$n - 8.75 = 12.64$

Part B: Solve the equation to find the original price of the shirt.

$21.39

9. Circle all of the equations that have the same solution as the equation $m - 10 = 6$. 6.EE.7

$6 = y + 10$ ($48 = 3a$)   ($5 + n = 21$) $2x = 8$

($8 = \frac{x}{2}$) $18 = n - 2$ $\frac{a}{10} = 6$ ($y - 6 = 10$)

10. Kenji wants to know how many quarters equal $7.50. Select whether each equation represents the number of quarters q that equal $7.50. 6.EE.7

Yes	No	
☐	■	$q + 0.25 = 7.50$
■	☐	$0.25q = 7.50$
☐	■	$\frac{q}{0.25} = 7.50$
☐	■	$q - 0.25 = 7.50$

11. Select all of the equations that can be solved in one step by dividing each side by 8. 6.EE.7

- ☐ $\frac{n}{8} = 2$
- ☐ $4n = 8$
- ■ $8n = 24$
- ☐ $24 = n - 8$
- ■ $40 = 8n$
- ☐ $n + 8 = 16$

12. The equation $P = 4n$ relates the perimeter P of a square to the length of a side n. 6.EE.7, 6.RP.3

Part A: The side length of a square is 8.5 inches. What is the perimeter?

34 in.

Part B: The perimeter of a square is 60 inches. What is the side length?

15 in.

Part C: One side of a square measures 10 inches. What is the perimeter in feet?

$3\frac{1}{3}$ ft

13. Bethany solved the equation $3x = 12$. Her work is shown. Select whether each statement is true or false. 6.EE.7

$3x = 12$
$3x - 3 = 12 - 3$
$x = 9$

True	False	
☐	■	Bethany solved the equation correctly.
■	☐	Bethany should have divided each side by 3 instead of subtracting.
☐	■	Bethany should have multiplied each side by 3 to get $x = 36$.
■	☐	The solution should be $x = 4$.

14. Hakeem drives his car at a constant rate of 60 miles per hour. 6.RP.3, 6.EE.7

Part A: Hakeem travels 450 miles. Write a multiplication equation to find the number of hours n he drove.

$60n = 450$

Part B: Solve the equation to find how long Hakeem drives on his trip.

7.5 hours

15. A teacher wrote the equation $\frac{x}{5} = 3$ on the board.

Part A: Write the numbers or letter to make each statement true. 6.EE.7

15 | 5 | 3 | 1 | $\frac{1}{5}$ | x

The variable is [x].

The coefficient of x is [$\frac{1}{5}$].

The quotient is [3].

To solve, multiply each side of the equation by [5].

Part B: Find the value of x that makes the equation true.

15

16. The quotient of a number n and 6 is 9. 6.EE.7

Part A: Write an equation to find the number.

$\frac{n}{6} = 9$

Part B: Solve the equation to find the number n.

54

17. Selena solved $\frac{x}{7} = 14$ by dividing each side by 7. She found that $x = 2$. Describe and correct Selena's error. 6.EE.7

Sample answer: Selena needs to multiply each side by 7, not divide by 7. The solution is $x = 98$.

18. Write the appropriate numbers in the spaces to show the solution of each equation. 6.EE.5

2 | 3 | 4 | 6 | 8 | 9 | 12 | 16 | 18 | 20

$\frac{n}{2} = 6$ — $n =$ [12]

$12 - n = 4$ — $n =$ [8]

$2n = 18$ — $n =$ [9]

$n + 6 = 12$ — $n =$ [6]

19. Jingdan is trying to solve the equation $\frac{n}{5} = 12$. Select whether each statement is true or false. 6.EE.5

True	False	
☐	■	The equation $5n = 12$ has the same solution as Jingdan's equation.
■	☐	The equation $5 = \frac{n}{12}$ has the same solution as Jingdan's equation.
■	☐	The equation $n - 12 = 48$ has the same solution as Jingdan's equation.
☐	■	Jingdan was correct in adding 5 to each side to solve his equation.
☐	■	Jingdan was correct in multiplying each side by 12 to solve his equation.
■	☐	The solution to Jingdan's equation is 60.

20. Solve the equation $a = b - c$ for b. Select all of the expressions that are equivalent to b. 6.EE.7

- ☐ $a \times c$
- ■ $a + c$
- ☐ $a - b$
- ☐ $a - c$
- ■ $c + a$
- ☐ $c - a$

NAME ______________________ DATE __________ PERIOD ________ SCORE ________

Chapter 8 Test

1. Isabel plans to make apple pies. She buys a pack of pie pans for \$10 and some apples for \$2 per pound. 6.EE.2, 6.EE.2c

Part A: Complete the table to show Isabel's total cost for the various amounts of apples.

Apples (lb), x	$2x + 10$	Cost (\$), y
2	2(2) + 10	14
4	2(4) + 10	18
6	2(6) + 10	22
8	2(8) + 10	26

Part B: Isabel buys 15 pounds of apples. What is the total cost?

\$40

2. The expression $\frac{9}{5}C + 32$ can be used to determine the temperature in degrees Fahrenheit, given the temperature C in degrees Celsius. Chuck claims that for any temperature less than 0°C, the temperature in degrees Fahrenheit will always be less than 0°F. Is Chuck's claim true? Justify your answer. 6.EE.2, 6.EE.2c

no; Sample answer: The temperature –5°C is equivalent to 23°F because $\frac{9}{5}(-5) + 32 = -9 + 32 = 23$.

3. The table shows the total cost of admission to a museum for different numbers of guests. Select whether each statement is true or false. 6.EE.9

Museum Admission	
Number of Guests, x	Total Cost (\$), y
1	9
2	18
3	27
4	36

True	False	
☐	■	The total cost for 14 guests is \$22.
■	☐	The total cost for 8 guests is \$72.
☐	■	The equation $y = x + 8$ can be used to find the total cost for x guests.
■	☐	The equation $y = 9x$ can be used to find the total cost for x guests.

4. A store's rewards program awards 5 points for joining and 2 points for every item purchased. Select all of the representations that determine the number of reward points earned. 6.EE.9

■

Items Purchased, x	1	2	3	4
Number of Points, y	7	9	11	13

■ $y = 5 + 2x$, where y represents the total number of points earned, and x represents the number of items purchased.

☐

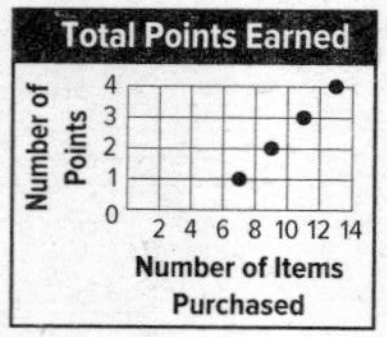

5. An infant car seat manufacturer uses the inequality $w \leq 22$, where w is the infant's weight in pounds, to determine the weight of infants who can be safely transported in their car seats. Sort the names of the infants shown in the table into their appropriate bins based on their weights. 6.EE.5

Name of Infant	Weight (lb)
Marion	20
Taye	18
Quincy	22
Sonia	23
Beth	15
Cory	40

Can be Transported Safely	Cannot be Transported Safely
Marion Taye Quincy Beth	Sonia Cory

6. Emilio has at least 6 coins in his piggy bank. Let c represent the number of coins in the bank. 6.EE.6, 6.EE.8

Part A: Write an inequality to represent this situation.

$c \geq 6$

Part B: Graph the inequality on the number line.

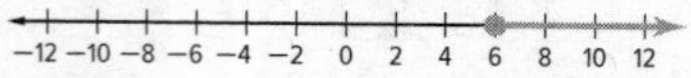

7. Consider the inequality $x + 7 \geq 12$. 6.EE.5

Part A: Select whether each value of x makes the inequality true.

Yes	No	
☐	■	$x = 3.75$
■	☐	$x = 5$
■	☐	$x = 8\frac{5}{8}$
☐	■	$x = -19$

Part B: Kiah claims that all of the values of x that make $x + 7 \geq 12$ true are the same values of x that make $x + 7 > 12$ true. Is Kiah's claim correct? Justify your answer.

no; Sample answer: When $x = 5$, $x + 7 \geq 12$ is true, but $x + 7 > 12$ is not true.

8. Five groups of people are standing in line to buy concert tickets. The table shows the number of tickets each group wants to buy. 6.EE.2

Group Number, x	Number of Tickets
1	1
2	4
3	7
4	10
5	13

Part A: The pattern in the table continues. How many tickets does Group 6 want to buy?

16 tickets

Part B: Use the pattern in the table to write a rule for the number of tickets each group wants to buy.

$3x - 2$

9. Jorge wrote the phrase "7 more than the product of 6 and the number n" to represent the values in an arithmetic sequence. He let n represent a number's position in the sequence. 6.EE.6

Part A: Write the appropriate numbers and symbols to create an expression that represents Jorge's statement.

1 6 7 n
+ − × ÷

6 n + 7

Part B: What are the first five numbers in the sequence?

13, 19, 25, 31, 37

10. The library does not charge a fee for books returned no more than 3 days late in a month. The library does charge a monthly late fee represented by $\$1.25(d - 3)$ where $d > 3$. The table shows the number of days late d for four months that Margaret borrowed books. Find the total late fees Margaret was charged in the four months. 6.EE.8

Month	Number of Days Late, d
January	5
February	1
March	3
April	7

$7.50

11. An office box has a height of 1.5 inches. Jen claims that a stack of 9 of these office boxes will have an overall height of 6 inches. Use the rule $h = 1.5n$, where n is the number of boxes and h is the total height, to determine if Jen's claim is true. Justify your answer. 6.EE.9

not true; Sample answer: When $n = 9$, $h = 1.5(9) =$ 13.5 in., not 6 in.

12. A sales associate at a furniture store receives a bonus of $200 for every couch she sells. Her goal is to earn at least $1,250 in bonuses. 6.EE.6, 6.EE.8

Part A: Write an inequality to represent the number of couches the associate must sell to reach her goal. Identify any variables you include.

Sample answer: $200c \geq 1{,}250$, where c represents the number of couches the associate must sell.

Part B: Solve the inequality for your variable. What is the least number of couches the associate must sell to reach her goal?

Inequality: **$c \geq 6.25$** **7** couches

13. The table shows the relationship between x and y. Graph the given ordered pairs. Then complete the table. 6.EE.9

Input (x)	Output (y)
0	0
1	2
1.5	**3**
2	4
3	6
x	**$2x$**

14. Select whether each statement can be represented by the equation $y = 0.1x + 2$. 6.EE.9

Yes	No	
■	□	A server earns 10% of a check plus \$2.
■	□	Students must solve two test items of their choice and 10% of the remaining items.
□	■	10% of the workers received 2 bonuses.
■	□	A veterinarian wants a dog to lose $\frac{1}{10}$ of its weight plus 2 pounds.
□	■	It is 2 degrees cooler than $\frac{1}{10}$ of the temperature in Florida.

15. Sort the values of x into the appropriate bin based on the inequality $17 > 20 - x$. 6.EE.5

$x = 0$ | $x = 2$ | $x = 5$ | $x = 3$ | $x = 6$ | $x = 10$

Solution	Not a Solution
$x = 5$	$x = 0$
$x = 6$	$x = 2$
$x = 10$	$x = 3$

16. A bicyclist takes 3 hours to travel 12 miles to a campsite. He cycles at least 1 mile but no more than 5 miles during the first hour. He cycles at least 2 miles during the second hour. He cycles exactly 3 miles during the third hour. Find the least number of miles the bicyclist could have traveled during the second hour. 6.EE.8

4 miles

17. Doug earns at most x dollars per day. His wife earns at least twice as much per day as Doug. Select whether each statement is true or false in representing their incomes. 6.EE.6

True	False	
■	□	Doug and his wife could earn \$$3x$ per day.
■	□	Doug and his wife could earn $(3x - 1)$ dollars per day.
□	■	If Doug earns \$100 in a day, he and his wife could earn a total income of \$150 that day.

18. Lorena determined that she weighs 3 pounds more than 4 times the weight of her baby brother Omar. She represented her weight with the expression $4x + 3$, where x is Omar's weight. Lorena weighs 67 pounds. How many more pounds does Lorena weigh than Omar? 6.EE.9

51 lb

19. Consider the sequence: 1, 4, 16, 64, ... Describe the pattern. Then determine the sixth term in the sequence. 6.EE.9

Sample answer: Each term after the first term is found by multiplying the previous term by 4.

Sixth term: 1,024

20. For each function table, write the corresponding equation in the space provided. 6.EE.9

$y = 5x + 1$ | $y = x + 5$ | $y = x + 1$ | $y = 2x - 1$ | $y = 3x - 2$

Input (x)	1	2	3	4
Output (y)	6	7	8	9

Equation: $y = x + 5$

Input (x)	1	2	3	4
Output (y)	1	3	5	7

Equation: $y = 2x - 1$

Input (x)	1	2	3	4
Output (y)	6	11	16	21

Equation: $y = 5x + 1$

NAME ______________________ DATE __________ PERIOD ______ SCORE ______

Chapter 9 Test

1. Select all of the base and height dimensions of a parallelogram with an area of 12 square feet. 6.G.1

- ☐ base = 2 ft, height = 4 ft
- ☐ base = 3 ft, height = 8 ft
- ■ base = 5 ft, height = 2.4 ft
- ■ base = 12 ft, height = 1 ft
- ☐ base = 3 ft, height = 3 ft

2. The diagram shows two parallelograms. For what value of n is the area of parallelogram B twice the area of parallelogram A? 6.G.1

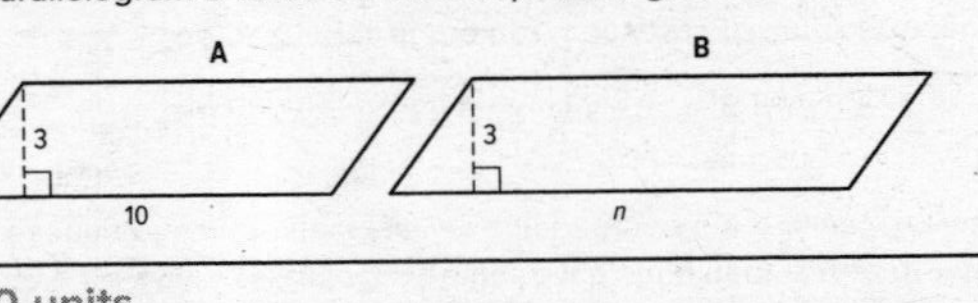

20 units

3. The diagram shows a sign that Alice is designing for a restaurant. The sign is in the shape of a parallelogram. 6.G.1

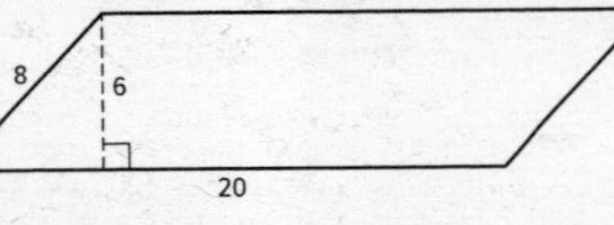

Part A: Alice wants to paint the front of the sign blue before adding white lettering. One quart of paint covers 100 square feet. How many quarts of blue paint does she need to buy? Justify your answer.

2 qt; The area is 6(20) = 120 ft². Because 1 quart covers 100 ft², she needs to buy 2 qt of paint.

Part B: Alice wants to string lights around the edges of the sign. A box of lights contains 12 linear feet of lights. How many boxes of lights does Alice need to buy? Justify your answer.

5 boxes; The perimeter is 2(20) + 2(8) = 56 ft. Because each box contains 12 ft of lights, she needs 56 ÷ 12 ≈ 4.6, which rounds up to 5 boxes.

4. The two triangles shown have the same area. Select whether each statement is true or false in representing the dimensions of the triangles. 6.G.1

Not drawn to scale.

True	False	
☐	■	$n = \frac{x}{2}$
☐	■	$n = x$
■	☐	$n = 2x$
☐	■	$n = 4x$
■	☐	$x = \frac{n}{2}$

5. Andrew found the area of the triangle. His work is shown. Describe and correct Andrew's error. 6.G.1

$A = \frac{1}{2} \cdot 6 \cdot 10$

$A = 30$ unit²

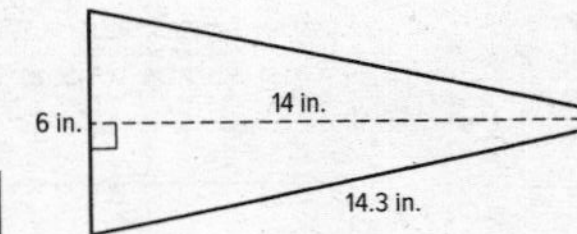

The height is not 10. Andrew should have written that the height is 8. So, the area should be $A = \frac{1}{2} \cdot 6 \cdot 8 = 24$ unit².

6. The diagram shows the pennant hanging on Henrietta's bedroom wall. How much wall space does the pennant cover? 6.G.1

42 in²

7. The area of the triangular plot in front of Adrianna's house is 28 square feet. Select all of the sets of dimensions that could be the dimensions of the triangular plot. 6.G.1

- ☐ base = 4 feet, height = 7 feet
- ■ base = 20 feet, height = 2.8 feet
- ☐ base = 7 feet, height = 16 feet
- ■ base = 14 feet, height = 4 feet
- ☐ base = 2 feet, height = 7 feet

8. The area of a trapezoid is 20 square units. The sum of the base lengths is 10 units. What is the height of the trapezoid? 6.G.1

4 units

9. The stage in a theater is in the shape of a trapezoid. The length of the front of the stage is 80 feet. The length of the back of the stage is 50 feet. The distance from the front to the back of the stage is 40 feet. What is the area of the stage? 6.G.1

2,600 ft²

10. The trapezoid shown has an area of 80 square units. Select all of the possible values for a and b. 6.G.1

- ☐ a = 4 units, b = 6 units
- ■ a = 5 units, b = 15 units
- ☐ a = 7 units, b = 9 units
- ■ a = 18 units, b = 2 units

a

8

b

11. The dimensions of a rectangular canvas are multiplied by a factor of 5 to create a new canvas. Select whether each statement is true or false in representing how the new canvas compares to the original canvas. 6.G.1

True	False	
■	☐	The perimeter of the new canvas is 5 times greater.
☐	■	The perimeter of the new canvas is 10 times greater.
☐	■	The perimeter of the new canvas is 25 times greater.
☐	■	The area of the new canvas is 5 times greater.
■	☐	The area of the new canvas is 25 times greater.

12. The carpeting that Elizabeth has selected for her bedroom floor is sold by the square yard. The floor measures 10 feet by 12 feet. 6.G.1

Part A: How many square feet are in one square yard?

9 ft²

Part B: How many square yards of carpeting will Elizabeth need to carpet the entire bedroom floor?

$13\frac{1}{3}$ yd²

13. Carla printed out a photo on a standard sheet of paper. Then she reduced the dimensions of the photo to be $\frac{1}{4}$ the original dimensions. How many smaller photos can Carla print on the same standard sheet of paper? 6.G.1

16 smaller photos

14. The perimeter of one square is $8x$. The perimeter of another square is $6x$. What is the ratio of the area of the smaller square to the area of the larger square? 6.G.1

9:16

15. The locations of four corner flags of a soccer field are plotted on the coordinate plane. Diego points out that 1 square unit on the coordinate plane represents 60 square feet. What is the area of the soccer field? Explain how you found your answer. 6.G.1, 6.G.3, 6.NS.8

2,400 ft²; Sample answer: rectangular area on coordinate plane = 4 × 10 = 40 units²; area of soccer field = 40 × 60 = 2,400 ft²

y
6
4
2
−2 O 2 4 6 8 x
−2
−4

16. Yoruba is creating a logo on a coordinate plane. She identifies the vertices of the logo as (2, –1), (3, 5), (6, 5), and (7, –1). 6.G.1, 6.G.3, 6.NS.8

Part A: Graph the ordered pairs that show the vertices of the logo, and connect the vertices to outline the shape of the logo.

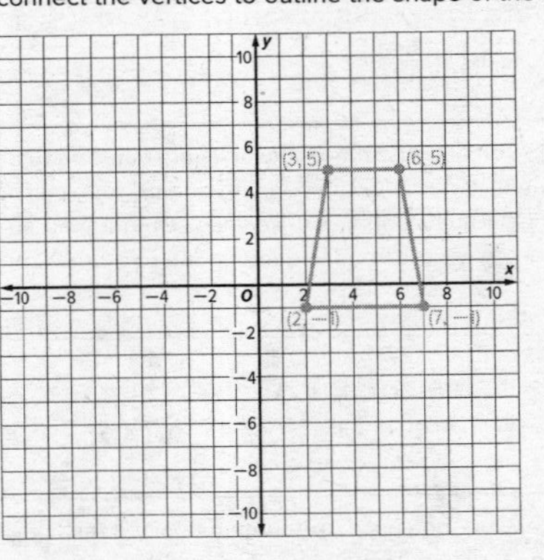

Part B: What is the area of the logo?

24 units²

17. A rectangle has a perimeter of 20 units and an area of 21 square units. The coordinate plane shows two vertices of the rectangle. Select all of the ordered pairs that could represent the other two vertices of the rectangle. 6.G.1, 6.G.3, 6.NS.8

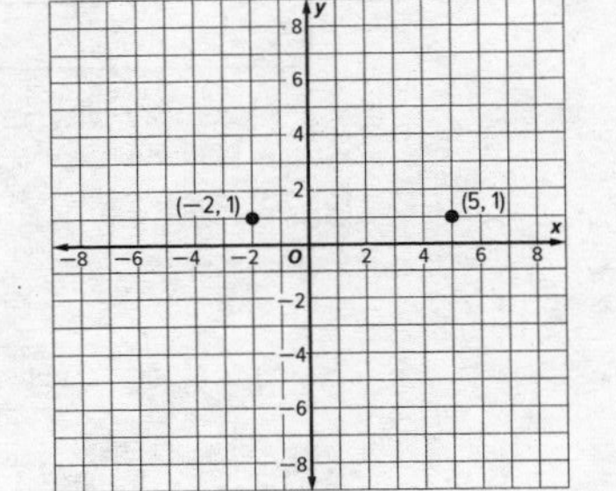

- ☐ (0, –2) and (10, –2)
- ■ (–2, 4) and (5, 4)
- ☐ (–2, 8) and (5, 8)
- ■ (–2, –2) and (5, –2)
- ☐ (1, 1) and (8, 1)

18. Aaron wants to paint a wall in his office. There are two windows in the wall. The windows have dimensions of 4 feet by 3 feet. The height of the wall is 8 feet and the width is 12 feet. What area of wall is to be painted? 6.G.1

72 ft²

19. Eduardo lives on the corner of two streets. The diagram shows the dimensions of the sidewalk around Eduardo's house. The width of the sidewalk is 3 feet. What is the total area of the sidewalk? 6.G.1

3 ft
150 ft
Eduardo's House
70 ft

651 ft²

20. The diagram shows the dimensions of a school playground. The student council wants to paint the surface of the playground in the school color. A one-gallon can of paint covers 40 square yards. How many cans of paint will they need? Explain how you found the answer. 6.G.1

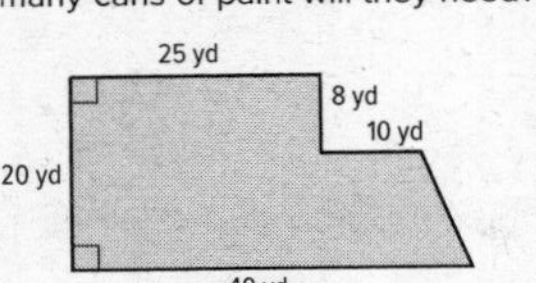

17 cans; Sample answer: I divided the area by the amount covered by a can. Rectangle area: 25(20) = 500 yd². Trapezoid: height = 20 – 8 = 12, bottom base = 40 – 25 = 15; area = $\frac{1}{2}$(12)(10 + 15) = 150 yd². Total area = 500 + 150 = 650 yd². Divide: 650 ÷ 40 = 16.25, so 17 cans are needed.

NAME ______________ DATE ________ PERIOD ______ SCORE ______

Chapter 10 Test

1. A fish tank has a width of 4 feet, a length of 3 feet, and a height of 2.5 feet. Ariana fills the tank with water until the height of the water is 12 inches from the top of the tank. What is the volume of water in the fish tank? 6.G.2

6	12	18	20
22.5	24	30	144

18 ft^3

2. The ratio of side lengths of two square prisms is 2:3. What is the ratio of the volumes? 6.G.2

8:27

3. A sporting goods company ships products in a 30-inch by 20-inch by 10-inch rectangular carton. Footballs are packaged in a 5-inch by 5-inch by 8-inch box. The company places 20 football boxes in a carton and fills the rest of the space with packing material. What volume of space was filled with packing material? Explain your answer. 6.G.2

2,000 in^3; Sample answer: volume of carton: (30)(20)(10) = 6,000 in^3; Volume of footballs: 20(5)(5)(8) = 4,000 in^3; Volume of packing material: 6,000 – 4,000 = 2,000 in^3

4. The volume of the cereal box shown is 121.6 cubic inches. The height of the shelves in Valerie's pantry is 10.75 inches. Is it possible for Valerie to place this cereal box in an upright position on her pantry shelf? Justify your response. 6.G.2

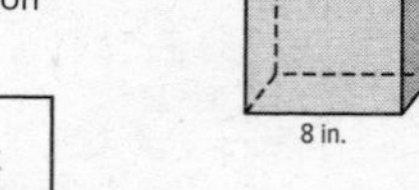

yes; $V = \ell wh$, so $h = \frac{V}{\ell w} = \frac{121.6}{(8)(1.6)} = 9.5$; the box is 9.5 in. tall. Since 9.5 < 10.75, the box can be placed upright on the shelf.

5. Edgardo created a rectangular prism with a square base. The volume of the prism is 45 cubic inches. The dimensions of the prism are all whole numbers. What is the height of the prism? 6.G.2

5 in.

6. The diagram shows the tent the Wilsons used on a camping trip. The front and back of the tent are isosceles triangles. Write the number and measurement to indicate the capacity of the tent. 6.G.2

240	174	144	ft^2
136	130	120	ft^3

120 ft^3

7. The diagram shows the dimensions of a triangular prism. Select all of the values for a and b that would give the prism a volume of 90 cubic inches. 6.G.2

- ☐ $a = 1, b = 9$
- ■ $a = 3, b = 6$
- ☐ $a = 4, b = 9$
- ■ $a = 9, b = 2$
- ☐ $a = 3, b = 3$

8. The diagram shows the dimensions of a building block. A set of these blocks is packaged in a box 10 inches long, 6 inches wide, and 3 inches high. What is the greatest number of blocks in a set? 6.G.2

6 in.
2 in.
0.75 in.

40 blocks

9. The volume of a triangular prism is equal to half the volume of a rectangular prism. Select whether each statement is true or false. 6.G.2

True	False	
☐	■	Each dimension of the triangular prism is half the measure of the corresponding dimension of the rectangular prism.
■	☐	The two prisms have the same dimensions.
☐	■	Each dimension of the triangular prism is twice the measure of the corresponding dimension of the rectangular prism.
☐	■	The dimensions of the two prisms are never equal.

10. The diagram shows a 3,300-cubic-foot greenhouse. What is the height of the greenhouse? 6.G.2

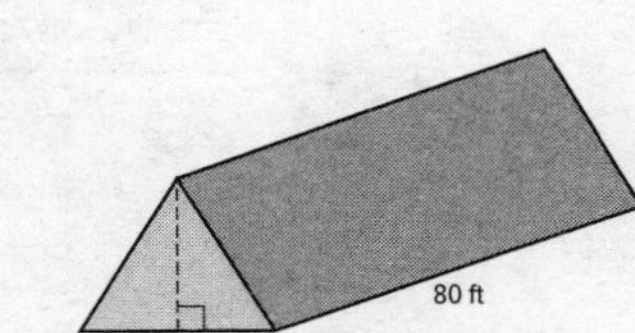

8.25 ft

11. The diagram shows the gift box Fernando plans to wrap. He wants to use the least amount of wrapping paper needed to completely cover the box. A sheet of wrapping paper is 600 square inches. How much wrapping paper would Fernando have left after wrapping the box? 6.G.4

1.5 in.
8 in.
10 in.

386 in²

12. Select whether each statement is a method for finding the surface area of a rectangular prism with length ℓ, width w, and height h. 6.G.4

Yes	No	
☐	■	Find the product of ℓ, w, and h.
☐	■	Find ℓwh, and then divide the product by 2.
■	☐	Find $\ell w + h\ell + wh$, and then multiply the sum by 2.
■	☐	Find $\ell w + h\ell + wh + wh + h\ell + \ell w$.

13. The dimensions of rectangular prism X are twice the dimensions of rectangular prism Y. 6.G.4

Part A: The surface area of prism X is 100 square inches. What is the surface area of prism Y?

25 in²

Part B: The dimensions of rectangular prism Z are three times the dimensions of rectangular prism Y. What is the surface area of prism Z?

225 in²

14. Select all of the situations for which surface area is the appropriate measure. 6.G.4

- ☐ The amount of water inside a fish tank.
- ■ The amount of glass needed to make a fish tank.
- ☐ The amount of space inside a wooden toy chest.
- ■ The amount of stain needed to paint a wooden toy chest.

Chapter Tests

15. The diagram shows the net of a cardboard box. How much cardboard is needed to make the box? 6.G.4

8 in.
0.75 in.
12 in.

222 in²

16. The diagram shows the dimensions of a canvas tent. How much canvas fabric does Charlie need to make the tent, including the floor? 6.G.4

4.3 ft
4.3 ft
4 ft
3 ft
5 ft

70 ft²

17. The diagram shows the net of a three-dimensional solid. 6.G.2, 6.G.4

4 in.
6.7 in.
7 in.
2 in.

Part A: Identify the name of the solid represented by the net.

triangular prism

Part B: Find the surface area and volume of the solid.

Surface area: 76.2 in²

Volume: 26.8 in³

18. A mailing container for posters is made from 87.4 square inches of cardboard. The container is in the shape of a triangular prism. The base of the prism is an equilateral triangle with 2-inch side lengths and a height of 1.7 inches. What is the length of the container? 6.G.4

14 in.

19. David uses a sheet of paper to make a model of an Egyptian pyramid. The model has a square base with side lengths of 4 inches. The slant height of the model is 5 inches. 6.G.4

Part A: How much paper was used to make the model, including the base?

56 in²

Part B: David wants to cover his model with colored squares of paper. Each colored square has 1.5-inch side lengths. What is the least number of colored squares needed to cover the model of the pyramid?

25 squares

20. The diagram shows a net of a triangular pyramid. 6.G.4

10 in.
8 in.
12 in.
12 in.
12 in.

Part A: What is the lateral area of the triangular pyramid?

144 in²

Part B: What additional steps are needed to find the surface area of the triangular pyramid?

Find the area of the base and add it to the lateral area.

NAME ______________ DATE ________ PERIOD ______ SCORE ______

Chapter 11 Test

1. In 7 days, Jessica walked an average of 30 minutes per day. Select whether each set of data has the same average as Jessica. 6.SP.3

Yes	No	
■	☐	30, 30, 30, 30, 30, 30, 30
☐	■	20, 24, 25, 30, 31, 32, 35
☐	■	30, 30, 30, 20, 15, 25, 40
■	☐	40, 20, 15, 22, 32, 40, 41

2. Greg earned $15, $18, $12, $20, and $25 for each of five lawns he mowed. Greg wants to earn a mean of $20 per lawn. How much must he charge for his next mowing job? Justify your answer. 6.SP.3

$30; The total he must earn for 6 lawns is $20(6), or $120. He has earned $90. So, he must charge 120 – 90 = $30.

3. The table shows the number of personalized greeting cards that artists created to send to veterans. 6.SP.3

Greeting Cards Made	
Artist	**Number of Cards**
Gilberto	36
Isabel	35
Taye	40
Selam	38
Kenji	34
Sue	81

Part A: What is the mean number of cards created?

44 cards

Part B: How does the number of cards Sue made affect the mean of the data?

Sample answer: Sue created many more cards than the others, causing the mean to be greater than the other data values. The mean without Sue's value is 36.6 cards, which is a better description of the data.

4. Larry needs to gather data for a science report. Select whether each question can be classified as a statistical question. 6.SP.1

Yes	No	
☐	■	What is the distance between Mars and Earth?
■	☐	How many articles were published in various science magazines about planets last year?
☐	■	What percent of students know that the sun is a star and not a planet?
■	☐	How many moons does each planet have?

5. The list shows the number of seconds it took eight phones to receive the same text message. 6.SP.3, 6.SP.5, 6.SP.5c

4 5 7 4 2 6 3 5

Part A: Write the appropriate value(s) for each data measure.

2	5
3	6.5
3.5	7
4	8
4.5	9

number of data values: 8

mean: 4.5

median: 4.5

modes: 4 and 5

range: 5

interquartile range: 2

Part B: What is the mean absolute deviation of the data? Explain how you found your answer.

1.25; Sample answer: I found the absolute value of the difference between the mean, 4.5, and each data value. Then I found the sum of the differences, 10, and divided 10 by 8 to get 1.25.

6. The table shows the shoe sizes of a group of boys. Find and compare the median and mode of the data. 6.SP.5, 6.SP.5c

Shoe Size			
6	8	7	6
10	9	7.5	5
5	5.5	6	7.5

median: 6.5; mode: 6; The median is half a size larger than the mode.

7. The line plot shows the ages of people enrolled in a pottery class. Select all of the data values that are outliers. 6.SP.5, 6.SP.5c

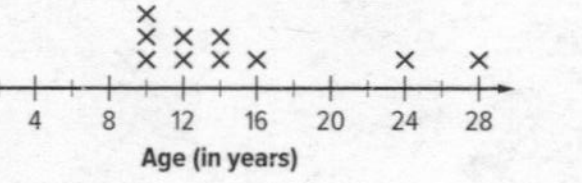

- ☐ 10
- ☐ 12 and 14
- ☐ 16
- ☐ 24
- ■ 28

8. The table shows the number of trees in some city parks. 6.SP.3, 6.SP.5, 6.SP.5c

Number of Trees in City Parks			
20	22	34	50
42	28	20	52

Part A: Order the values from least to greatest, and find the median.

20, 20, 22, 28, 34, 42, 50, 52; median: 31

Part B: Determine the first quartile and third quartile.

Q_1: 21; Q_3: 46

Part C: What is the range of the data? What is the interquartile range?

range: 32; IQR: 25

9. A student conducted a survey by asking 20 people, "Do you know how to knit, crochet, do both, or do neither?" The results showed that 7 people knit and 5 people crochet. Of these people, 4 know how to do both. How many of those surveyed do not know how to knit or crochet? 6.SP.1

12 people

10. The double stem-and-leaf plot shows the temperature, in degrees Fahrenheit, taken on the hour in two different classrooms. 6.SP.3, 6.SP.5, 6.SP.5c

Room 100		Room 103
8	6	5
8 5 5 4 2 0	7	0 0 0 2 3 3 4
0	8	

8|6 = 68°F 6|5 = 65°F

Part A: What is the median temperature for each room?

Room 100: 74.5°F; Room 103: 71°F

Part B: What are the range and interquartile range for each room? Justify your answer.

Room 100: range: 12°F, IQR: 5.5°F; Since Q_1 = 71 and Q_3 = 76.5, IQR = 76.5 − 71 = 5.5.
Room 103: range: 9°F, IQR: 3°F; Since Q_1 = 70 and Q_3 = 73, IQR = 73 − 70 = 3.

Part C: Compare and contrast the measures of variation for both rooms.

Sample answer: Room 103 median = Room 100 Q_1. So, the temperatures in Room 100 are warmer than in Room 103. The ranges indicate that the temperatures in Room 100 vary more than those in Room 103. The interquartile range shows that the temperatures for Room 103 are more clustered around the median, and those in Room 100 are more spread out.

11. The table shows the hourly parking fees of three different garages. Margaret found the mean absolute deviation as 0.75. Explain Margaret's error. 6.SP.5, 6.SP.5b, 6.SP.5c

Hourly Parking Fee	
Garage A	$5.50
Garage B	$9.00
Garage C	$6.50

Margaret divided the wrong numbers. Sample answer: The mean is $7.00. The mean absolute deviation is 4 ÷ 3 ≈ 1.33. Margaret found 3 ÷ 4, instead of 4 ÷ 3.

12. The table shows the maximum speeds of car drivers on a residential road. Circle the values that are more than one mean absolute deviation away from the mean. 6.SP.5, 6.SP.5b, 6.SP.5c

Maximum Speeds (mph)			
35	36	32	40
37	38	29	33

(29) (32) 33 35
36 37 (38) (40)

13. The list shows the number of phone calls made by five people in one month: 132, 28, 40, 35, 20. Select whether each statement is true or false in representing the data. 6.SP.3, 6.SP.5, 6.SP.5c

True	False	
■	☐	The median better represents the data than the mean.
☐	■	The mean is less than the median.
■	☐	The range is affected by the outlier.
☐	■	The mode is affected by the outlier.

14. A company pays seven employees $10 per hour and one employee $60 per hour. 6.SP.5, 6.SP.5c

Part A: Find the median and mean of the hourly wages.

median: $10; mean: $16.25

Part B: The company claims that their employees earn an average of $16.25 per hour. Assume you were interviewing for a job at this company. What question should you ask to validate the claim?

Sample answer: Were outliers included in your calculation for average hourly wage?

Part C: Which measure(s) of center best describe(s) the data? Explain.

median and mode; Sample answer: Both measures equal $10 and best represent the hourly wage, with or without the $60 outlier.

15. For each data set, write the most appropriate measure of center. Use each answer once. 6.SP.5, 6.SP.5d

mean
median
mode

median Club fees: $35, $225, $36, $45, $60

mode Age of dancers: 51, 25, 64, 51, 51, 51

mean Number of lunges: 9, 9, 17, 24, 20, 16, 30

16. Fatima asked, "How tall is the tallest female in your household?" Is her question a statistical question? If so, explain why it is statistical. If not, rephrase it so it is a statistical question. 6.SP.1

no; Sample answer: How tall are the women in your household?

17. The list shows the number of homework problems out of ten that Juan answered correctly for eight assignments: 9, 4, 10, 6, 10, 8, 7, 10. Select whether each statement is true or false in representing the data. 6.SP.3

True	False	
■	☐	10 is a mode of the data set.
☐	■	8 is the median of the data set.
☐	■	8.5 is the mean of the data set.
☐	■	There is no mode in the data set.

18. Use the data: 27, 21, 22, 20, 21, 23, 25, 25, 25, 26, 26, 27. Write the appropriate term to correctly complete each statement. 6.SP.5, 6.SP.5b, 6.SP.5c

interquartile range
mean
median
mean absolute deviation

The **mean absolute deviation** is approximately 2.

The **median** is 25.

The **mean** is 24.

19. The data show the time, in seconds, that members of a track team ran 100 meters: 11, 12, 11, 10, 20, 12, 12, 11. Sort the terms into the appropriate bin based on the effect of the outlier. 6.SP.3

mean
median
mode

Affected by the Outlier	Not Affected by the Outlier
mean	**median** **mode**

20. The table shows the number of times students have visited their state capital. Describe the effect on the mean when the outlier is removed from the data. Justify your answer. 6.SP.5, 6.SP.5d

Visits to the State Capital		
0	1	3
2	4	3
2	1	11

The mean decreases. Sample answer: The mean is 3. Without the outlier, the mean is 2. The mean decreases by 1.

NAME ______________ DATE ________ PERIOD ______ SCORE ______

Chapter 12 Test

1. Select whether each statement is true or false about data represented by a line plot. 6.SP.5, 6.SP.5a, 6.SP.5b

True	False	
■	☐	Each individual data value is shown.
☐	■	The mean is more easily determined than the mode.
☐	■	The median cannot be computed.
■	☐	The range can be easily computed.

2. The table shows the amount of time 15 students spent reading last night. 6.SP.4, 6.SP.5, 6.SP.5c

Time Spent Reading (min)				
45	38	27	15	45
30	40	27	18	24
15	45	18	22	27

Part A: Complete the line plot to represent the data.

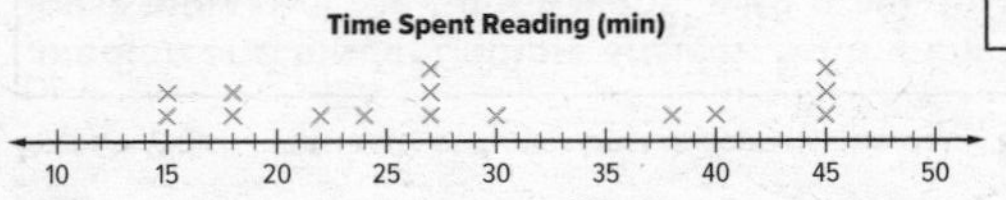

Time Spent Reading (min)

10 15 20 25 30 35 40 45 50

Part B: Find the median, the mode(s), and the interquartile range.

median: 27; modes: 27 and 45; IQR: 22

3. Select whether each statement is true or false about data represented by a histogram with intervals on the horizontal axis. 6.SP.5, 6.SP.5a, 6.SP.5b

True	False	
☐	■	Each individual data value is shown.
☐	■	The median can be easily identified.
☐	■	The mode can be easily identified.
■	☐	The bars touch each other because the data are in ranges with consecutive intervals.

4. The histogram shows test scores for one class. Select whether each statement is true or false. 6.SP.5, 6.SP.5c

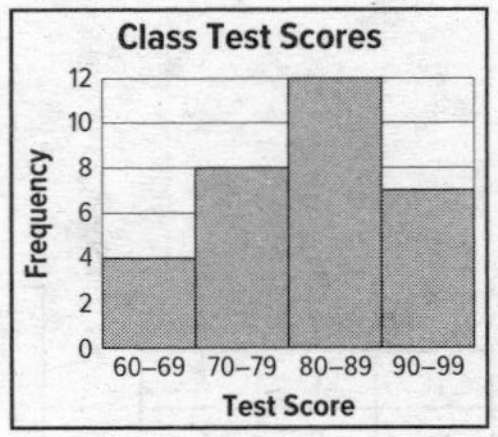

Class Test Scores

Frequency: 0, 2, 4, 6, 8, 10, 12

Test Score: 60–69, 70–79, 80–89, 90–99

True	False	
☐	■	The mode is 85.
■	☐	Twelve students scored below 80.
■	☐	The median is in the interval 80–89.
☐	■	The range is 39.

5. The table shows the number of points Michael scored in each of 20 games. 6.SP.4, 6.SP.5, 6.SP.5a

Number of Points Scored				
22	15	0	9	16
9	11	22	30	27
15	18	31	15	2
10	16	8	27	23

Part A: Complete the histogram to represent the data.

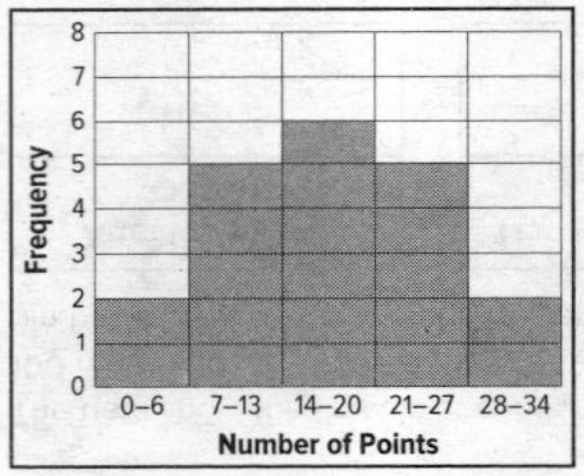

Frequency: 0, 1, 2, 3, 4, 5, 6, 7, 8

Number of Points: 0–6, 7–13, 14–20, 21–27, 28–34

Part B: In how many games did Michael score more than 13 points?

13 games

6. Select whether each statement is true or false in representing data by a box-and-whisker plot. 6.SP.5, 6.SP.5a, 6.SP.5b

True	False	
☐	■	The mean is located outside of the box.
■	☐	The median can be easily determined.
☐	■	The mode is always a point inside of the box.
■	☐	The range can be computed from two of the plotted points.
☐	■	The number of data values can be determined.

7. The box-and-whisker plot shows the number of books checked out of a library each day. Select all of the statements that are valid. 6.SP.5, 6.SP.5c

Number of Books Checked Out Each Day

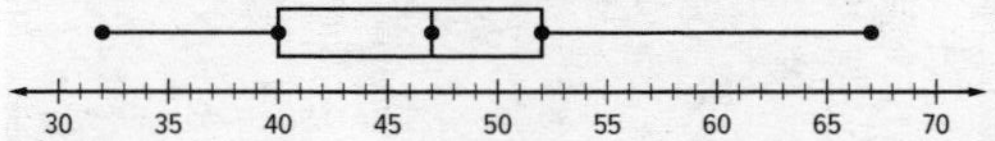

30 35 40 45 50 55 60 65 70

- ☐ There are more data values from 52 to 67 than from 32 to 40.
- ■ Half the values are between 40 and 52.
- ■ The least number of books checked out is 32.
- ■ There are the same number of values between 47 and 52 as from 52 to 67.

8. The table shows the heights, in inches, of 15 students. 6.SP.4, 6.SP.5, 6.SP.5c

Heights of Students (in.)				
50	60	58	64	62
52	61	54	60	50
53	62	58	55	60

Part A: Complete the box-and-whisker plot to represent the data.

Heights of Students (in.)

48 50 52 54 56 58 60 62 64 66

Part B: What is the interquartile range?

8

9. The diagram shows some points on a box-and-whisker plot. Write the appropriate point or expression that corresponds to each measure. 6.SP.5, 6.SP.5c

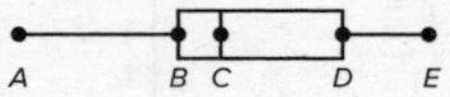

A B C D E

$D-B$	$E-A$	A to C	E	D to E	C

Median: C Range: $E-A$

Interquartile range: $D-B$ Greatest value: E

Same number of values as from A to B: D to E

10. Piano students were asked to name their favorite musical note. The line plot shows the survey results. Select whether each statement is true or false. 6.SP.2, 6.SP.5, 6.SP.5c

Favorite Musical Notes of Piano Students

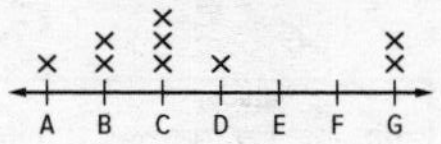

A B C D E F G

True	False	
■	☐	There is a peak in the data.
■	☐	There is a gap in the data.
☐	■	The distribution is symmetrical.
■	☐	There is a data cluster.

11. A survey asked students how many sit-ups they completed in a physical education class. The histogram shows the results. Answer each question about the data in the histogram. 6.SP.2, 6.SP.5, 6.SP.5c

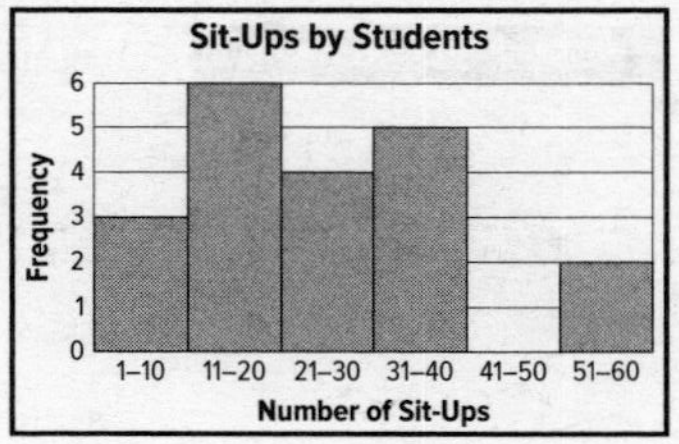

Sit-Ups by Students

Frequency: 0 1 2 3 4 5 6

Number of Sit-Ups: 1–10 11–20 21–30 31–40 41–50 51–60

Yes	No	
☐	■	Is there an outlier in the interval 51–60?
■	☐	Is there a gap from 41–50?
☐	■	Is the distribution symmetrical?
☐	■	Is the peak 15 sit-ups?
■	☐	Is there a cluster from 1–40?

12. Select whether each statement is true or false in representing the data shown by the box-and-whisker plot. 6.SP.5, 6.SP.5c

Test Scores

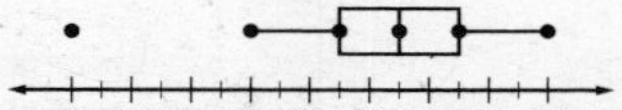

20 30 40 50 60 70 80 90 100

True	False	
■	☐	There is an outlier at 20.
☐	■	There is a peak at 75.
☐	■	The distribution is symmetrical.
■	☐	There is a gap from 20 to 50.

13. Select all of the situations that are best represented with a line graph. 6.SP.4

- ■ the high temperature recorded each day for a week
- ☐ the test scores of students in a class
- ■ the population in a town for each of eight years
- ☐ the amount of protein in a protein bar

14. Joseph wants to make a data display so that the median is easily identifiable. What type of data display should he use? Explain. 6.SP.4, 6.SP.5, 6.SP.5d

Sample answer: He should use a box-and-whisker plot because the median is represented by the middle line in the box.

15. Juanita wants to display her standardized test scores for the last few years. What type of display should she use? Explain. 6.SP.4

Sample answer: a line graph; It shows changes over time.

16. Harold created a line plot to show research data. He now wants to present the data using a different type of display that shows the data in categories. 6.SP.4

Part A: What other type of display should Harold use?

Sample answer: bar graph

Part B: Compare the line plot with the display you identified in Part A. How are the two displays alike and how are they different?

Sample answer: Both show individual values and peaks and gaps. The bar graph uses an axis and a bar to show how many, whereas a line plot uses X's to show how many.

17. A principal wants to make a data display of the amount of time the 500 students in the school spend on homework each evening. What type of data display should the principal use? Explain your choice. 6.SP.4

Sample answer: a box-and-whisker plot; It shows the measures of variation and can easily represent this large set of data, since it does not show all the individual values.

18. A set of data has an outlier. Which measures of center and spread would be more appropriate to represent the data: mean and mean absolute deviation, or median and interquartile range? Explain your reasoning. 6.SP.5, 6.SP.5c, 6.SP.5d

median and interquartile range; Sample answer: A value that is an outlier usually means that the distribution is not symmetric, and the outlier has a greater effect on the mean than it does on the median.

19. Select all of the displays that show individual data values. 6.SP.4, 6.SP.5, 6.SP.5a

- ■ bar graph
- ☐ histogram
- ■ line plot
- ■ line graph
- ☐ box-and-whisker plot

20. Select all of the statements that are valid in representing the data shown in the line graph. 6.SP.4

- ■ The temperatures increase from June to July.
- ☐ The temperatures increase from August to September.
- ■ The greatest change in temperature is between September and October.
- ■ The highest temperatures are in August.

Average High Temperatures
Temperature (°F): 0, 10, 20, 30, 40, 50, 60, 70, 80, 90
Month: June, July, Aug, Sep, Oct

Page 125 • Triathlon Bound

<table>
<tr><td colspan="3">Task Scenario
Students will describe a ratio, make tables of equivalent ratios, plot the pairs of values on the coordinate plane, use tables to compare ratios, and solve unit rate problems.</td></tr>
<tr><td colspan="2">CCSS Content Standard(s)</td><td>6.RP.1, 6.RP.2, 6.RP.3, 6.RP.3a, 6.RP.3b, 6.NS.4</td></tr>
<tr><td colspan="2">Mathematical Practices</td><td>MP1, MP2, MP4, MP5, MP6, MP7, MP8</td></tr>
<tr><td colspan="2">Depth of Knowledge</td><td>DOK2, DOK3, DOK4</td></tr>
<tr><th>Part</th><th>Maximum Points</th><th>Scoring Rubric</th></tr>
<tr><td>A</td><td>2</td><td>Full Credit:
The ratio between swimming and biking is 30:75, or 2:5.
On Monday and Friday, for every 2 minutes of swimming, there will be 5 minutes of biking.
The ratio between swimming and running is 30:60, or 1:2.
On Wednesday, for every minute of swimming, there will be 2 minutes of running.
The ratio between running and biking is 60:75, or 4:5.
On Tuesday and Thursday, for every 4 minutes of running, there will be 5 minutes of biking.

Partial Credit (1 point) will be given for correct ratios OR the correct explanation of what the ratio means.

No credit will be given for an incorrect answer.</td></tr>
<tr><td>B</td><td>3</td><td>Full Credit:
Sample answer: Tables may include different values for the first four columns, but the final pair of values must match the samples.

<table>
<tr><th colspan="6">Monday and Friday Training</th></tr>
<tr><td>Swim (min)</td><td>2</td><td>4</td><td>10</td><td>20</td><td>30</td></tr>
<tr><td>Bike (min)</td><td>5</td><td>10</td><td>25</td><td>50</td><td>75</td></tr>
</table>

<table>
<tr><th colspan="6">Wednesday Training</th></tr>
<tr><td>Swim (min)</td><td>1</td><td>5</td><td>10</td><td>20</td><td>30</td></tr>
<tr><td>Run (min)</td><td>2</td><td>10</td><td>20</td><td>40</td><td>60</td></tr>
</table>

<table>
<tr><th colspan="6">Tuesday and Thursday Training</th></tr>
<tr><td>Run (min)</td><td>4</td><td>12</td><td>20</td><td>40</td><td>60</td></tr>
<tr><td>Bike (min)</td><td>5</td><td>15</td><td>25</td><td>50</td><td>75</td></tr>
</table>

Partial Credit (1 point) will be given for each correct table.

No credit will be given for an incorrect answer.</td></tr>
</table>

Part	Maximum Points	Scoring Rubric
C	3	Full Credit: Sample graph: Each set of points appears to be in a straight line. The line for Swim/Bike training is the steepest, and the line for Run/Bike training is the flattest. 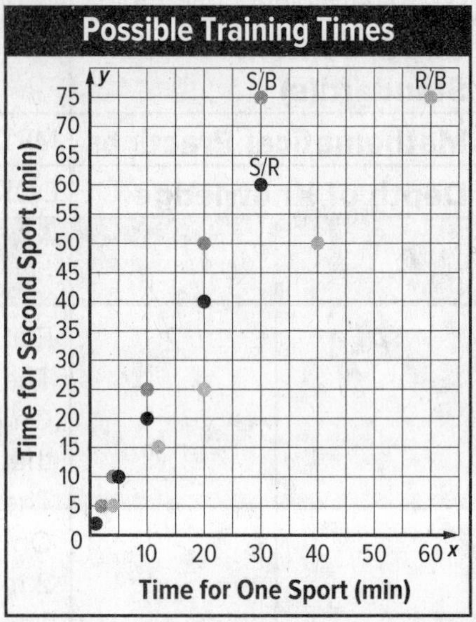 Partial Credit (1 point) will be given for the correct graph of two sets of points OR an accurate comparison of the data. No credit will be given for an incorrect answer. **Possible Training Times** Time for Second Sport (min) vs. Time for One Sport (min); y-axis 0–75, x-axis 10–60; lines labeled S/B, S/R, R/B
D	1	Full Credit: Swim: 1 mile in 30 minutes, or 1 mi ÷ 0.5 h = 2 mph Bike: 25 miles in 75 minutes, or 25 mi ÷ 1.25 h = 20 mph Run: 6 miles in 60 minutes, or 6 mi ÷ 1 h = 6 mph No credit will be given for an incorrect answer.
E	2	Full Credit: Sample answer: First week: Swim: 2 mph for 2 min; $\frac{2 \text{ mi}}{60 \text{ min}} = \frac{? \text{ mi}}{2 \text{ min}}$; $\frac{1}{15}$ mi Bike: 20 mph for 5 min; $\frac{20 \text{ mi}}{60 \text{ min}} = \frac{? \text{ mi}}{5 \text{ min}}$; $1\frac{2}{3}$ mi Run: 6 mph for 4 min; $\frac{6 \text{ mi}}{60 \text{ min}} = \frac{? \text{ mi}}{4 \text{ min}}$; $\frac{2}{5}$ mi Fourth week: Swim: 2 mph for 20 min; $\frac{2 \text{ mi}}{60 \text{ min}} = \frac{? \text{ mi}}{20 \text{ min}}$; $\frac{2}{3}$ mi Bike: 20 mph for 50 min; $\frac{20 \text{ mi}}{60 \text{ min}} = \frac{? \text{ mi}}{50 \text{ min}}$; $16\frac{2}{3}$ mi Run: 6 mph for 40 min; $\frac{6 \text{ mi}}{60 \text{ min}} = \frac{? \text{ mi}}{40 \text{ min}}$; 4 mi Partial Credit (1 point) will be given for the correct distances for one week. No credit will be given for an incorrect answer.
TOTAL	**11**	

Chapter 1 Performance Task

Part A

Monday	Tuesday	Wednesday	Thursday	Friday
30:75	60:75	30:60	60:75	30:75
2:5	4:5	1:2	4:5	2:5
Swim:Bike	Run:Bike	Swim:Run	Run:Bike	Swim:Bike

On Monday, the athletes will swim two minutes for every five minutes they bike.

On Tuesday, the athletes will run four minutes for every five minutes they bike.

On Wednesday, the athletes will swim one minute for every two minutes they run.

On Thursday, the athletes will run four minutes for every five minutes they bike.

On Friday, the athletes will swim two minutes for every five minutes they bike.

Part B

Swimming and Biking (M+F)

Min. Swim	2	4	6	8	30
min Bike	5	10	15	20	75

Swimming and Running (W)

Min. Swim	1	2	3	4	30
Min. Run	2	4	6	8	60

Running and Biking (T+Th)

Min. Run	4	8	12	16	60
min. Bike	5	10	15	20	75

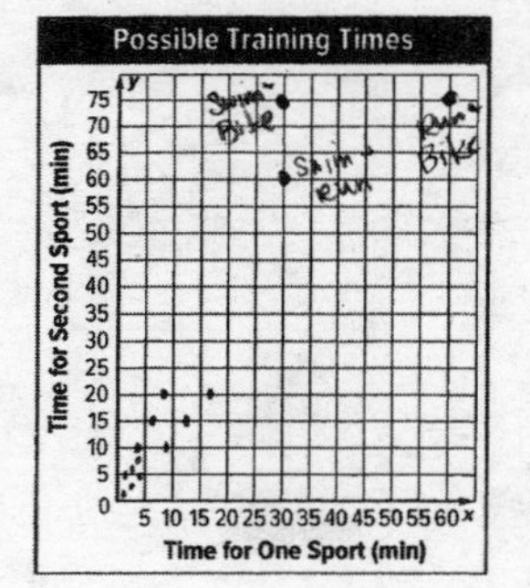

Part C

Even though all the tables are different, the points from each table form a straight line. The steepest line is swimming and biking and the least steep line is running and biking.

Part D

Swim

1 mile in 30 minutes

1 mile in 0.5 hr

$1 \div 0.5 = 2$

2 miles/hour

Run

6 miles in 60 minutes

6 miles in 1 hour

$6 \div 1 = 6$

6 mph

Bike

25 miles in 75 minutes

25 miles in 1.25 hrs

$25 \div 1.25 = 20$

20 mph

Part E

Swim:

1st week - 2 minutes @ 2mph

$\frac{2mi}{60min} = \frac{x}{2min}$

$\frac{60x}{60} = \frac{4}{60}$

$x = \frac{1}{15}mi$

4th week - 8min @ 2mph

$\frac{2mi}{60min} = \frac{x}{8min}$ → $\frac{60x}{60} = \frac{16}{60}$

$x = \frac{4}{15}mi$

Bike:

1st week - 5min @ 20mph

$\frac{20mi}{60min} = \frac{x}{5min}$

$\frac{60x}{60} = \frac{100}{60}$

$x = 1\frac{40}{60} = 1\frac{4}{6}$ miles

Run:

1st week - 4 min @ 6mph

$\frac{60mi}{60min} = \frac{x}{4min}$

$\frac{24}{60} = \frac{60x}{60}$

$\frac{2}{5}mi = x$

4th week

$\frac{6mi}{60min} = \frac{x}{16}$

$\frac{60x}{60} = \frac{96}{60}$

$x = 1\frac{36}{60} = 1\frac{3}{5}mi$

4th week - 20min @ 20mph

$\frac{20mi}{60min} = \frac{x}{20min}$

$\frac{60x}{60} = \frac{400}{60}$

$x = 6\frac{4}{6} = 6\frac{2}{3}mi$

Student Work Sample

Chapter 1 Performance task

Part A

On Monday, the ratio of swimming to biking is 30 to 75 which reduces to 2:5.

On Tuesday, the ratio of running to biking is 60 to 75 which reduces to 4:5.

On Wednesday, the ratio of swimming to running is 30 to 60 which reduces to 1:2.

On Thursday, the ratio of running to biking is 60 to 75, which reduces to 4:5.

On Friday, the ratio of swimming to biking is 30 to 75 which reduces to 2:5

Part B

Mon/Fri Swim/Bike

Swim	2	4	8	16	32
Bike	5	10	20	40	80

Tu/Th Run/Bike

Run	4	8	16	32	64
Bike	5	10	20	40	80

Wed Swim/Run

Swim	1	2	4	8	16
Run	2	4	8	16	32

Part C

Possible Training Times

Time for Second Sport (min)

Time for One Sport (min)

swim/bike

run/bike

swim/run

The lines are long and hit 80. The other line is short.

Part D

Swim

1 mile in 30 minutes

$\frac{1 \text{ mi}}{30 \text{ min}} = \frac{2 \text{ mi}}{60 \text{ min}}$

2 mph

Run

$\frac{6 \text{ mi}}{60 \text{ min}}$

6mph

Bike

$\frac{25 \text{ mi} \times 4}{75 \text{ min} \times 4} = \frac{100 \text{ mi} \div 5}{300 \text{ min} \div 5} = \frac{20 \text{ mi}}{60 \text{ min}}$ 20 mph

Part E

Week 1

Swim

$\frac{1 \text{ mi} \div 15}{30 \text{ min} \div 15} = \frac{?}{2 \text{ min}}$ $\frac{1}{15}$ mi

Bike

$\frac{25 \text{ mi} \div 15}{75 \text{ min} \div 15} = \frac{?}{5 \text{ min}}$ $\frac{25}{15} = 1\frac{2}{3}$ mi

Run

$\frac{6 \text{ mi} \div 15}{60 \text{ min} \div 15} = \frac{?}{4 \text{ min}}$ $\frac{6}{15} = \frac{2}{5}$ mi

Week 4

Swim

$\frac{1 \text{ mi}}{30 \text{ min} \div ?} = \frac{?}{16 \text{ min}}$

Bike

$\frac{25 \text{ mi}}{75 \text{ min} \div ?} = \frac{?}{40 \text{ min}}$

Run

$\frac{6 \text{ mi}}{60 \text{ min}} = \frac{?}{32 \text{ min}}$

Don't know what to divide by

Chapter 1 Performance Task

Part A

Mon	Tues	Wed	Thurs	Fri
Swim:Bike	Run:Bike	Swim:Run	Run:Bike	Swim:Bike
30:75	60:75	30:60	60:75	30:75

Part B

Mon + Fri

Swim	Bike
2	5
4	10
6	15
10	25
30	75

Tu + Thurs

Run	Bike
4	5
8	10
20	25
40	50
60	75

WeD

Swim	Run
1	2
5	10
10	20
15	30
30	60

Part C

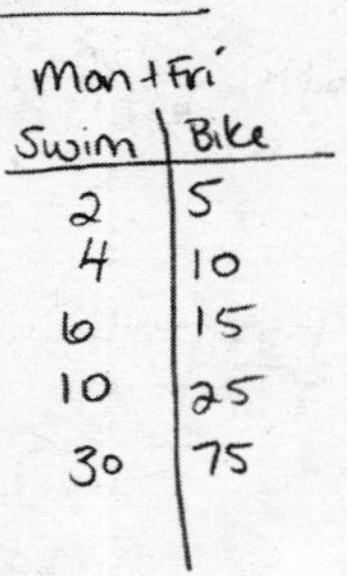

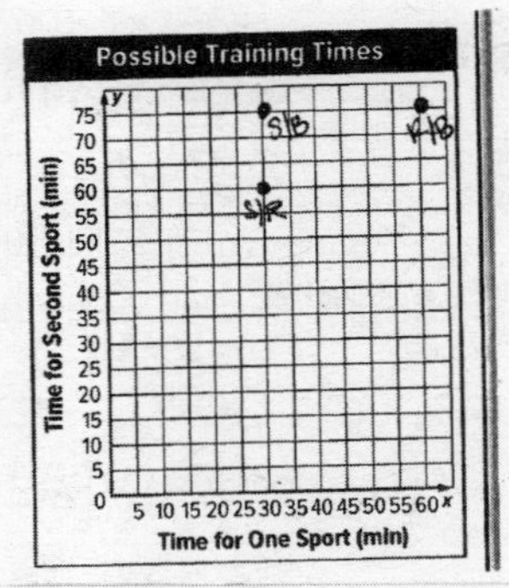

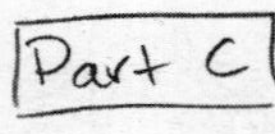

Part D

Swim

$\frac{1 \text{ mi}}{0.5 \text{ hr}} = 2 \text{ mph}$

Run

$\frac{6 \text{ mi}}{1 \text{ hr}} = 6 \text{ mph}$

Bike

$\frac{25 \text{ mi}}{75 \text{ min}} = \frac{25 \text{ mi}}{1.25 \text{ hr}} = 20 \text{ mph}$

Part E

Swim

WK1: 2 min × 2 mph = 4 mi

WK4: 10 min × 2 mph = 20 mi

Run

WK1: 4 × 6 mph = 24 mi

WK4: 40 × 6 mph = 240 mi

Bike

WK1: 5 × 20 = 100 mi

WK4: 50 × 20 = 1000 mi

Student Work-Sample

Chapter 1 Performance Task

PART A

Monday 30:75
Tuesday 60:75
Wednesday 30:60
Thursday 60:75
Friday 30:75

PART B

Mon

Bike	10	15	20	25	30
Swim	55	60	65	70	75

PART C

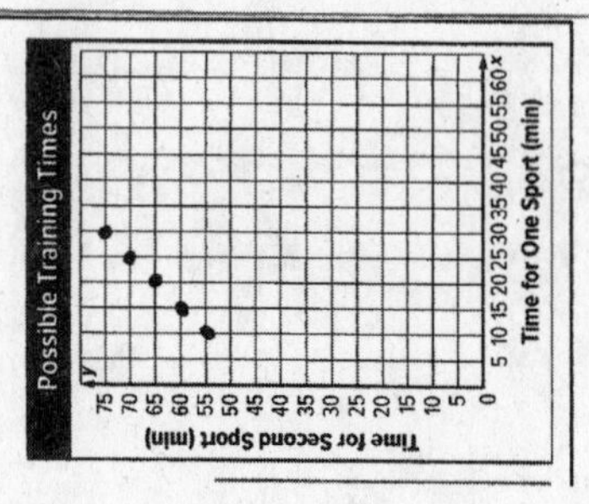

It is a straight line.

PART D

Swim
$30 \div 1 = 30$ mph

Run
$60 \div 6 = 10$ mph

Bike
$75 \div 25 = 3$ mph

PART E

They would go more in week four than in week one.

Page 127 • Home Interior Paint

<table>
<tr><td colspan="3">Task Scenario
Students will determine the percent of different pigment colors given the ratio values, determine ratio values given the percent of pigments, correct ratio values to arrive at the correct percent, determine the percent of an amount given the parts and the whole, determine the amount after a 25% increase, and calculate sales tax.</td></tr>
<tr><td colspan="2">CCSS Content Standard(s)</td><td>6.RP.3, 6.RP.3c</td></tr>
<tr><td colspan="2">Mathematical Practices</td><td>MP1, MP2, MP4, MP5, MP6</td></tr>
<tr><td colspan="2">Depth of Knowledge</td><td>DOK2</td></tr>
<tr><th>Part</th><th>Maximum Points</th><th>Scoring Rubric</th></tr>
<tr><td>A</td><td>2</td><td>Full Credit:
<table>
<tr><th>Paint Color</th><th>Ratio of Red Pigment to Total Amount</th><th>Percent of Red Pigment</th></tr>
<tr><td>Coral Paradise</td><td>8:19</td><td>42%</td></tr>
<tr><td>Sunset Shine</td><td>5:13</td><td>38%</td></tr>
<tr><td>Peach Pie</td><td>6:18</td><td>33%</td></tr>
</table>
Peach Pie has the lowest percentage of red pigment because 33% is less than both 38% and 42%.

Partial Credit (1 point) will be given for the correct percent of red pigment for each paint color OR the correct answer without the percents.

No credit will be given for an incorrect answer.</td></tr>
<tr><td>B</td><td>1</td><td>Full Credit:
Sample answer: The total number of drops is 100%. Divide a bar diagram into sections representing 5% each. Group the sections to show the percentages for each paint color.

0% 100%
<table>
<tr><td>R</td><td>R</td><td>R</td><td>R</td><td>R</td><td>B</td><td>B</td><td>B</td><td>B</td><td>B</td><td>B</td><td>B</td><td>Y</td><td>Y</td><td>Y</td><td>Y</td><td>Y</td><td>Y</td><td>Y</td><td>Y</td></tr>
<tr><td colspan="5">Red, 25%</td><td colspan="7">Blue, 35%</td><td colspan="8">Yellow, 40%</td></tr>
</table>
Each section represents 1 drop of color.
Red: 5 drops; Blue: 7 drops; Yellow: 8 drops

No credit will be given for an incorrect answer.</td></tr>
</table>

<table>
<tr><th>Part</th><th>Maximum Points</th><th>Scoring Rubric</th></tr>
<tr><td>C</td><td>2</td><td>Full Credit:
Sample answer: Because the blue pigment has the correct number of drops, 4 drops = 25% of total drops. Multiplying by 3 shows that 12 drops = 75% of the total drops.
The red pigment already has 8 drops in the paint.
12 – 8 = 4
Ava needs to add 4 red drops to correct her mistake.
Partial Credit (1 point) will be given for the correct total number of red drops OR the correct number of red drops to be added
No credit will be given for an incorrect answer.</td></tr>
<tr><td>D</td><td>2</td><td>Full Credit:
Total amount: 8 + 12 + 12 = 32 ounces
Percent red: $\frac{8}{32} = 0.25 = 25\%$
Percent blue: $\frac{12}{32} = 0.375 = 37.5\%$
Percent yellow: $\frac{12}{32} = 0.375 = 37.5\%$
Partial Credit (1 point) will be given for the correct total amount OR two or more of the correct percentages of the colors.
No credit will be given for an incorrect answer.</td></tr>
<tr><td>E</td><td>2</td><td>Full Credit:
100% + 25% = 125% = 1.25
8 × 1.25 = 10; 12 × 1.25 = 15
<table><tr><th>Pigment Color</th><th>Amount Ordered Last Month</th><th>Amount to Order This Month</th></tr><tr><td>Red</td><td>8 oz</td><td>10 oz</td></tr><tr><td>Blue</td><td>12 oz</td><td>15 oz</td></tr><tr><td>Yellow</td><td>12 oz</td><td>15 oz</td></tr></table>
Total = 10 + 15 + 15 = 40 oz of pigment
Partial Credit (1 point) will be given for correctly completing the table OR finding the total amount.
No credit will be given for an incorrect answer.</td></tr>
<tr><td>F</td><td>1</td><td>Full Credit:
Cost for pigment: $30.50(40) = $1,220
Sales tax on pigment: 0.06(1,220) = $73.20
There is no sales tax on shipping costs.
Ava paid $73.20 in sales tax.
No credit will be given for an incorrect answer.</td></tr>
<tr><td>**TOTAL**</td><td>**10**</td><td></td></tr>
</table>

Chapter 2 Performance Task

Part A

Paint Color	Total Drops	Ratio of Red to Total	Percent of Red
Coral Paradise	8 + 1 + 10 = 19	8:19	42%
Sunset Shine	5 + 1 + 7 = 13	5:13	38%
Peach Pie	6 + 12 = 18	6:18	33%

33% < 38% < 42%

Peach Pie

Part B

The total number of drops is 100%. Each section is 5%.

0% | R | R | R | R | R | B | B | B | B | B | B | B | Y | Y | Y | Y | Y | Y | Y | Y | 100%

Red, 25% — Blue, 35% — Yellow, 40%

Red: 5 drops, Blue: 7 drops, Yellow: 8 drops

Part C

Blue has correct number of drops. 4 drops = 25% of total drops.

0% | 4 | 25% | 4 | 50% | 4 | 75% | 4 | 100%

Blue, 25% — Red, 75%

Red: 75% of the total drops = 12 drops

Red already has 8 drops. 12 − 8 = 4

Ava needs to add 4 red drops.

Part D

Total amount: 8 + 12 + 12 = 32 ounces

Percent red: $\frac{8}{32} = 0.25 = 25\%$

Percent blue: $\frac{12}{32} = 0.375 = 37.5\%$

Percent yellow: $\frac{12}{32} = 0.375 = 37.5\%$

Part E

100% + 25% = 125% = 1.25

8 × 1.25 = 10 12 × 1.25 = 15

Pigment Color	Amount Ordered Last Month	Amount to Order This Month
red	8 oz	10 oz
blue	12 oz	15 oz
yellow	12 oz	15 oz

Total 40 oz

Order 40 oz of pigment this month.

Part F

No sales tax on shipping

Cost for pigment:

$30.50 (40) = $1,220

Sales tax on pigment only:

0.06 (1,220) = $73.20

Ava paid $73.20 in sales tax.

Student Work Sample

Chapter 2 Performance Task

Part A

Coral Paradise $\frac{8}{19} \approx 0.42105 \approx 42\%$ biggest

Sunset Shine $\frac{5}{13} \approx 0.384615 \approx 38\%$

Peach Pie $\frac{6}{18} \approx 0.333333 \approx 33\%$ smallest

Ava should advise Peach Pie as the color.

Part B

0% — Red, 25% | Blue, 35% | Yellow, 40% — 100%

Red = 25 drops
Blue = 35 drops
Yellow = 40 drops

Part C

Blue

4 is 25% of what number?

$25\% = \frac{1}{4}$

$\frac{4}{\text{whole}} = \frac{1}{4} = \frac{1 \times 4}{4 \times 4} = \frac{4}{16}$

16 total drops

Red

16 total
4 blue
− 8 red
4

4 red drops are needed.

Part D

$8 + 12 + 12 = 32$ oz

Red: $\frac{8}{32} = 0.25 = 25\%$

Blue: $\frac{12}{32} = 0.333 \approx 33\%$

Yellow: $\frac{12}{32} = 0.333 \approx 33\%$

Part E

25% of $8 = 0.25 \times 8 = 2$

$8 + 2 = 10$

25% of $12 = 0.25 \times 12 = 3$

$12 + 3 = 15$

Color	Last Month	This Month
red	8 oz	10 oz
blue	12 oz	15 oz
yellow	12 oz	15 oz

Part F

6% tax

$100\% + 6\% = 106\% = 1.06$

$30.50
× 1.06
18300
0000
3050
32.3300

$32.33 with sales tax

Chapter 2 Performance Task

Part A

Drops not red: $1+10+1+7+0+12=31$

Coral Paradise $\frac{8}{31} \approx 25.8\%$

Sunset Shine $\frac{5}{31} \approx 16.1\%$

Peach Pie $\frac{6}{31} \approx 19.4\%$

Sunset Shine is the color.

Part B

0%	10%	20%	25%	40%	50%	60%	70%	80%	90%	100%
2	2	1	1	2	2	2	2	2	2	2

Red, 25% Blue, 35% Yellow, 40%

Red: 5 drops
Blue: 7 drops
Yellow: 8 drops

Part C

Blue: 4 is 25% of what number?

$25\% = 0.25$

$4 \div 0.25 = 16$

16 total drops

16 drops − 4 blue = 12 drops for red

12 red drops − 8 red = 4 drops

Add 4 red drops to the gallon.

Part D

Total = $8+12 = 20$ ounces

$\frac{8}{20} = 0.4 = 40\%$

$\frac{12}{20} = 0.6 = 60\%$

Part E

$8 + 12 + 12 = 32$ ounces this month

25% of $32 = 0.25 \times 32 = 8$

$32 + 8 = 40$

Order 40 oz this month.

Part F

$30.50 (40) = $1,220

$1,220 + $7.99 = $1,227.99

$1,227.99 (0.06) = 73.6794 ≈ $73.68

$73.68 sales tax

Chapter 2 Performance Task

PART A

SS   PP   CP

5 drops < 6 drops < 8 drops

Sunset Shine has the lowest number of drops.

PART B

25% + 35% + 40% = 100%

Red   100 ÷ 25 = 4   4 drops

Blue   100 ÷ 35 = 2.8   3 drops

Yellow   100 ÷ 40 = 2.5   3 drops

PART C

8 red + 4 blue = 12 drops

Red:

75% of 12 drops

$\frac{3}{4} \times 12 = \frac{36}{4} = 9$ red drops

9 − 8 = 1

1 red drop is needed.

PART D

Pigment	Red	Blue	Yellow
Amount Ordered (oz)	8	12	12
Percent	8%	12%	12%

Red: 8%

Blue: 12%

Yellow: 12%

PART E

25% of 8

$\frac{1}{4} \times 8 = 2$

25% of 12

$\frac{1}{4} \times 12 = 3$

Color	Last Month	This Month
red	8 oz	2 oz
Blue	12 oz	3 oz
yellow	12 oz	3 oz

PART F

6% tax = 0.06

\$30.50 (0.06) = \$1.83

1.83 (40) = \$73.20

\$73.20 in sales tax

Page 129 • Welcome to our School Store!

Note to Teacher: Students may perform the operations in a different order and still arrive at the correct answer. Other correct solution methods are acceptable.

Task Scenario Students will add, subtract, multiply, or divide amounts of money involving multi-digit decimals using the standard algorithms to solve problems about costs and profits at a school store.		
CCSS Content Standard(s)	6.NS.2, 6.NS.3	
Mathematical Practices	MP1, MP2, MP6, MP7, MP8	
Depth of Knowledge	DOK2, DOK3	

Part	Maximum Points	Scoring Rubric
A	2	Full Credit: Binder: \$12.92 × 2 = \$25.84 Copy Paper: \$2.99 × 2 = \$5.98 Notebooks: \$2.48 × 3 = \$7.44 Pens: \$0.99 × 5 = \$4.95 \$25.84 + \$5.98 + \$7.44 + \$4.95 = \$44.21 tax: \$44.21 × 0.06 = 2.6526 \$44.21 + \$2.65 = \$46.86 \$60.00 − \$46.86 = \$13.14 change The student should receive \$13.14 change. Partial Credit (1 point) will be given for correct total cost with tax OR correct final answer. No credit will be given for an incorrect answer.
B	2	Full Credit: 1 of each item: \$11 + \$14 + \$32 = \$57 12 of each item: \$57 × 12 = \$684 37)684.000 = 18.486 −37 314 −296 180 −148 320 −296 240 −222 18 The cost per person is \$18.49. Partial Credit (1 point) will be given for correct total cost OR correct final answer. No credit will be given for an incorrect answer.

<table>
<tr><th>Part</th><th>Maximum Points</th><th>Scoring Rubric</th></tr>
<tr><td>C</td><td>3</td><td>Full Credit:
<table>
<tr><td>1 of each</td><td>14 of each</td><td>sales tax</td><td>total cost</td><td>60% owed</td></tr>
<tr><td>$24.59
$ 12.92
$32.00
$1.25
$1.99
+ $2.14
$74.89</td><td>$74.89
× 14
29956
+ 74890
$1,048.46</td><td>$1,048.46
× 0.06
$62.9076</td><td>$1,048.46
+ $62.91
$1,111.37

47.63
14)666.82</td><td>$1,111.37
× 0.6
666.822
total:
$666.82</td></tr>
</table>
Each member owes $47.63.

Partial Credit (2 points) will be given for 2 of 3: correct cost with tax OR correct total owed by all members OR correct final answer. Partial Credit (1 point) is given for 1 of the above.

No credit will be given for an incorrect answer.</td></tr>
<tr><td>D</td><td>2</td><td>Full Credit:
<table>
<tr><td>Portfolio</td><td>Notebk.</td><td>Binder</td><td>Pen</td><td>Pencil</td><td>M. Pad</td></tr>
<tr><td>$24.59
−16.00
$8.59
× 3
$25.77</td><td>$2.48
−2.00
$0.48
× 15
$7.20</td><td>$12.92
−9.00
$3.92
× 12
$47.04</td><td>$0.99
−0.50
$0.49
× 22
$10.78</td><td>$0.99
−0.70
$0.29
× 34
$9.86</td><td>$2.14
−1.75
$0.39
× 11
$4.29</td></tr>
</table>
25.77 + 7.20 + 47.04 + 10.78 + 9.86 + 4.29 = 104.94
The total profit for that week was $104.94.

Partial Credit (1 point) will be given for correct costs for all items OR correct final answer.

No credit will be given for an incorrect answer.</td></tr>
<tr><td>E</td><td>2</td><td>Full Credit:
<table>
<tr><td>Sc. Calc.</td><td>Portfolio</td><td>Notebk.</td><td>M. Pad</td><td>Eras.</td><td>Binder</td></tr>
<tr><td>$175.65
−150.00
$25.65
× 3
$76.95</td><td>$8.59
× 15
$128.85</td><td>$0.48
× 48
$23.04</td><td>$0.39
× 12
$4.68</td><td>$0.59
−0.30
$0.29
× 57
$16.53</td><td>$3.92
× 26
$101.92</td></tr>
</table>
76.95 + 128.85 + 23.04 + 4.68 + 16.53 + 101.92 = 351.97
351.97 ÷ 6 ≈ 58.662; Each program will receive $58.66.

Partial Credit (1 point) will be given for correct costs for all items OR correct final answer.

No credit will be given for an incorrect answer.</td></tr>
<tr><td>TOTAL</td><td>11</td><td></td></tr>
</table>

Chapter 3 Performance Task

Part A

Binders: $12.92 × 2 = $25.84

Copy Paper: $2.99 × 2 = $5.98

Notebooks: $2.48 × 3 = $7.44

Pens: $0.99 × 5 = $4.95

Total cost, pre tax: $25.84 + 5.98 + 7.44 + 4.95 = $44.21

Tax: $44.21 × 0.06 = 2.6526; $2.65 in tax

Total: $44.21 + 2.65 = $46.86

Change: $60.00 − 46.86 = $13.14

Part B

T-shirts: 12 × 11 = 132

Sweatpants: 14 × 12 = 28 + 140 = 168

Sweatshirts: 32 × 12 = 64 + 320 = 384

Total cost: 132 + 168 + 384 = 684

37) 684.000 = 18.486

When split among 37 people, the cost per person is $18.49.

Part C

Portfolio 24.59
Binder 12.92
Sweatshirt 32.00
Music case 1.25
Phone case 1.99
Mouse pad + 2.14
$74.89

74.89 × 14 = 299 56 + 748 90 = $1048.46

$1048.46 × 0.06 = $62.9076 Tax

$1048.46 + 62.91 = $1111.37 Total with tax

Kids pay: $1111.37 × 0.6 = 666.822

Cost per person: 14) 666.82 = $47.63

Part D

Portfolio Profit: 24.59 − 16.00 = $8.59

Notebook Profit: $2.48 − 2.00 = $0.48

Binder Profit: $12.92 − 9.00 = $3.92

Pen Profit: $0.99 − 0.50 = $0.49

Pencil Profit: $0.99 − 0.70 = $0.29

Mouse Pad Profit: $2.14 − 1.75 = $0.39

8.59 × 3 = $25.77

$0.48 × 15 = 240 + 480 = $7.20

$3.92 × 12 = 784 + 3920 = $47.04

$0.49 × 22 = 98 + 980 = $10.78

$0.29 × 34 = 116 + 870 = $9.86

$0.39 × 11 = 39 + 390 = $4.29

25.77 + 7.20 + 47.04 + 10.78 + 9.86 + 4.29 = $104.94 ← Is the total profit for the week

Part E

Scientific Calc: $175.65 − 150.00 = $25.65; $25.65 × 3 = $76.95

Portfolio: $8.59 × 15 = 4295 + 8590 = $128.85

Notebooks: $0.48 × 48 = 384 + 1920 = $23.04

Mouse Pad: $0.39 × 12 = 78 + 390 = $4.68

Erasers: $0.59 − .30 = $0.29

$0.29 × 57 = 203 + 1450 = 16.53

Binder: $3.92 × 26 = 2352 + 7840 = $101.92

Total Profit: $76.95 + 128.85 + 23.04 + 4.68 + 16.53 + 101.92 = $351.97

6) 351.970 = 58.661

Each group gets $58.66.

Student Work Sample

Chapter 3 Performance Task

Part A

12.92 × 2 = 25.82

25.84 + 5.98 + 7.44 + 4.95 = 44.21

44.21 × 1.06: 26526; 442100; $46.8626

Part B

11 + 14 + 32 = $57

57 × 12: 114; 570; $684

Part C

24.59 + 12.92 + 32.00 + 1.25 + 1.99 + 2.14 = $74.89

74.89 × 1.06: 44934; 748900; 79.3834

$79.38 × .6 = $47.628 → $47.63

Part D

PP: 8.59 × 3 = $25.77

NP: 0.48 × 15 = $7.20

BP: 3.92 × 12 = $47.04 → 7.84 + 39.20 = 47.04

PenP: 0.49 × 22 = $10.78

Pencil P: 0.29 × 34 = $9.86

MP: 0.39 × 11 = $4.29

$104.94

0.29 × 34: 116; 870; 986

Part E

CP: 25.65 × 3 = $76.95

PP: 8.59 × 15 = 128.85

NP: 0.48 × 48 = 23.04

MP: 0.39 × 12 = 4.68

EP: 0.29 × 57 = 16.53

BP: 3.92 × 26 = 101.92

$351.97

25.65 × 3 = 76.95

8.59 × 15: 4295; 8590; 128.85

0.48 × 48: 384; 1920; 23.04

392 × 26: 2352; 7840; 101.92

0.29 × 57: 203; 1450; 1653

0.39 × 12: 78; 390; 468

Chapter 3 Performance Task

Part A

$100.00 − 44.21 = $15.79

12.92 + 2.99 = 15.91
15.91 × 2 = 31.82

2.48 × 3 = 7.44

4.95

31.82 + 7.44 + 4.95 = 44.21

Part B

11 + 14 + 32 = $57

57 × 12: 114, 570, $684

Part C

24.59
12.92
32.00
1.25
1.99
+ 2.14
74.89

74.89 × .4 = 29.956

The discount is $29.96.

Part D

16 × 3 = 48
15 × 2 = 30
12 × 9 = 108
22 × .5 = 11
34 × .7 = 23.8
1.75 × 11: 175, 1750, 19.25

48
30
108
11
23.80
+ 19.25
$240.05

Part E

150 × 3 = 450
15 × 16: 90, 150, 240
48 × 2 = 96
1.75 × 12: 350, 1750, 21.00
57 × .3 = 17.1
26 × 9 = 234

450
240
96
21
17.10
234
1058.10

6) 1058.10 = $176.35
6
45
42
38
36
21
18
30

Chapter 3 Performance Task

PART A

```
  12.92
   2.99
   2.48
 + 0.99
 ------
  19.38
```

```
  $ 20.00
  - 19.38
  -------
  $ 00.62
```

PART B

```
  12
  12
  12
  --
  36 items
```

37 − 36 = 1

Everyone will get one item and there will be one leftover.

PART C

```
  24.59
  12.92
  32.00
   1.25
   1.99
 + 2.14
 ------
  74.89
```

```
  74.89
  − .40
  -----
 $ 74.49
```

PART D

```
   16
    2
    9
   .50
   .70
  1.75
  ----
 $ 3.22
```

PART E

```
    3
   15
   48
   12
   57
 + 26
 ----
  161
```

```
     26.5
  6 ) 161
      12
      --
      41
      36
      --
       5
```

Page 131 • Treasure Box

Note to Teacher: Students may perform different operations or conversions and still arrive at the correct answer. Other correct solution methods are acceptable.

Task Scenario	
Students will use diagrams and multiply and divide fractions and mixed numbers to determine the quantities of wood that Mr. Penny needs for his students to build treasure boxes and to find the cost of ribbons.	
CCSS Content Standard(s)	6.NS.1, 6.RP.3, 6.RP.3d
Mathematical Practices	MP1, MP2, MP3, MP4, MP5, MP6, MP7
Depth of Knowledge	DOK2

Part	Maximum Points	Scoring Rubric
A	2	Full Credit: First convert measurements to feet or inches. Sample answer: $9\frac{5}{8} \times 12 = \frac{77}{\cancel{8}_{2}} \times \frac{\cancel{12}^{3}}{1} = \frac{231}{2} = 115\frac{1}{2}$ in. $\frac{9}{16} \times 12 = \frac{9}{\cancel{16}_{4}} \times \frac{\cancel{12}^{3}}{1} = \frac{27}{4} = 6\frac{3}{4}$ in. The plank width is the same as the width of the pieces needed. So divide: $115\frac{1}{2} \div 8\frac{1}{4} = \frac{231}{2} \div \frac{33}{4} = \frac{231}{2} \times \frac{4}{33} = \frac{924}{66} = 14$. Mr. Penny can cut 14 rectangular pieces from the plank. Partial Credit (1 point) will be given for correct conversions OR the correct number of pieces. No credit will be given for an incorrect answer.
B	2	Full Credit: First convert measurements to feet or inches. Sample answer: $4\frac{1}{8} \times 12 = \frac{33}{\cancel{8}_{2}} \times \frac{\cancel{12}^{3}}{1} = \frac{99}{2} = 49\frac{1}{2}$ in. Both the plank and the pieces needed are squares. So divide: $49\frac{1}{2} \div 8\frac{1}{4} = \frac{99}{2} \div \frac{33}{4} = \frac{\cancel{99}^{3}}{\cancel{2}_{1}} \times \frac{\cancel{4}^{2}}{\cancel{33}_{1}} = 6$ Mr. Penny can cut the plank into 6 strips and then each strip into 6 of the desired pieces for the treasure box. Mr. Penny can cut 36 square pieces from the wooden plank. $8\frac{1}{4}$ in. $49\frac{1}{2}$ in. Partial Credit (1 point) will be given for the correct conversion OR a diagram and the correct number of pieces. No credit will be given for an incorrect answer.

Part	Maximum Points	Scoring Rubric
C	1	Full Credit: Each plank makes 14 rectangular sides (from Part A). Each box needs 4 pieces. For 18 students: 18 × 4 = 72 pieces needed; 72 ÷ 14 ≈ 5.14 planks. Mr. Penny will need 6 wooden planks. No credit will be given for an incorrect answer.
D	1	Full Credit: Each plank makes 36 square bases (from Part B). Each box needs 2 pieces. For 18 students: 18 × 2 = 36 pieces needed; 36 ÷ 36 = 1 plank. Mr. Penny will need 1 wooden plank. No credit will be given for an incorrect answer.
E	2	Full Credit: Model $2\frac{1}{4}$. Divide the bars into eighths. Count the $\frac{3}{8}$ sections. 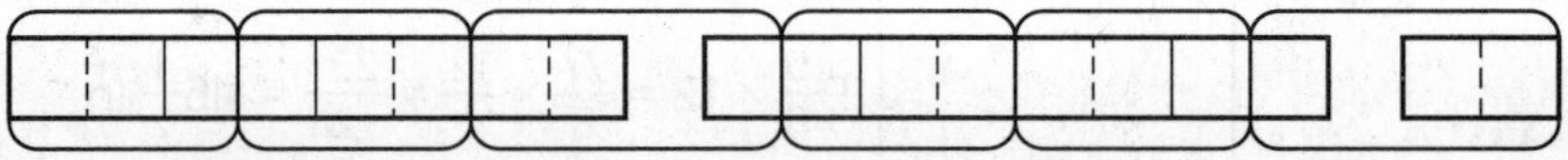 There are 6 groups. Mr. Penny can cut 6 pieces of ribbon from one long ribbon. Partial Credit (1 point) will be given for correct model OR the correct number of pieces. No credit will be given for an incorrect answer.
F	1	Full Credit: Each box will have 3 pieces of ribbon. Each long ribbon makes 6 pieces (from Part E). For 18 students: 18 × 3 = 54 pieces needed; 54 ÷ 6 = 9 long ribbons. Mr. Penny needs 9 long ribbons. No credit will be given for an incorrect answer.
G	2	Full Credit: Convert the long ribbon to inches. $2\frac{1}{4} \times 12 = \frac{9}{4} \times \frac{12}{1} = \frac{9}{1} \times \frac{3}{1} =$ 27 in. Mr. Penny needs 9 ribbons: 9 × 27 = 243 inches needed. Divide to find the number of $\frac{1}{4}$ inch pieces. Multiply to find the cost. $243 \div \frac{1}{4} = \frac{243}{1} \times \frac{4}{1} = 972$ pieces; $\frac{972}{1} \times \frac{1}{10} = 97\frac{2}{10} = 97.2$ The total cost of the ribbon is $97.20. Partial Credit (1 point) the total number of inches of ribbon needed OR the correct total cost. No credit will be given for an incorrect answer.
TOTAL	**11**	

Chapter 4 Performance Task

Part A

$9\frac{5}{8}$ ft, $\frac{9}{16}$ ft; $8\frac{1}{4}$ in, $6\frac{3}{4}$ in

$9 \times 12 = 108$ in.

$\frac{5}{8} \times \frac{12}{1} = \frac{15}{2} = 7\frac{1}{2}$ in

$108 + 7\frac{1}{2} = 115\frac{1}{2}$ in

$\frac{9}{16} \times \frac{12}{1} = \frac{27}{4} = 6\frac{3}{4}$ in ← same width

$115\frac{1}{2} \div 8\frac{1}{4} = \frac{231}{2} \div \frac{33}{4} = \frac{231}{2} \times \frac{4}{33} = \frac{14}{1} = 14$

Mr. Penny can cut 14 boards from the wooden plank.

Part B

$4\frac{1}{8}$ ft $\times 12 = 49\frac{1}{2}$ in

$\frac{1}{8} \times \frac{12}{1} = \frac{3}{2} = 1\frac{1}{2}$

$49\frac{1}{2} \div 8\frac{1}{4}$

$\frac{99}{2} \div \frac{33}{4} = \frac{99}{2} \times \frac{4}{33} = \frac{18}{3} = 6$

$8\frac{1}{4}$, $8\frac{1}{4}$; $4\frac{1}{8}$ ft, $4\frac{1}{8}$ ft

Mr. Penny can cut 36 total pieces.

Part C

18 students
4 sides each
$18 \times 4 = 72$ pieces

From each $9\frac{5}{8}$ ft $\times \frac{9}{16}$ ft board he gets 14 pieces.

So $72 \div 14$ is a little over 5, so he will need 6 planks.

$72.0 \div 14 = 5.1$ (70, 2.0)

Part D

Each student need 2 pieces measuring $8\frac{1}{4}" \times 8\frac{1}{4}"$.

So $18 \times 2 = 36$.

Each $4\frac{1}{8}$ ft $\times 4\frac{1}{8}'$ board gives 36 pieces, so Mr. Penny will only need 1 board.

Part E

1 ft, 1 ft, $\frac{1}{4}$ ft; 1, 2, 3, 4, 5, 6

Mr. Penny can get six pieces of ribbon from the one longer ribbon.

Part F

18 students
3 pieces each
$18 \times 3 = 54$ pieces
$54 \div 6 = 9$

Mr. Penny needs 9 lengths of ribbon $2\frac{1}{4}$ ft long.

Part G

$\frac{1}{10}$ of a dollar $= \$0.10$

\$0.10 per $\frac{1}{4}$ inch
\$0.40 for 1 inch

$2\frac{1}{4}$ ft $\times 9 = \frac{9}{4} \times \frac{9}{1} = \frac{81}{4}$

$\frac{81}{4} \times \frac{12}{1} = 243$ inches

$243 \times 4 = 972$

$243 \times \frac{40}{100} = \frac{972}{10} = 97.2 = \$97.20$

It will cost \$97.20.

Chapter 4 Performance Task

Part A

$8\frac{1}{4} \div 12 = \frac{33}{4} \div \frac{12}{1} = \frac{\cancel{33}^{11}}{4} \times \frac{1}{\cancel{12}_4} = \frac{11}{16}$ ft

$6\frac{3}{4} \div 12 = \frac{\cancel{27}^{9}}{4} \times \frac{1}{\cancel{12}_4} = \frac{9}{16}$ ft ← same width

$9\frac{5}{8} \div \frac{11}{16} = \frac{77}{8} \div \frac{11}{6} = \frac{\cancel{77}^{7}}{\cancel{8}_1} \times \frac{\cancel{16}^{2}}{\cancel{11}_1} = 14$ pieces

Part B

$8\frac{1}{4}$ inches $= \frac{11}{16}$ ft

$4\frac{1}{8}$ ft $\div \frac{11}{16}$ ft $= \frac{\cancel{33}^{3}}{\cancel{8}_1} \times \frac{\cancel{16}^{2}}{\cancel{11}_1} = 6$ pieces

Part C

kids, each

$18 \times 4 = 72$

$14\overline{)72}$ = 5 R2 ($72 - 70 = 2$)

5 planks

Part D

kids, each

$18 \times 2 = 36$

$36 \div 6 = 6$ boards

Part E

$2\frac{1}{4} \div \frac{3}{8} = \frac{9}{4} \div \frac{3}{8} = \frac{\cancel{9}^{3}}{\cancel{4}_1} \times \frac{\cancel{8}^{2}}{\cancel{3}_1} = 6$ pieces

Part F

kids, each

$18 \times 3 = 54$

$54 \div 6 = 9$ ribbons

Part G

$9 \div \frac{1}{4} = \frac{9}{1} \times \frac{4}{1} = 36$

$\frac{36}{1} \times \frac{1}{10} = \frac{36}{10} = 3\frac{6}{10} = \$3.60$

Chapter 4 Perfomance Task

Part A

$9\frac{5}{8} \times 12 = \frac{77}{\cancel{8}_2} \times \frac{\cancel{12}^3}{1} = \frac{231}{2} = 115\frac{1}{2}$ in

$\frac{9}{16} \times 12 = \frac{9}{\cancel{16}_4} \times \frac{\cancel{12}^3}{1} = \frac{27}{4} = 6\frac{3}{4}$ in

$115 \div 8 = 14 R 3$

About 14.

$$\begin{array}{r} 14\ R3 \\ 8\overline{)115} \\ 8\downarrow \\ \hline 35 \\ -32 \\ \hline 3 \end{array}$$

Part B

$4\frac{1}{8} \times 12 = \frac{33}{\cancel{8}_2} \times \frac{\cancel{12}^3}{1} = \frac{99}{2} = 49\frac{1}{2}$

$49\frac{1}{2} \div 8\frac{1}{4} = \frac{99}{2} \div \frac{33}{4} = \frac{\cancel{99}^3}{\cancel{2}_1} \times \frac{\cancel{4}^2}{\cancel{33}_1} = 6$

$6 \times 6 = 36$ pieces

Part C

$5\frac{2}{14} = 5\frac{1}{7}$ boards

$$\begin{array}{r} 5\ \frac{2}{14} \\ 14\overline{)72} \\ -70 \\ \hline 2 \end{array}$$

Part D

$72 \div 36 = 2$ boards

Part E

$2\frac{1}{4}$ ft

$\leftarrow \frac{3}{8} \rightarrow$

$2\frac{1}{4} \div \frac{3}{8} = \frac{9}{4} \div \frac{3}{8} = \frac{\cancel{9}^3}{\cancel{4}_1} \times \frac{\cancel{8}^2}{\cancel{3}_1} = 6$

Part F

$18 \div 6 = 3$ pieces

Part G

$2\frac{1}{4} \times 3 = \frac{9}{4} \times \frac{3}{1} = \frac{27}{4}$

$\frac{27}{4} \div \frac{1}{4} = \frac{27}{\cancel{4}_1} \times \frac{\cancel{4}^1}{1} = 27$

$27 \times \frac{1}{10} = \frac{27}{10} = 2\frac{7}{10} = \$2.70$

Student Work Sample

Chapter 4 Performance Task

Part A

$9\frac{5}{8} \div 8\frac{1}{4} = \frac{77}{8} \div \frac{33}{4} = \frac{\overset{7}{77}}{\underset{2}{8}} \times \frac{\overset{3}{33}}{\underset{1}{4}} = \frac{21}{2} = 10\frac{1}{2}$

$\begin{array}{r} 77 \\ \times 33 \\ \hline 231 \\ 2310 \\ \hline 2541 \end{array}$

$6\frac{3}{4} \div \frac{9}{16} = \frac{27}{4} \div \frac{9}{16} = \frac{\overset{3}{27}}{\underset{1}{4}} \times \frac{\overset{1}{9}}{\underset{4}{16}} = \frac{3}{4}$

$10\frac{1}{2} + \frac{3}{4} = 10\frac{4}{6}$

Part B

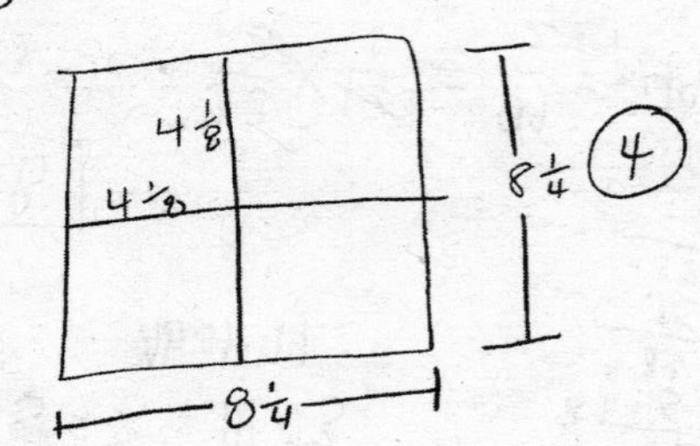

Part C

(2)

18 kids = 18 pieces

Part D

$18 \div 4 = 4.2$

Part E

$3 \times 2\frac{1}{4} = 6\frac{3}{4}$

Part F

(18)

Part G

$\frac{1}{10} \times \frac{1}{4} = \frac{1}{40}$

Page 133 • Adventure Party

Task Scenario Students will use rational numbers, number lines, and coordinate planes to describe the locations of the participants and distances traveled during an adventure party.	
CCSS Content Standard(s)	6.NS.5, 6.NS.6, 6.NS.6a, 6.NS.6b, 6.NS.6c, 6.NS.7, 6.NS.7a, 6.NS.7b, 6.NS.8
Mathematical Practices	MP1, MP2, MP4, MP6, MP7
Depth of Knowledge	DOK2, DOK3

Part	Maximum Points	Scoring Rubric
A	3	Full Credit: Students should plot and label the points on a vertical number line, as shown. Point 0 represents ground level. Sample answer: Positive numbers are above the ground, and negative numbers are below the ground, so 0 represents ground level. Partial Credit (2 points) will be given for 2 correct of these answers: the correct graph OR accurate description of what 0 represents OR appropriate explanation. Partial Credit (1 point) will be given for one correct answer of the three listed above. No credit will be given for an incorrect answer. 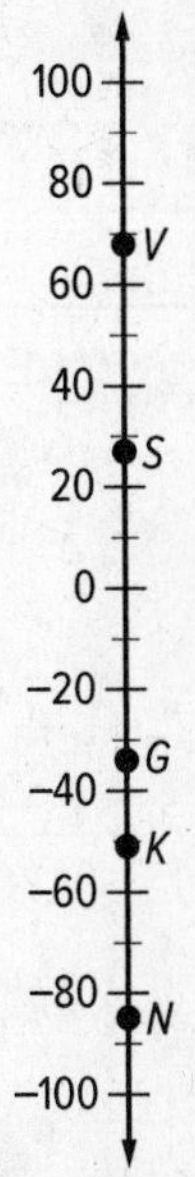
B	1	Full Credit: Nannette will be at ground level, or 0, because +85 is the opposite of –85. Sheila will be at 54 feet because 27 + 27 = 54. Grace will be at 51 feet because 51 is the same distance from 0 as –51, Kendra's position, but in the opposite direction. No credit will be given for an incorrect answer.
C	2	Full Credit: A negative sign means that the person's rate was slower than the day's record. A positive sign means that the person's rate was faster than the record. Slowest to fastest: $-2.5, -1\frac{3}{4}, -1\frac{2}{5}, -0.8, 1.25$ Partial Credit (1 point) will be given for the correct interpretation of the signs OR for the correct order. No credit will be given for an incorrect answer.

Part	Maximum Points	Scoring Rubric
D	3	Full Credit: The points are $A(-7, 3)$ in quadrant II, $B(-2, -3)$ in quadrant III, $C(5, 8)$ in quadrant I, and $G(5, -8)$ in quadrant IV. Sample answer: Point *C* is 5 blocks from the *y*-axis and 8 blocks above the *x*-axis. So its reflection, point *G*, will also be 5 blocks from the *y*-axis, but it will be 8 blocks below the *x*-axis. Partial Credit (2 points) will be given for 2 correct of these answers: the ordered pairs for *A*, *B*, and *C* OR the quadrants for *A*, *B*, and *C* OR the location (ordered pair and quadrant) of *G* with explanation. Partial Credit (1 point) will be given for one correct answer of the three listed above. No credit will be given for an incorrect answer.
E	3	Full Credit: Students plot *D*, *E*, and *F* correctly. Area: 56 square blocks Sample answer: The path forms a right triangle with base $\|-6\| + \|2\| = 8$ blocks and height $\|5\| + \|-9\| = 14$ blocks. The area is $A = \frac{1}{2}(8)(14) = 56$. 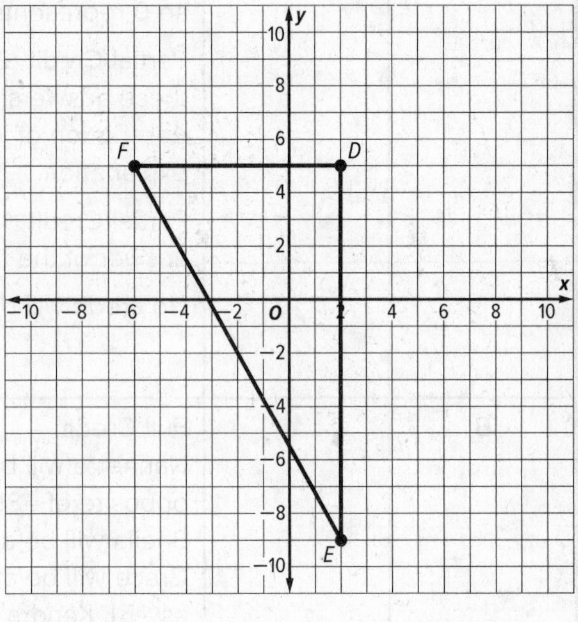 Partial Credit (1 point) will be given for the correct plotted points OR the correct area without explanation OR an appropriate explanation using absolute value. No credit will be given for an incorrect answer.
F	1	Full Credit: $\frac{5}{9}$ of the pizza was consumed. There are 9 equal parts, and there are 5 pieces that are not shaded. $0.\overline{5}$ of the pizza was eaten; Divide 5 by 9 to find the decimal. No credit will be given for an incorrect answer.
TOTAL	**13**	

Chapter 5 Performance Task

Part A

V 80, 60, 40, S 20, 0, -20, G -40, K -60, -80, N

zero represents ground level because positive numbers are above ground and negative numbers are below.

Part B

If Nannette moves up 85 feet, she would be at ground level. $-85+85=0$

If Shelia moves up 27 feet, she would be at 54 feet. $27+27=54$

If Grace moves opposite to Kendra's location, she would be at 51 feet because the opposite of -51 is 51.

Part C

A negative sign means the person was slower than the record of 11 ft/s.

A positive sign means the person was faster.

$-2.5, -1\frac{3}{4}, -1\frac{2}{5}, -0.8, 1.25$

#4	#1	#3	#5	#2
-0.8	-2.5	$-1\frac{2}{5}=-1.4$	1.25	$-1\frac{3}{4}=-1.75$
V	G	S	N	K

Part D

A: (-7,3) II B(-2,-3) III C(5,8) I G(5,-8) IV

I knew point G had to have the same x value but the opposite y value of C.

Part E

From D to E, the group traveled 14 blocks because $5+|-9|=14$.

From F to D, the group traveled 8 blocks because $|-6|+2=8$.

Then, because the points form a right triangle, I can use the area formula.

$A=\frac{1}{2}b\cdot h$

$A=\frac{1}{2}(8)(14)$

$A=56$ square blocks

Part F

There is $\frac{4}{9}$ of the pizza left, so the girls ate $\frac{5}{9}$ which is approximately $0.\overline{5}$. I know because

$\frac{9}{9}-\frac{4}{9}=\frac{5}{9}$ and $5\div9-0.555\ldots$

Student Work Sample

Chapter 5 Performance Task

Part A

Ground level b/c that is where the #'s change from + to −

Nannette, 80, Valentina, 60, 40, Shelia, 20, 0, −20, Grace, −40, Kendra, −60, −80

Part B

Nannette @ 190 ft b/c 85+85=190.

Shelia @ 54 b/c 27+27= 54.

Grace @ 51 b/c she moved up 85 feet to be at 51.

Part C

− means slower than 11 ft/sec

\+ means faster

−2.5, −1.75, −1.4, −0.8, 1.25

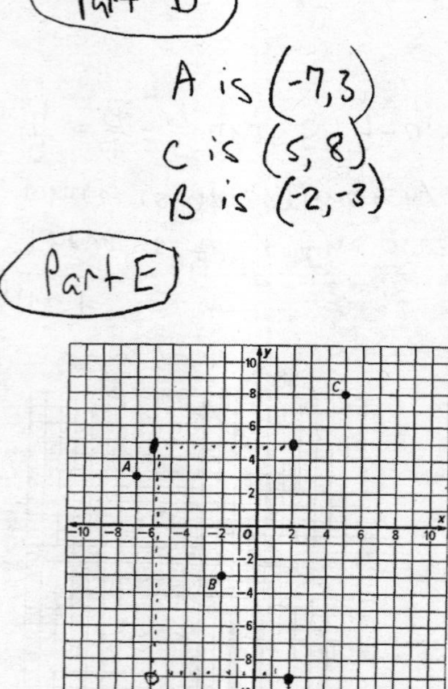

Part D

A is (−7,3)

C is (5, 8)

B is (−2,−3)

Part E

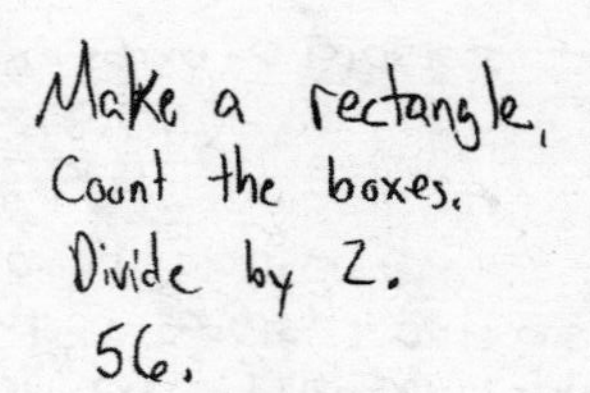

Make a rectangle.

Count the boxes.

Divide by 2.

56.

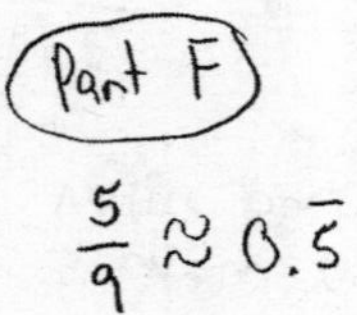

Part F

$\frac{5}{9} \approx 0.\overline{5}$

Chapter 5 Performance Task

Part A

N K G The Ground! S V

-90 -80 -70 -60 -50 -40 -30 -20 -10 0 10 20 30 40 50 60 70 80

Part B

N = D feet
-85 + 85 = D

S = 54 ft
27 + 27 = 54

G = 51 ft
that's the opposite of Kendra
-(-51) = 51

Part C

If the difference is recorded person, negative means faster (ex. 11-12=-1) and positive means slower (ex 11-8=3)

-2.5, -1 3/4, -1 2/5, -0.8, 1.25 is the order of the numbers.

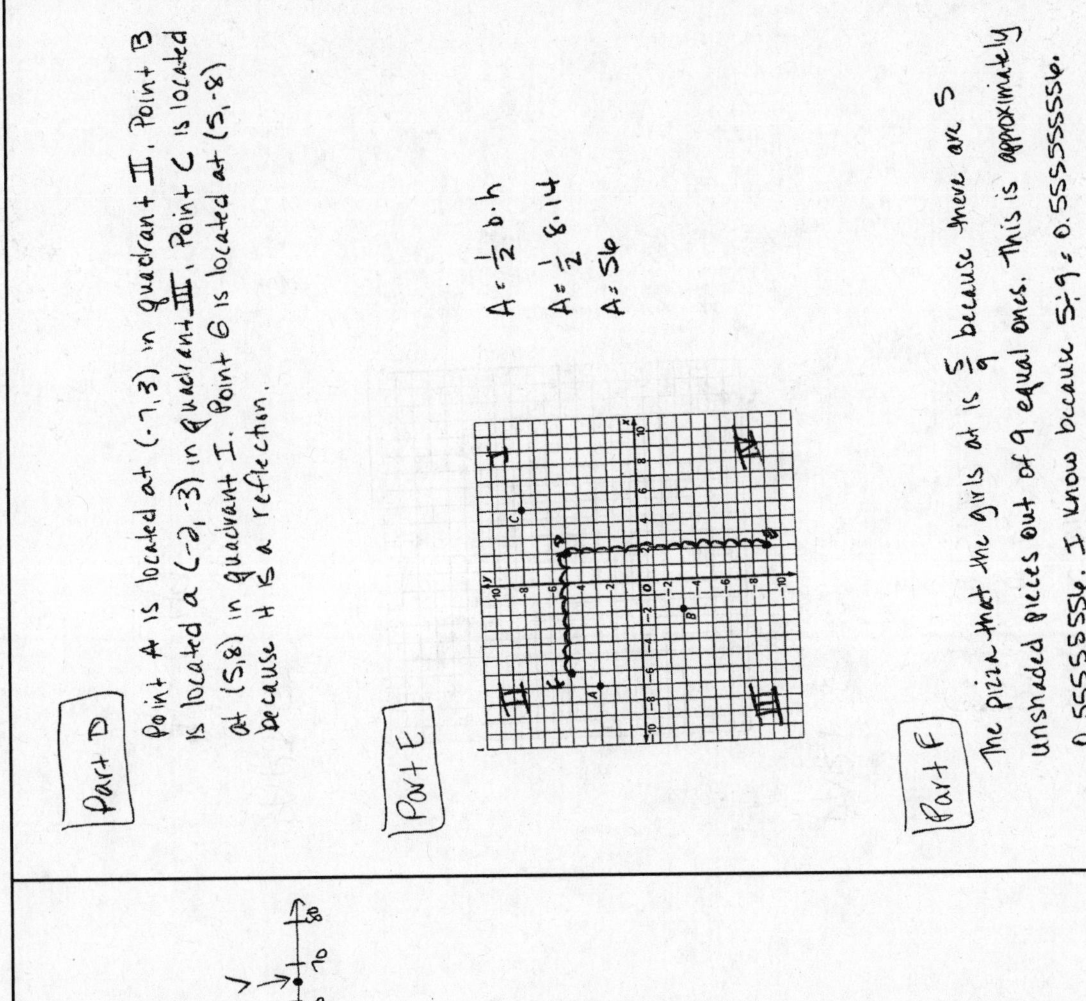

Part D
Point A is located at (-7,3) in quadrant II. Point B is located a (-2,-3) in quadrant III. Point C is located at (5,8) in quadrant I. Point G is located at (5,-8) because H is a reflection.
Part E
II I III IV
A = 1/2 b·h
A = 1/2 8·14
A = 56
Part F
The pizza that the girls at is 5/9 because there are 5 unshaded pieces out of 9 equal ones. This is approximately 0.5555556. I know because 5÷9 = 0.55555556.

Student Work Sample

Chapter 5 Performance Task

PART A

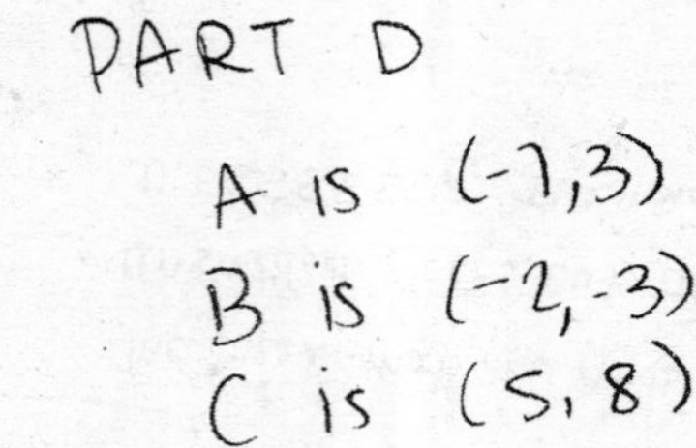

PART B

Nannette is 85 further up.
Shelia is 27 ft further up.
Grace is opposite Kendra.

PART C

−0.8 −2.5 − 1.25 1.25 − 1.34

−2.5, −1.34, −1.25, −0.8, 1.25

PART D

A is (−7,3)
B is (−2,−3)
C is (5,8)

PART E

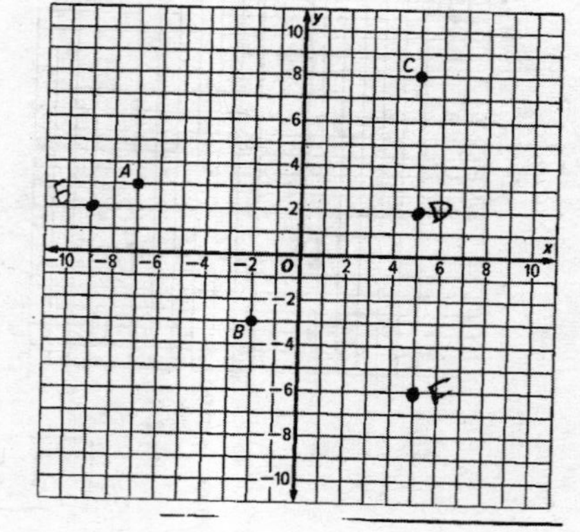

PART F

$\frac{4}{9} = 0.49$

Page 135 • Movie Night

Task Scenario		
Students will write, simplify, and evaluate numerical and algebraic expressions to calculate ticket sales and concession costs at a movie night fundraiser.		
CCSS Content Standard(s)	6.NS.3, 6.EE.1, 6.EE.2, 6.EE.2a, 6.EE.2c, 6.EE.3, 6.EE.4, 6.EE.6	
Mathematical Practices	MP1, MP2, MP3, MP4, MP6, MP7	
Depth of Knowledge	DOK2, DOK3	

Part	Maximum Points	Scoring Rubric
A	2	Full Credit: Total ticket sales: 4(132) + 6.5*a*, which simplifies to 528 + 6.5*a* No, Paige is not correct. Substitute 76 for *a* in the expression. 528 + 6.5*a* = 528 + 6.5(76) = 528 + 494 = 1,022. Ticket sales are \$1,022, not \$3,926. Partial Credit (1 point) will be given for the correct algebraic expression OR an appropriate response and the correct amount of ticket sales. No credit will be given for an incorrect answer.
B	2	Full Credit: The expressions for volume are (18)(18)*h* and $(18^2)h$. The height of the stand is 36 inches. Sample answer: I found the height using guess, check, and revise. I simplified $(18^2)h$ to be 324*h*. I substituted different values for *h* into the expression 324*h*. I stopped when the product equaled 11,664. That was when *h* = 36. Partial Credit (1 point) will be given for both correct expressions OR the correct height with an appropriate strategy explained. No credit will be given for an incorrect answer.
C	1	Full Credit: The expression for volume is $2(18^3)$. Sample answer: The length and width of the stand are 18 in. The height is 36, which is 2 × 18. So, the stand's volume can be divided into the volume of 2 cubes with side lengths of 18 in. The volume of each cube is 18^3, and the volume of the two cubes is $2(18^3)$. No credit will be given for an incorrect answer.

Part	Maximum Points	Scoring Rubric
D	3	Full Credit: Paulo's expression: $2(0.75) + 1(0.50) + 4(1.25)$ Paulo spent $2(0.75) + 1(0.50) + 4(1.25) = 1.5 + 0.50 + 5.00 = \$7$. The bills will be the same. Sample answer: Laurie orders the same number of the same items as Paulo, but in a different order. The Commutative Property of Addition states that the order of addends does not change the sum. In this case, each addend is a product. So changing the order does not change the total cost. $2(0.75) + 1(0.50) + 4(1.25) = 1(0.50) + 4(1.25) + 2(0.75)$ Partial Credit (1 point) will be given for each of 3 answers: Paulo's expression and cost OR the correct answer for the comparison OR an appropriate explanation using properties for the costs being the same. No credit will be given for an incorrect answer.
E	2	Full Credit: They are both correct. Sample answer: The expressions are equivalent. Michael's expression results from applying the Distributive Property to Laurie's expression. Laurie: $2(x + 0.60 + 0.40 + 0.35) = 2(x + 1.35) = 2x + 2.7$ Michael: $2x + 2(0.60) + 2(0.40) + 2(0.35) = 2x + 1.2 + 0.8 + 0.7 = 2x + 2.7$ Partial Credit (1 point) will be given for the correct answer and correct reason, OR the expressions simplified correctly. No credit will be given for an incorrect answer.
TOTAL	**10**	

Chapter 6 Performance Task

Part A

An algabraic expression could be $6.5a + 4(132)$ which simplifies to $6.5a + 528$. If 76 adults attend, the cost would be $6.5(76) + 528 =$ \$1022. I do not agree with Paige's calculation because when you put in 76 for a, you get \$1022 to be the total.

Part B

Using the formula $V = l \cdot w \cdot h$, an expression for the volume would be $18 \cdot 18 \cdot h$. Using exponents, it would be 18^2h. If the volume is 11,664 in^3, the height can be found by dividing 11664 by 18^2. The height is 36 in. ($11{,}664 \div 324 = 36$).

Part C

The volume of one cube would be $18 \cdot 18 \cdot 18$, or 18^3. If there are two cubes of side length 18, the expression for the volume of the stand is

$2(18^3)$.

$18 + 18 = 36$ so the height of the stand is correct.

Part D

The expression for what Pablo ordered is $2(0.75) + 0.5 + 4(1.25)$. His total is $1.50 + 0.5 + 5 = \$7$. Laurie orders the same things, just in a different order, so their bills will be the same. The Commutative Property allows you to switch the order and still get the same total.

Part E

Michael and Laurie are both right. Michael multiplied each item by 2 and then added them together while Laurie added each piece and then multiplied by 2.

Michael's expression simplified is

$2x + 1.2 + 0.8 + 0.70$

$2x + 2.7$.

Laurie's expression simplified is

$2(x + 1.35)$

$(x + 1.35)$

$+ (x + 1.35)$

$2x + 2.7$.

They are the same.

Chapter 6 Performance Task

Part A

$4(132) + 6.50a$

$528 + 6.50a$

$528 + 6.50(76) = \$1022.$

Paige was wrong

Part B

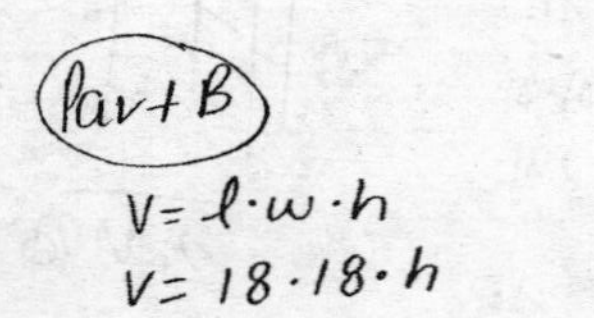

$V = l \cdot w \cdot h$

$V = 18 \cdot 18 \cdot h$

$V = 18^2 h$

l·wxh	Volume
324x10	3,240
324x50	16,2000
324x40	12,960
324x35	11,340
324x36	11,664

Height is 36.

Guess and Check.

Part C

$18^2 \times 36$ I used an exponet to find the volume of the stand (h=36 from above).

Part D

Paolo	Laurie
$2(.75)+1(.5)+4(1.25)$	$1(.5)+4(1.25)+2(.75)$
$1.50 + .5 + 5$	$.5 + 5 + 1.5$
7	7

The same amount.

It is the associative property because I grouped 1.5+.5 for Paolo and then added 5, but for Laurie .5+5 and then 1.5.

Part E

Michael	Laurie
$2x+2(.6)+2(.4)+2(.35)$	$2(x+.6+.4+.35)$
$2x + 1.2 + .8 + .7$	$2(x + 1.35)$
$2x + 2.7$	$2x + 2.7$

They are both right. I uses the distributive property but they are really just the same.

Chapter 6 Performance Task

Part A

132(4) + 6.50 (76) = 528 + 494 = 1022

Paige was incorrect because the total is $1022.00.

Part B

18 x 18 x h

$2(18)^2 h$

36 x h = 11,664

11664 ÷ 36 = 324

Check

$2 \cdot 18^2 \cdot 324 = 11664$

The height is 324.

I know this because 18 x 2 x 324 is 11664.

Part C

18, 18, 18, 18

2(18 x 18 x 324)

Part D

P => 2p + f + 4d

P => 2(.75) + 0.5 + 4(1.25)

1.5 + .5 + 5

7

L => f + 4d + 2p

L => 0.5 + 4(1.25) + 2(.75)

L => 0.5 + 5 + 1.5

7

They are the same price!

Part E

Laurie

2(x + 1.35)

Michael

2x + 1.2 + .8 + .7

2x + 2 + .7

2x + 2.7

They are not the same.

Chapter 6 Performance Task

Part A

132 × 4 + 6.50A

No.

Part B

18 × 18 × h

Cannot find h. Sorry.

Part C

2 (18 × 18 × h)

Part D

[p × 2] + (f) + {d × 4}

0.75 × 2 + 0.5 + 1.25 × 4

(f) + {d × 4} + [p × 2]

0.5 + 1.25 × 4 + 0.75 × 2

Part E

Michael

2x + 1.20 + 0.80 + 0.70

4.70x

Laurie

2(2.7x)

5.4x

Not the same.

Page 137 • Selling Scones

Task Scenario	
Students will model, write, solve, and compare equations to solve problems related to making and selling scones and drinks to help fund a trip for the chorus.	
CCSS Content Standard(s)	6.EE.5, 6.EE.7, 6.RP.3
Mathematical Practices	MP1, MP2, MP3, MP4, MP6, MP7
Depth of Knowledge	DOK2, DOK3, DOK4

Part	Maximum Points	Scoring Rubric
A	3	Full Credit: Sample model: $2\frac{3}{4}$ cups | Cups of flour, f $6\frac{1}{2}$ cups Equation: $2\frac{3}{4} + f = 6\frac{1}{2}$ Subtract $2\frac{3}{4}$ from each side to get $f = 3\frac{3}{4}$. Duyi needs $3\frac{3}{4}$ more cups of flour. To check the answer, substitute $3\frac{3}{4}$ for f and verify that the equation is true: $2\frac{3}{4} + 3\frac{3}{4} = 6\frac{1}{2}$. Partial Credit (2 points) will be given for 2 of these 3: the correct model OR the correct equation and solution OR the correct check. Partial Credit (1 point) will be given for 1 of the 3 listed above. No credit will be given for an incorrect answer.
B	2	Full Credit: Equation: $\frac{p}{5} = 11$; Multiply each side by 5 to get $p = 55$. 55 students preferred almond scones. The division equation is shown. The equivalent multiplication equation, $\frac{1}{5}p = 11$, could also be used because multiplying by $\frac{1}{5}$ is the same as dividing by 5. Partial Credit (1 point) will be given for the correct equation and number of students OR for an appropriate explanation of using both types of equations. No credit will be given for an incorrect answer.

<table>
<tr><th>Part</th><th>Maximum Points</th><th>Scoring Rubric</th></tr>
<tr><td>C</td><td>3</td><td>Full Credit:
Kijika's error was that he subtracted 140 from each side of the equation $m - 371 = 140$ instead of adding 371 to each side. He did not isolate the variable m on one side.
When 231 is substituted for m, $231 - 371 \neq 140$, so 231 is not a solution.
Solve: $m - 371 = 140$
$\underline{\quad + 371 + 371}$
$m \quad = 511$
The chorus will sell 511 scones this year.
Partial Credit (2 points) will be given for 2 of these 3: the explanation of the error OR the explanation of why 231 is not the solution OR the correct solution.
Partial Credit (1 point) will be given for 1 of the 3 listed above.
No credit will be given for an incorrect answer.</td></tr>
<tr><td>D</td><td>1</td><td>Full Credit:
Let x represent the total sales; 80% = 0.8.
Equation: $0.8x = 578.40$
Divide each side by 0.8 to get $x = 723$.
The sales total is $723.
Let y represent the number of scones sold.
Equation: $1.50y = 723$
Divide each side by 1.50 to get $x = 482$.
The chorus members have sold 482 scones.
No credit will be given for an incorrect answer.</td></tr>
<tr><td>E</td><td>2</td><td>Full Credit:
Sample answer:
Let x represent the number of scones.
$2 + 1.50x = 8$
$1.50x = 6$
$x = 4$
The teacher purchased 4 scones.
This equation required two steps, subtraction and division. The other equations need only one step to solve.
Partial Credit (1 point) will be given for the correct number of scones OR the correct equation and a comparison explanation.
No credit will be given for an incorrect answer.</td></tr>
<tr><td>TOTAL</td><td>11</td><td></td></tr>
</table>

Chapter 7 Performance Task

Part A

6 1/2 c. flour

2 3/4 c	x

$2\frac{3}{4} + x = 6\frac{1}{2}$

$-2\frac{3}{4} \quad -2\frac{3}{4}$

$x = 3\frac{3}{4}$

$\frac{13}{2} - \frac{11}{4} = \frac{26}{4} - \frac{11}{4} = \frac{15}{4} = 3\frac{3}{4}$

Duyi needs to add $3\frac{3}{4}$ cups of flour. I can check that this is right by adding $3\frac{3}{4}$ and $2\frac{3}{4}$.

$3\frac{3}{4} + 2\frac{3}{4} = \frac{15}{4} + \frac{11}{4} = \frac{26}{4} = 6\frac{2}{4} = 6\frac{1}{2}$.

This adds up to the original amount of flour.

Part B

$p \div 5 = 11$ p = students who like almond

$5 \times (p \div 5) = 11 \times 5$

$p = 55$

I used division, but you could do multiplication if you multiplied a by $\frac{1}{5}$. Multiplying by $\frac{1}{5}$ is the same as dividing by 5.

Part C

$m - 371 = 140$

$+371 \quad +371$

$m = 511$

check

$511 - 371 = 140$

$140 = 140$ ✓

If the two previous years sold 371 scones total, the number they sell this year would be greater. Kijika subtracted 140 from 371 to get 231 instead of adding 371 to both sides. You know he is wrong if you check. $231 - 371 = {}^{-}140$ not $+140$ like in the equation.

Part D

80% × sales = profit

$\frac{0.8(s)}{0.8} = \frac{578.40}{0.8}$

$s = 723$

sales = 1.50 × number sold

$\frac{723}{1.5} = \frac{1.5n}{1.5}$

$482 = n$

They have sold 482 scones

Part E

$1.5n + 2 = 8$

$-2 \quad -2$

$\frac{1.5n}{1.5} = \frac{6}{1.5}$

$n = 4$

n = # of scones

She bought four scones. This was an equation that took both subtracting and dividing to solve. The others just took one step.

Student Work Sample

Chapter 7 Performance Task

Part A

$6\frac{1}{2} = \overset{5}{\cancel{6}}\,\frac{\cancel{2}^{6}}{4}$

$-2\frac{3}{4} \quad -2\frac{3}{4}$

$3\frac{3}{4}$ cups of floor

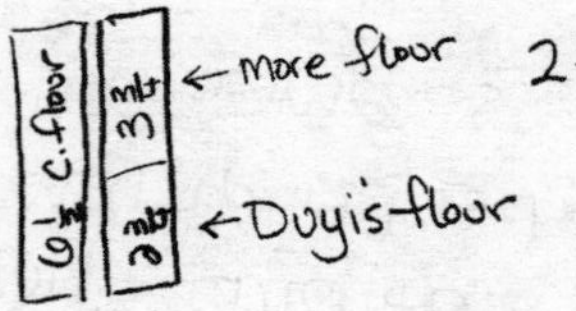

$2\frac{3}{4} + m = 6\frac{1}{2}$

Check: $2\frac{3}{4} + 3\frac{3}{4} = 6\frac{1}{2}$

$5\frac{6}{4} = 6\frac{1}{4}$

Part B

$\frac{0.2p}{0.2} = \frac{11}{0.2}$

$p = 55$

I multiplied p by 0.2 and then I used division to solve it.

Part C

231 can't be right because $231 - 371 \neq 140$. It is -140.

The answer is 511 because $m - 371 = 140$

$m - 371 + 371 = 140 + 371$

$m = 511$.

Kijika just made a mistake.

Part D

$1.5(0.8) = 1.2$ ← \$1.20 profit for each scone.

$\$578.40 \div \$1.20 = 482$

482 Scones

Part E

$1.50s + 2 = 8$

$1.5s + 2 - 2 = 8 - 2$

$\frac{1.5s}{1.5} = \frac{6}{1.5}$

$s = 4$

This equation has more steps.

Chapter 7 Performance Task

Part A

$6.5 - c = 2.75$

2.75	c

(total: 6.5)

$6.5 - 2.75 = 3.75$

Check

$6.5 - 3.75 = 2.75$

Right

Part B

$\frac{1}{5}(11) = p$

$2.2 = p$

I used multiplication ($\frac{1}{5} \times 11$) but I could have divided 11 by 5.

Part C

$m - 371 = 140$

$231 - 371 = 140$

$-140 = 140$

Subtracted in the wrong order. He should have done $371 - 231 = 140$.

Part D

$\frac{80}{100} = \frac{p}{s}$

$\frac{80}{100} = \frac{578.40}{s}$

$\frac{80s}{80} = \frac{57840}{80}$

$s = 723$

They have sold 723 scones.

Part E

$8 - 2 = 1.5s$

$\frac{6}{1.5} = \frac{1.5s}{1.5}$

$4 = s$

Different numbers in this equation.

Chapter 7 Performance Task

PART A

$6\frac{1}{2} + 2\frac{3}{4} = T$

$8\frac{4}{6} = T$

$8\frac{2}{3} = T$

Flour

PART B

$11 = p + \frac{1}{5}$

$p = 10\frac{4}{5}$

You can't use multiplication and division.

You have to Subtract.

PART C

$$\begin{array}{r} 146 \\ +\ 225 \\ \hline 371 \\ +\ 140 \\ \hline 511 \end{array}$$

PART D

$578.40\ (80\%) = 462.72 \div 1.50 = 308.48$

So 309 scones.

PART E

$8 + 2 = 10 \div 1.5 = 6.7$

So 6 scones.

Page 139 • Field Trip Meeting

<table>
<tr><td colspan="3">Task Scenario
Students will write, solve, and apply functions, equations, and inequalities, and use tables and graphs, to solve problems involving attendance and costs of a field trip.</td></tr>
<tr><td colspan="2">CCSS Content Standard(s)</td><td>6.EE.2, 6.EE.2c, 6.EE.5, 6.EE.6, 6.EE.8, 6.EE.9</td></tr>
<tr><td colspan="2">Mathematical Practices</td><td>MP1, MP2, MP4, MP6, MP7, MP8</td></tr>
<tr><td colspan="2">Depth of Knowledge</td><td>DOK2, DOK3, DOK4</td></tr>
<tr><th>Part</th><th>Maximum Points</th><th>Scoring Rubric</th></tr>
<tr><td>A</td><td>2</td><td>Full Credit:
Function rule: $50 - 0.5x$
No. Sample answer: If x is an odd number of minutes, the number of students in the room is not a whole number. For 3 min, $50 - 0.5(3) = 50 - 1.5 = 48.5$ students. (Also, if $x > 100$, the number of students in the room is a negative number, which doesn't make sense.)
Partial Credit (1 point) will be given for a correct function rule OR a correct explanation for all positive integers.
No credit will be given for an incorrect answer.</td></tr>
<tr><td>B</td><td>2</td><td>Full Credit:
The inequality is $s \geq 40$.
−50 −40 −30 −20 −10 0 10 20 30 40 50
Partial Credit (1 point) will be given for the correct inequality OR the correct graph.
No credit will be given for an incorrect answer.</td></tr>
<tr><td>C</td><td>3</td><td>Full Credit:
<table><tr><th>Month</th><th>Balance ($)</th></tr><tr><td>1</td><td>50</td></tr><tr><td>2</td><td>40</td></tr><tr><td>4</td><td>20</td></tr></table>The equation is $y = 60 - 10x$.
At month 3, there is a balance due of $30. Sample answer: Using the graph, I located month 3 on the x-axis and read the corresponding point on the line at $y = 30$. Using the equation, I substituted 3 for x, and simplified: $y = 60 - 10(3) = 30$.
Partial Credit (2 points) will be given for 2 of these 3: a completed table OR a correct equation OR the correct explanations.
Partial Credit (1 point) will be given for 1 of the 3 above.
No credit will be given for an incorrect answer.</td></tr>
</table>

Part	Maximum Points	Scoring Rubric
D	2	Full Credit: Sample answer: At $x = 1$, $y = 50$, so the balance due at month 1 is \$50. Each student also has to pay a \$20 deposit. 50 + 20 = \$70 The total cost of the trip for each student is \$70. Partial Credit (1 point) will be given for the correct total cost OR for showing work. No credit will be given for an incorrect answer.
E	1	Full Credit: Yes, Jake will have enough. Sample answer: The total amount of money Jake has saved by the end of each week is 2 times that of the previous week. So by week 6, Jake should have 2(32) = \$64, which is \$4 more than the \$60 he wants. No credit will be given for an incorrect answer.
TOTAL	**10**	

Chapter 8 Performance Task

Part A

Function rule: $50-\frac{1}{2}x$

No because when there are 7 minutes left, there are 46.5 students which isn't possible. It doesn't work for any odd integer.

Part B

$s \geq 40$

0 10 20 30 40 50

Part C

Month	Balance
1	50
2	40
4	20

$y=60-10x$

At three months, there is $30 left. I can tell because when I follow the line up from $x=3$ and hit the line and then follow it over, it hits at $y=30$. I can use the equation if I put $x=3$, $60-10(3)=30$.

Part D

The cost is $70 per person. I know this because at month 1, $50 is the balance but they had already paid a $20 deposit.

$50 + $20 = $70.

Part E

Yes, I think he will, because the amount he has saved doubles every week and $32 \times 2 = 64$. By week 6 he will have $64 saved.

Student Work Sample

Chapter 8 Performance Tast

Part A

Function

$50 - 0.5x$

Yes because there are always people coming in.

Part B

$S \geq 40$

0 10 20 30 40 50

Part C

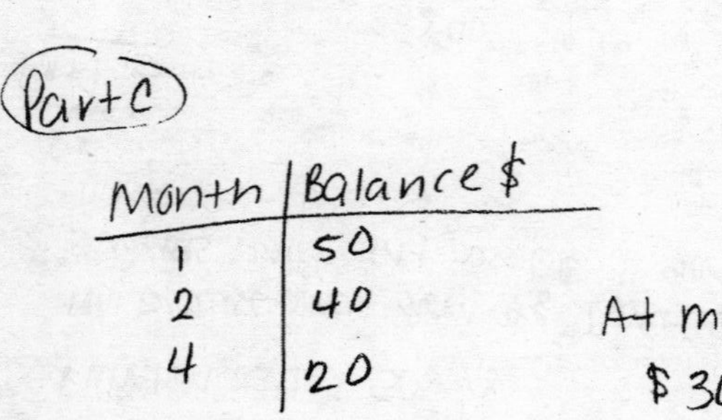

Month	Balance $
1	50
2	40
4	20

At month three, there is $ 30 left to pay.

Part D

$70 because they pay $10 per month and the line starts at (1, 50) but they pay $20 at the meeting.

Part E

Jake will have $64 because his money doubles every week.

Chapter 8 Performance Task

Part A

10	45
8	46
6	47
5	47.5
4	48
3	48.5
2	49
1	49.5
0	50

Rule $= 45 + \frac{1}{2}x$

No because there would be half people.

Part B

0 10 20 30 40 50

Part C

1	50
2	40
3	30

$y = 60 - 10x$

At 3 months there is $30 left.

$60 - 10(3) = 30$

Also point (3, 30) is on the line.

Part D

The trip costs $60 because (1, 60) is the first point on the line

Part E

The pattern looks like the money doubles each week, so yes.

Chapter 8 Performance Task

PART A

There is no Steady patten on the table
So there is no function rule.

PART B

$S \leq 40$

PART C

M	B
1	60
2	50
3	40
4	30
2	20
1	10

PART D

$60

PART E

No. The week is multiplied by 2 then 3 then 4 then 5.
$6 \times 6 = 36$, which is not enough.

Page 141 • The Recreation Room

<table>
<tr><td colspan="3">Task Scenario
Students will draw polygons on a coordinate plane, apply area and perimeter formulas, and use scale drawings to solve problems involving the design of a recreation room.</td></tr>
<tr><td colspan="2">CCSS Content Standard(s)</td><td>6.G.1, 6.G.3, 6.NS.8</td></tr>
<tr><td colspan="2">Mathematical Practices</td><td>MP1, MP2, MP3, MP4, MP7</td></tr>
<tr><td colspan="2">Depth of Knowledge</td><td>DOK2, DOK3, DOK4</td></tr>
<tr><th>Part</th><th>Maximum Points</th><th>Scoring Rubric</th></tr>
<tr><td>A</td><td>3</td><td>Full Credit:
Graph of ABCD:
The figure is a trapezoid.
Area: $\frac{1}{2}h(b_1 + b_2) =$
$\frac{1}{2}(9)(20 + 12) =$
144; 144 square units
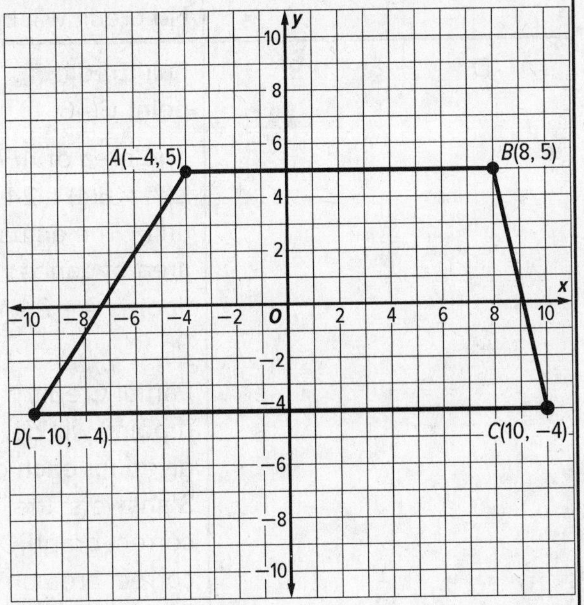

Partial Credit (1 point) will be given for each of 3 answers: the correct graph OR correct figure OR correct area.
No credit will be given for an incorrect answer.</td></tr>
<tr><td>B</td><td>2</td><td>Full Credit:
Sample answer: 3 figures: a rectangle with vertices A(−4, 5), B(8, 5), (8, −4), and (−4, −4), one triangle to the left of the rectangle, one triangle to the right of the rectangle
Rectangle: $A = \ell w = 12(9) = 108$ square units
Triangle at left: $A = \frac{1}{2}bh = \frac{1}{2}(6)(9) = 27$ square units
Triangle at right: $A = \frac{1}{2}bh = \frac{1}{2}(2)(9) = 9$ square units
Total area: $27 + 9 + 108 = 144$ units^2, which equals Part A's area
Partial Credit (1 point) will be given for the areas of the shapes from a correct decomposition OR the total area.
No credit will be given for an incorrect answer.</td></tr>
</table>

Part	Maximum Points	Scoring Rubric
C	2	Full Credit: The sides of the original shape are half the sides of *ABCD*. So, the perimeter of the original shape is half that of *ABCD*. The area of the original shape is $(0.5)^2 = 0.25$ that of *ABCD*. The area of the original space was 0.25(144) = 36 square units. The approximate perimeter of *ABCD* is 26(2) = 52 units. Partial Credit (1 point) will be given for correctly comparing the perimeters and areas OR the correct measurements. No credit will be given for an incorrect answer.
D	3	Full Credit: point *G*(–6, 1) The area of *AEFG* is *A* = 6(4) = 24 unit². The actual area of dance floor is *A* = 24(4) = 96 ft². 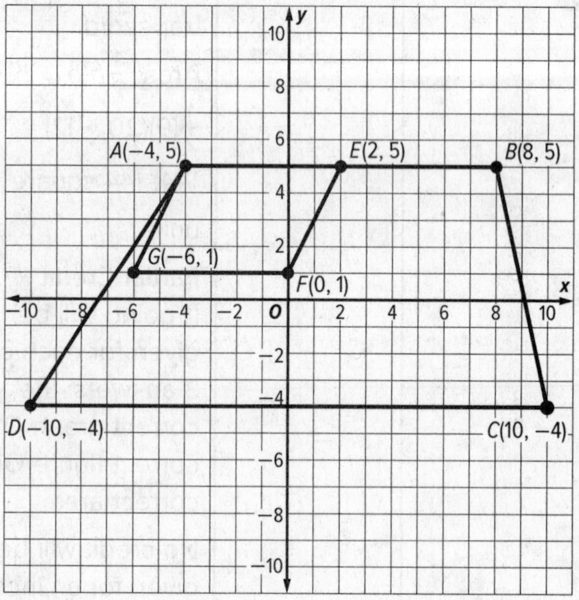 Partial Credit (1 point) will be given for each of 3 answers: the correct graph OR correct area on the blueprint OR correct actual area. No credit will be given for an incorrect answer.
E	2	Full Credit: Wood flooring for dance floor: area = 96 ft² Cost = (96)(4.99) = $479.04 Carpet for rest of floor: area of *ABCD* – area of *AEFG* = 144 – 24 = 120 square units; Actual carpet area: 120(4) = 480 ft² Cost = (480)(7.99) = $3,835.20 Total Cost = 479.04 + 3,835.20 = $4,314.24 Budget: 4,500.00 – 4,314.24 = $185.76 Yes, Madison is under budget by $185.76. Partial Credit (1 point) will be given for the correct costs of the floor types OR the correct answer and explanation. No credit will be given for an incorrect answer.
TOTAL	**12**	

Chapter 9 Performance Task

Part A

It is a trapezoid. The area is 144 square units.

$A = \frac{1}{2}(b_1 + b_2)h$

$A = \frac{1}{2}(12 + 20)9$

$A = \frac{1}{2}(32)9$

$A = 144 \text{ un}^2$

Part B

I Right Triangle

$A = \frac{1}{2}bh$

$A = \frac{1}{2}(6)9$

$A = 27$

II Rectangle

$A = bh$

$A = 9 \cdot 12$

$A = 108$

III Rt Tri

$A = \frac{1}{2}bh$

$A = \frac{1}{2} \cdot 2 \cdot 9$

$A = 9$

Area of whole shape $= 27 + 108 + 9 = 144$

144 un² is the same as the area of the trapezoid I found in Part A.

Part C

Original Space

$A = \frac{1}{2}(b_1 + b_2)h$

$A = \frac{1}{2}(16)(4.5)$

$A = 36$

The area of new shape ABCD is four times the area of the original. I know because $144 \div 36 = 4$. The area of the original space was 36 un² (work to left). The perimeter of new ABCD will be twice as big as the old space when you double the length and then add them, the perimeter doubles. If the original perimeter is 26, the new perimeter is 52 units.

Also, when you double the lengths and then find area (units squared) the change is 4. $2^2 = 4$

Part D

See part A for graph.

G(−6,1)

$A = b \cdot h$

$A = 6 \cdot 4$

$A = 24 \text{ un}^2$

$\frac{1 \text{ un}^2}{4 \text{ ft}^2} = \frac{24 \text{ un}^2}{x}$

$x = 96 \text{ ft}^2$

The point for G is at (−6,1). The area of AEFG is 24 un². This is 96 ft² in real life.

Part E

Dance Floor

$96 \text{ ft}^2 \times \$4.99/\text{ft}^2 = \$479.04$

Rest of room

$144 \text{ un}^2 - 24 \text{ un}^2 = 120 \text{ un}^2$

$120 \times 4 = 480 \text{ ft}^2$

$480 \text{ ft}^2 \times \$7.99/\text{ft}^2 = \$3835.20$

Total cost of Flooring

$\$479.04 + \$3835.20 = \$4314.24$

Madison stayed within budget by $185.76.

Budget

$\$4500.00 - \$4314.24 = \$185.74$

Student Work Sample

Chapter 9 Performance Task

Part A

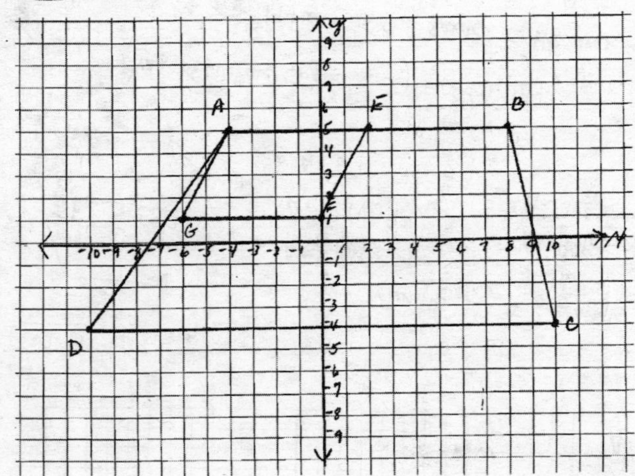

- Trapezoid
- Area : 144

$\frac{1}{2}(b+b)h$

$\frac{1}{2}(20+12)9$

Part B

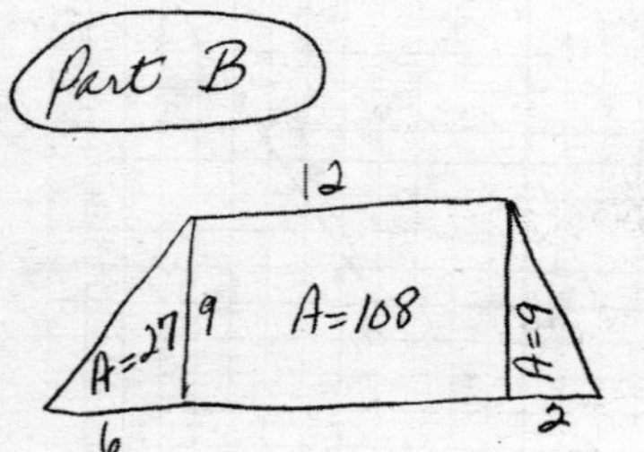

$A = 27 + 108 + 9 = 144$

Therefore part A is right.

Part C

- Perimeter will be doubled. New perimeter = 52 units.
- Area will be doubled. Area of original space = 72 units.

Part D

- G(−6, 1)
- See part A
- Area = 24 un^2

$A = b \cdot h$

$A = 46$

Part E

$24(4.99) = 119.76$

$120(7.99) = 958.80$

Cost: 1078.56

Amount under: $4500 - 1078.56 = \$3421.44$

Chapter 9 Performance Task

Part A

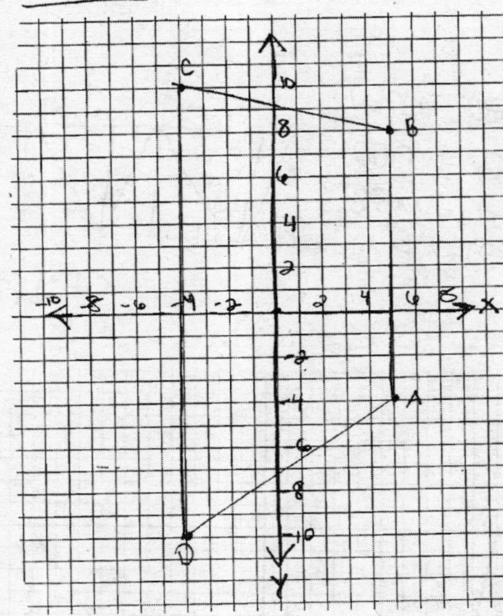

$A = \frac{1}{2}(b_1 + b_2)h$

$A = 0.5(20 + 12)9$

$A = 144$

Part B

$\frac{1}{2} \cdot 9 \cdot 2 + \frac{1}{2} \cdot 9 \cdot 6 + 9 \cdot 12 = 9 + 27 + 108 = 144$

Part C

Perimeter of the original is half as big because the sides are half as long.

Area is a quarter the size because $(\frac{1}{2})^2 = \frac{1}{4}$.

P of old = 26 A old = 36

P of new = 52.

Part D

$A = bh$

$A = 4 \cdot 6$

$A = 24$

$24 \times 4 = 96$

Part E

$96(4.99) = 479.04$

$48(7.99) = 383.52$

Total: \$862.56

Student Work Sample

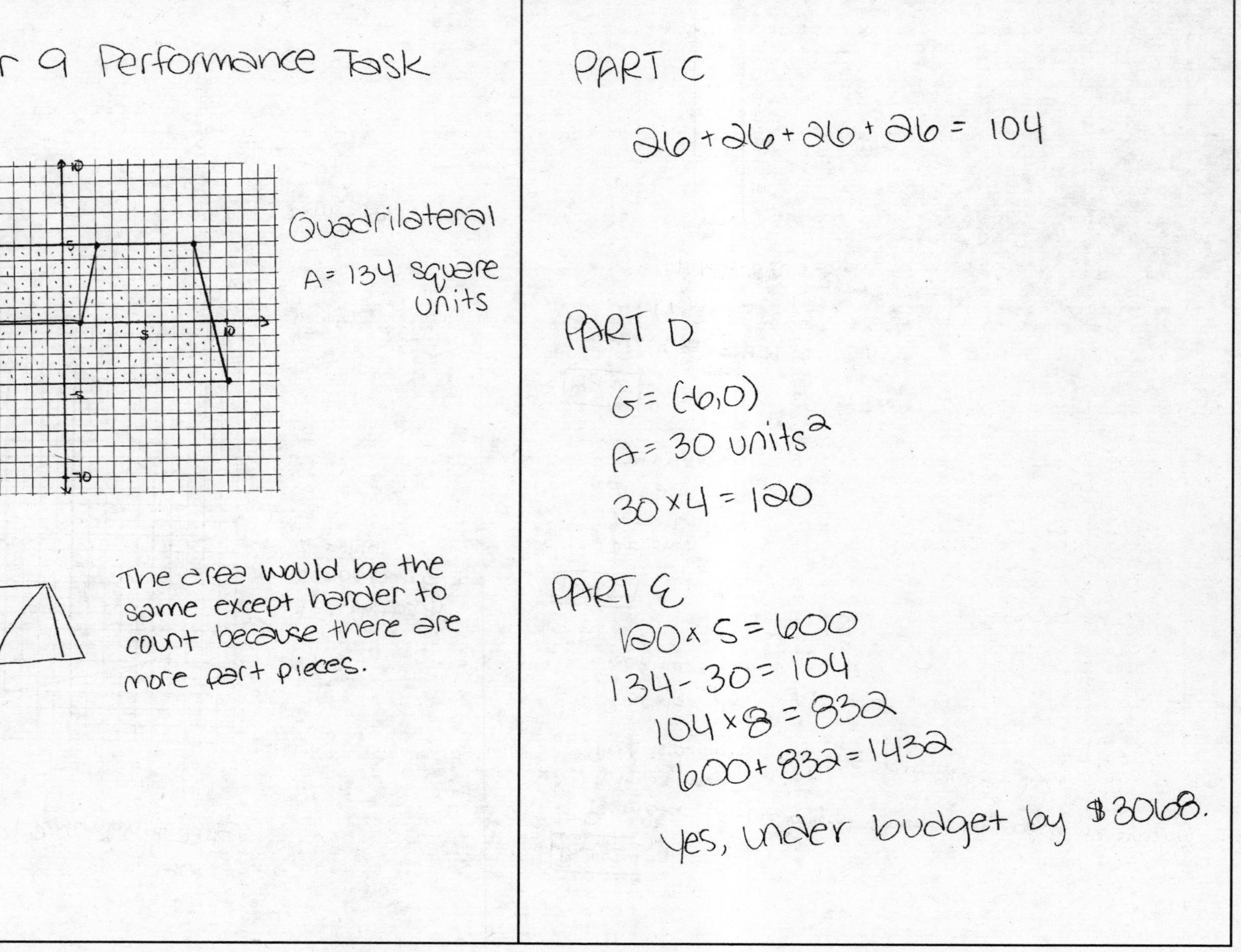

Chapter 9 Performance Task

PART A

Quadrilateral

A = 134 square units

PART B

The area would be the same except harder to count because there are more part pieces.

PART C

26 + 26 + 26 + 26 = 104

PART D

G = (-6,0)

A = 30 units²

30 × 4 = 120

PART E

120 × 5 = 600

134 − 30 = 104

104 × 8 = 832

600 + 832 = 1432

Yes, under budget by $3068.

Page 143 • Math Crunchies

Task Scenario	
Students will calculate the surface area and volume of different cereal box designs shaped like prisms and pyramids.	
CCSS Content Standard(s)	6.G.1, 6.G.2, 6.G.4
Mathematical Practices	MP1, MP2, MP4, MP6, MP7
Depth of Knowledge	DOK2, DOK3, DOK4

Part	Maximum Points	Scoring Rubric
A	2	Full Credit: Sample net: 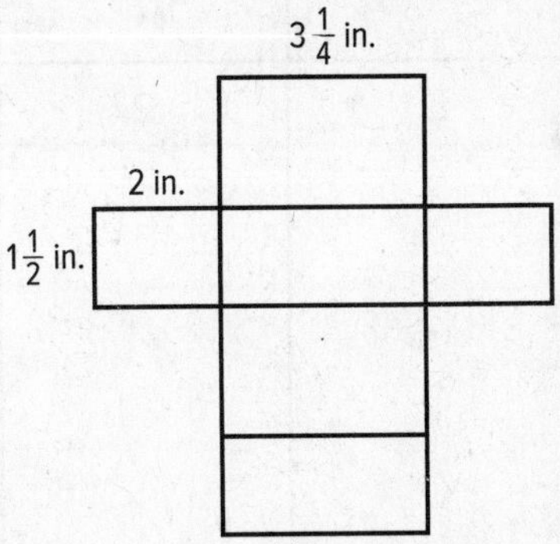 To find the amount of cardboard needed, find the surface area. *S.A.* = $2\left[\left(2 \times 1\frac{1}{2}\right) + \left(1\frac{1}{2} \times 3\frac{1}{4}\right) + \left(2 \times 3\frac{1}{4}\right)\right]$ $= 28.75$ in^2 He needs 28.75 in^2 of cardboard to make one box. Partial Credit (1 point) will be given for the correct net OR the correct amount of cardboard. No credit will be given for an incorrect answer.
B	3	Full Credit: The dimensions of the new box are $3 \times 2 = 6$; $3 \times 1\frac{1}{2} = 4\frac{1}{2}$; $3 \times 3\frac{1}{4} = 9\frac{3}{4}$. So, 6 in. × $4\frac{1}{2}$ in. × $9\frac{3}{4}$ in. The surface area of the new box is: *S.A.* = $2\left[\left(6 \times 4\frac{1}{2}\right) + \left(4\frac{1}{2} \times 9\frac{3}{4}\right) + \left(6 \times 9\frac{3}{4}\right)\right] = 258\frac{3}{4}$ in^2 The number of times more cardboard the new box needs: $258\frac{3}{4} \div 28.75 = 258\frac{3}{4} \div 28\frac{3}{4} = 9$ Vajra's cereal box requires 9 times as much cardboard as Osamu's cereal box. Partial Credit (1 point) will be given for each of the 3 answers: the correct dimensions OR the correct surface area OR the correct comparison of cardboard needed. No credit will be given for an incorrect answer.

<table>
<tr><th>Part</th><th>Maximum Points</th><th>Scoring Rubric</th></tr>
<tr><td>C</td><td>1</td><td>Full Credit:
Sample answer:
Volume of Vajra's cereal box: $V = 6 \times 4\frac{1}{2} \times 9\frac{3}{4} = 263\frac{1}{4}$ in^3
Osamu's cereal box holds a single serving:
$V = 2 \times 1\frac{1}{2} \times 3\frac{1}{4} = 9\frac{3}{4}$ in^3
Divide the total volume by the single-serving volume.
$263\frac{1}{4} \div 9\frac{3}{4} = 27$
Vajra's cereal box will hold 27 servings.
No credit will be given for an incorrect answer.</td></tr>
<tr><td>D</td><td>2</td><td>Full Credit:
Sample net:
$S.A. = (3 \times 3) + 4(0.5 \times 3 \times 3.6)$
$= 30.6$
30.6 in^2 of cardboard is needed to make this box.
3.9 in.
3.6 in.
3 in.
3 in.
3.9 in.
Partial Credit (1 Point) will be given for a correct net OR the correct amount of cardboard.
No credit will be given for an incorrect answer.</td></tr>
<tr><td>E</td><td>2</td><td>Full Credit:
Osamu's cereal box: volume = $9\frac{3}{4}$ in^3; height = $3\frac{1}{4}$ in.
Deondre's design: volume = triangle base area × height
$9\frac{3}{4}$ = triangle base area × $3\frac{1}{4}$
triangle base area = $9\frac{3}{4} \div 3\frac{1}{4} = 3$ in^2.
Because the area $A = \frac{1}{2}bh = 3$, the product of the base length and height of the triangular face must equal 6 in.
Sample answer: Possible dimensions of the triangular face are height = 4 in. and base = 1.5 in.
Partial Credit (1 Point) will be given for the correct base area OR a correct set of possible dimensions with explanation.
No credit will be given for an incorrect answer.</td></tr>
<tr><td>**TOTAL**</td><td>10</td><td></td></tr>
</table>

Chapter 10 Performance Task

Part A

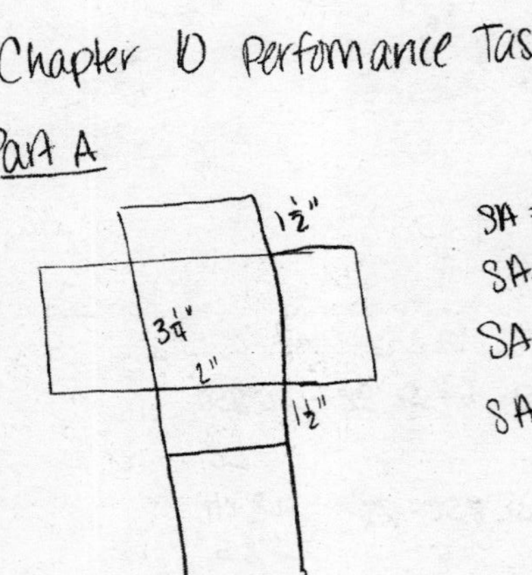

$SA = 2(3\frac{1}{4} \times 2) + 2(2 \times 1\frac{1}{2}) + 2(3\frac{1}{4} \times 1\frac{1}{2})$

$SA = 2(3.25 \times 2) + 2(2 \times 1.5) + 2(3.25 \times 1.5)$

$SA = 13 + 6 + 9.75$

$SA = 28.75 = 28\frac{3}{4}$ in2

Part B

$3\frac{1}{4} \times 3 = 9.75$

$2 \times 3 = 6$

$1.5 \times 3 = 4.5$

The new dimensions are $9\frac{3}{4} \times 6 \times 4\frac{1}{2}$. The surface area is 258.75 in2. which is nine times the SA of the original. This makes sense because each dimension was multiplied by three and then multiplied by another tripled dimension. $3 \times 3 = 9$.

$SA = 2(9.75 \times 6) + 2(6 \times 4.5) + 2(9.75 \times 4.5)$

$SA = 117 + 54 + 87.75$

$SA = 258.75$ in2

Part C

Osamu's Box $V = 3.25(2)(1.5)$
$V = 9.75$ in3

Vajra's Box $V = 9.75 \times 6 \times 4.5$
$V = 263.25$ in3

$263.25 \div 9.75 = 27$

It holds about 27 servings of cereal.

Part D

3.9" 3.9" 3.9" 3.9" 3" 3" 3.6"

$(10.8 - 3) \div 2 = 3.9$

$SA = 4(\frac{1}{2} b \cdot h) + l \cdot w$

$SA = 4(\frac{1}{2}(3)(3.6)) + 3^2$

$SA = 21.6 + 9$

$SA = 30.6$ in2

Part E

Osamu's box: $V = 9.75$, $h = 3\frac{1}{4}$"

$3\frac{1}{4}$

Deondre

$V =$ Area of base × height

$V =$ Area of base × $3\frac{1}{4}$

$V = 3 \times 3\frac{1}{4}$

$\frac{1}{2} \cdot b \cdot h = 3$

$b \cdot h = 6$

$9.75 \div 3\frac{1}{4} = 3$

The base of the triangle could be 2 and the height would be 3. That way the volume is $\frac{1}{2}(3)(2)(3.25) = 9.75$ in3

Student Work Sample

Chapter 10 Performance Task

PART A

$1\frac{1}{2}$" 3 in²

4.875 in² | 6.5 in² $3\frac{1}{4}$" | 4.875 in² | 6.5 in²

$1\frac{1}{2}$" | $1\frac{1}{2}$" 3 in² 2" | $1\frac{1}{2}$" | 2"

SA = 28.75 in²

PART B

9.75" x 6" x 4.5"

58.5
43.875 SA = 258.75 in²
27

258.75 ÷ 28.75 = 9 times as much

PART C

I think that 27 servings of cereal would fit in the box. Because all three dimensions are tripled and volume is found by multiplying length, width and height. $3^3 = 27$, so the new big box will hold 27 times as many servings as the single serve box.

PART D

5.4" 5.4" 3" 6 9" 9"

SA = 81 + $\left(\frac{1}{2}(3.6)(9)\right) \times 4$

SA = 81 + 64.8

SA = 145.8 in²

PART E

Osamu V = l·w·h

V = 3.25 x 2 x 1.5

V = 9.75 in3

Deondre

V = 9.75 in³

h = 3.25 in

1" x 6" x 3.25" triangle box

V = B·h

½ b·h → 3.25

9.75 ÷ 3.25 = 3

½ b·h = 3

b·h = 6

1 h = 6

Chapter 10 Performance Task

Part A

$SA = 2 \cdot l \cdot w + 2 \cdot l \cdot h + 2 \cdot w \cdot h$

$SA = 2(2)(1\frac{1}{2}) + 2(2)(3\frac{1}{4}) + 2(1\frac{1}{2})(3\frac{1}{4})$

$SA = 6 + 13 + 9.75$

$SA = 28.75 \text{ in}^2$

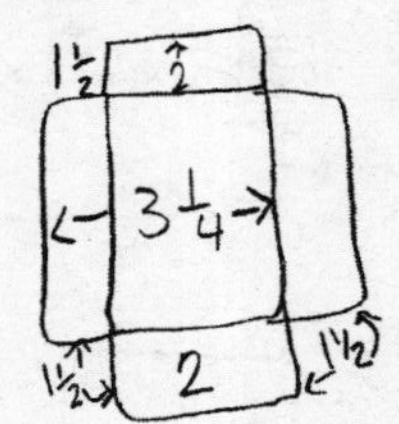

Part B

$SA = 2(6)(4.5) + 2(6)(9.75) + 2(4.5)(9.75)$

$SA = 54 + 117 + 87.75$

$SA = 258.75 \text{ in}^2$

New box 6" x 4.5" x 9.75"

Part C

Vajra's box holds 1 serving. Since all the dimensions are x3, the new box should hold x3 as many servings. 1x3=3.

Part D

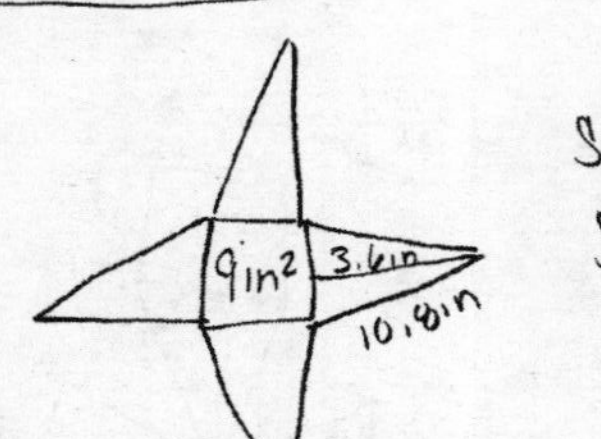

$SA = 9 + (3.6(3) \times 4) \times \frac{1}{2}$

$SA = 30.6 \text{ in}^2$

Part E

$V = l \cdot w \cdot h$

$9.75 = 1 \cdot w(3.25)$

$3 = 1 \cdot w$

$1 = 1$

$w = 3$

Chapter 10 Performance Task

PART A

$SA = l \cdot w + w \cdot h + l \cdot h$

$= 2 \times 1.5 + 1.5 \times 3.25 + 2 \times 3.25$

$= 3 + 4.875 + 6.5$

$= 14.375$

PART B

$9\frac{3}{4} \times 6 \times 4\frac{1}{2}$

Three times as much because I multiplied all sides by 3.

PART C

Three times as much.

PART D

$(10.8)4 + 9 = 52.2 \text{ in}^2$

PART E

The box should have the same other dimensions if it has the same volume and height.

Page 145 • Bird Watching

Task Scenario		
Students will find and compare measures of center and measures of variation to describe Sofia's bird watching and fish identifying data. Students will also determine how measures are affected when a data value is added to sets of data.		
CCSS Content Standard(s)	6.SP.2, 6.SP.3, 6.SP.5, 6.SP.5c, 6.SP.5d	
Mathematical Practices	MP1, MP2, MP3, MP4, MP6, MP7	
Depth of Knowledge	DOK2, DOK3, DOK4	

Part	Maximum Points	Scoring Rubric
A	2	Full Credit: The sum of the data values is 382. The data set consists of 15 items. The mean = 382 ÷ 15 ≈ 25.5. The mean will increase slightly. Sample answer: Because Sofia's value is greater than the mean, the mean will increase when her value is included in the data. However, her value is close to the mean, so the mean will change only slightly. The mean with Sofia's value included ≈ 25.6. Partial Credit (1 point) will be given for the correct mean for the survey data OR an appropriate explanation of the affected mean. No credit will be given for an incorrect answer.
B	2	Full Credit: Survey result data in order: 8, 17, 18, 19, 21, 22, 24, <u>24</u>, 24, 25, 28, 29, 33, 34, 56 The median is 24. Sofia's value added to the data: 8, 17, 18, 19, 21, 22, 24, <u>24, 24</u>, 25, 27, 28, 29, 33, 34, 56 The median is 24, the average of the two middle values. When Sofia's value is added to the data, the median does not change. Partial Credit (1 point) will be given for the correct median for the survey data OR the correct comparison with the median including Sofia's value. No credit will be given for an incorrect answer.

Part	Maximum Points	Scoring Rubric
C	3	Full Credit: Range: max. value – min. value = 56 – 8 = 48 IQR: $Q_3 - Q_1 = 28.5 - 20 = 8.5$ There is an outlier. (1.5)IQR = (1.5)(8.5) = 12.75 $Q_1 - 12.75 = 20 - 12.75 = 7.25$ $Q_3 + 12.75 = 28.5 + 12.75 = 41.25$ Because 56 > 41.25, 56 is an outlier. Partial Credit (1 point) will be given for each of the 3 answers: the correct range OR the correct IQR OR the correct outlier and justification. No credit will be given for an incorrect answer.
D	1	Full Credit: The mode is 12. It is the value that occurs most often. The value 12 appears four times in the data, which means that 4 people were each able to identify 12 different fish. No credit will be given for an incorrect answer.
E	2	Full Credit: Mean of fish data: 11.8125 Sum of absolute deviations: 3.8125 + 2.8125 + 2(1.8125) + 2(0.8125) + 5(0.1875) + 2(1.1875) + 2.1875 + 2(3.1875) = 23.75 MAD = 23.75 ÷ 16 ≈ 1.5 The MAD for the fish data is much less than the MAD for the bird data: 1.5 < 6.7. The fish data are much closer together than the bird data. Partial Credit (1 Point) will be given for the correct MAD for the fish data OR the correct comparison of the MAD values. No credit will be given for an incorrect answer.
F	2	Full Credit: Bird data: The median 24 is the most appropriate measure for the bird data. Although there is an outlier, there are no big gaps in the middle of the data values. Fish data: Sample answer: The mean 11.8125 is the most appropriate measure for the fish data because there are no extreme values. The mode 12 could also be the most appropriate because the data have many repeated numbers. Partial Credit (1 Point) will be given for the correct measure and explanation for the bird data OR the correct measure and explanation for the fish data. No credit will be given for an incorrect answer.
TOTAL	**12**	

CHAPTER 11 Performance TASK

PART A

22	17	24	56	19
34	8	28	25	21
+ 33	+ 24	+ 18	+ 29	+ 24
89	49	70	110	64

$89 + 49 + 70 + 110 + 64 = 382$

$\frac{382}{15} = 25.5$ birds

$\frac{409}{16} = 25.6$ birds

The average number of birds that can be identified is 25.5. If Sofia includes her data, the mean increases to 25.6 because her data value is greater than but close to the mean.

PART B

8 17 18 19 21 22 24 [24] 24 25 (27) 28 29 33 34 56

The original median 24.

If you add Sofia's value of 27, the median is still 24 because $(24 + 24) \div 2 = 24$.

PART C

The range is 48 because $56 - 8 = 48$.

The IQR is 8.5 because

First the upper quartile is 28.5 $(28 + 29) \div 2 = 28.5$

Second the lower quartile is 20 $(19 + 21) \div 2 = 20$

$28.5 - 20 = 8.5$

An outlier is more than 1.5 × IQR away from the upper & lower quartile.

$1.5(8.5) = 12.75$

$20 - 12.75 = 7.25$ so 8 is safe.

$28.5 + 12.75 = 41.25$ so 56 is an outlier.

PART D

#	Repeated
8	I
9	I
10	II
11	II
12	IIII
13	II
14	I
15	II

The mode is the most commonly repeated number. Here the mode is 12. I know because I tallied how many times each number was used, and 12 was there four times. This means four people could each identify 12 fish.

PART E

MAD for birds = 6.7
MAD for fish = 1.5

This means that the fish data is much closer than the bird data was.

$\text{Mean} = \frac{8+9+20+22+48+26+14+30+12}{15+1} = \frac{189}{16} = 11.8125$

$\frac{3.8125 + 2.8125 + 2(1.8125) + 2(0.8125) + 5(0.1875) + 2(1.1875) + 1(2.1875) + 2(3.1875)}{16}$

(3.625, 1.625, 0.9375, 2.375, 6.375 written above the products)

$23.75 \div 16 = 1.484375 \approx 1.5$

PART F

For the bird data, the median is the best measure of center. There is an outlier so that throws off the mean. The mode would be the same as the median (24). So that would be a good choice too.

For the fish, the mode (12) is the best because it is towards the middle of the data (very close to the mean). It is repeated a lot of times, too.

Student Work Sample

Chapter 11 Performance Task

Part A

$\frac{382}{15} = 25.5$ birds

If Sofia is included,

$\frac{409}{16} = 25.6$ birds because Sofia's data value was already close to the mean.

Part B

8 17 18 19 21 22 24 (24) 24 25 28 29 35 [illegible] 56

the median is 24.

8 17 18 (19) 21 22 24 [24] 24 25 27 (28) 29 35 47 56

24 is still the median after Sofia's data is added.

Part C

Range: 48

IQR: 8.5

Q_3 28.5

Q_1 20

yes, two outliers – 8 and 56.

Part D

8 9 10 10 11 11 12 12 12 12 13 13 14 15 15

Mode is 12. I counted each time a value was used and 12 was used most – 4 times.

Part E

Mean for fish: $\frac{177}{15} = 11.8$

3.8 + 2.8 + 1.8 + 1.8 + 0.8 + 0.8 + 0.2 + 0.2 + 0.2 + 0.2 + 1.2 + 1.2 + 2.2 + 3.2 + 3.2 =

23.6

$23.6 \div 15 = 1.57 \approx 1.6$

The MAD for the fish is a lot smaller which makes sense because the bird data is much more spread out.

Part F

Bird: Mode (24) because it was the most common and there were outliers.

Fish: Mean (11.8) because the data was all pretty close together.

Chapter 11 Performance Task

Part A

Average: 25.5

Sofia's Average: 26.25
(25.5 + 27) ÷ 2

It got brought up a lot when you included Sofia.

Part B

Median: 24

Adding Sofias value keeps it at 24 still.

Part C

Range: 48

IQR: 24

24 − 12 = 12

24 + 12 = 36

Took median and added half to it to get upper and subtracted half to get lower.

Outlier: 56 because it is way out there.

Part D

mode is 12 because it was repeated x4.

Part E

mean: $\frac{189}{16} = 11.8125 \approx 12$

2+3+2+0+4+2+1+1+0+1+0+0+3+1+3 = 23

23 ÷ 16 = 1.4375 ≈ 1.4

MAD of fish is smaller because there are no outliers

Part F

Fish: Mode because it is the most repeated

Birds: Median because it is the average.

Student Work Sample

Chapter 11 Performance Task

Part A

Mean: 25.5

With Sofia it changes it because it was a different number than any of the rest.

Part B

The median is 28 because it is in the middle of the numbers given.

Adding 27 to the list would change it to 26.5 because you have to average 28 and 25.

Part C

The range is 2 (24-22).

Outlier is 56.

Part D

The mode is 10, 11, 12, 13 and 15 because they were all repeated more than once.

Part E

Bird MAD = 6.7

Fish MAD = 11.8125

Part F

Any of them could be picked. For the birds I choose the mean and for the fish I pick the mean because they are the average, so it is in the middle.

Page 147 • Wagging the Dog

Note to teacher: For this Performance Task, have students research the ideal weight of ten different dog breeds. Have students share their findings with the class.

Task Scenario	
Students will draw data displays, find statistical measures, describe data, and choose appropriate ways to display the data they researched about the weights of different dogs.	
CCSS Content Standard(s)	6.SP.2, 6.SP.4, 6.SP.5, 6.SP.5a, 6.SP.5b
Mathematical Practices	MP2, MP4, MP5, MP6, MP7
Depth of Knowledge	DOK2, DOK3, DOK4

Part	Maximum Points	Scoring Rubric
A	2	Full Credit: Sample data: Poodle: 15 lb, Beagle: 25 lb, Cocker spaniel: 25 lb, Husky: 35 lb, Collie: 65 lb, Boxer: 65 lb, Golden retriever: 70 lb, Setter: 75 lb, Doberman pinscher: 85 lb, German shepherd: 90 lb **Ideal Dog Weights (lb)** 0 10 20 30 40 50 60 70 80 90 100 Sample answer: The distribution is not symmetric. There are no peaks. There is a cluster from 65–75. There is a big gap from 40–60, and smaller gaps at 20, 30, and 80. Most of the breeds researched are large or small dogs, not medium-sized dogs. Partial Credit (1 point) will be given for a correct line plot OR an accurate description of the data distribution. No credit will be given for an incorrect answer.
B	2	Full Credit: Sample frequency table and histogram: Weight (lb) / Frequency: 0–19: 1; 20–39: 3; 40–59: 0; 60–79: 4; 80–99: 2 **Ideal Dog Weights** (Frequency 0–5; Weight (lb): 0–19, 20–39, 40–59, 60–79, 80–99) Partial Credit (1 point) will be given for the correct frequency table OR the correct histogram. No credit will be given for an incorrect answer.

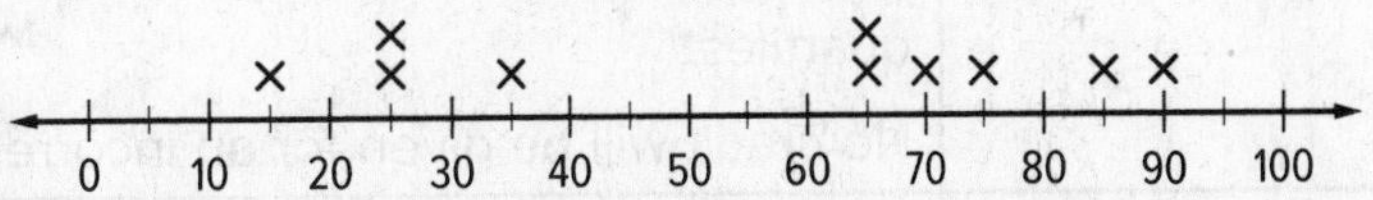

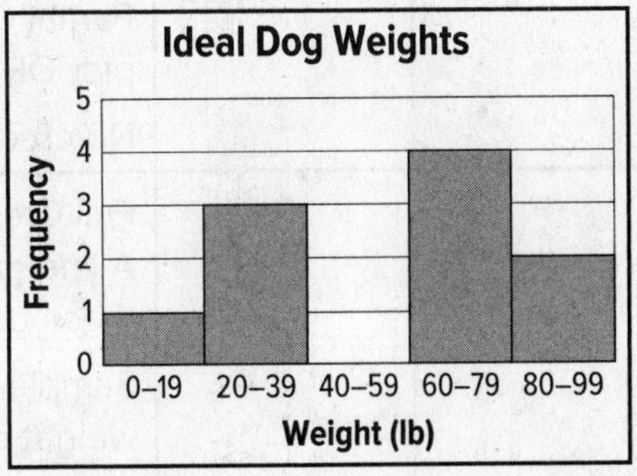

Weight (lb)	Frequency
0–19	1
20–39	3
40–59	0
60–79	4
80–99	2

Part	Maximum Points	Scoring Rubric
C	2	Full Credit: Sample answer: A line plot shows the individual data values. You can calculate the mean, median, mode(s), range, and quartiles. A histogram shows only how many data values are in various intervals. It is more concise, but less specific than a line plot. Sample answer: It depends on the information needed. For knowing the exact weights, a line plot would be better. For classifying dog breeds by their ideal weights in categories such as large, medium, and small dogs, a histogram would be appropriate. Partial Credit (1 Point) will be given for a correct comparison OR an appropriate choice of display with explanation. No credit will be given for an incorrect answer.
D	1	Full Credit: Sample answer: There are no outliers. The IQR is 50, so 1.5(IQR) = (1.5)(50) = 75. No data value is more than 75 from the first or third quartiles. No credit will be given for an incorrect answer.
E	2	Full Credit: Sample answer: 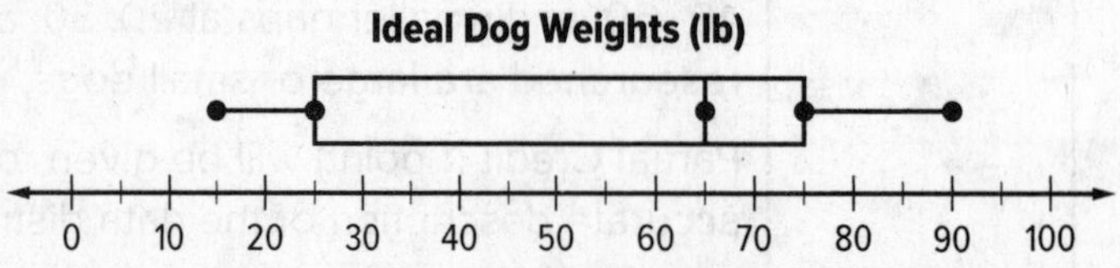 **Ideal Dog Weights (lb)** 0 10 20 30 40 50 60 70 80 90 100 Sample answer: The median divides the data in half, and the median is the center bullet in the box, or 65. Half of the dog breeds have an ideal weight that is at least 65 lb. Partial Credit (1 Point) will be given for a correct box-and-whisker plot OR an appropriate description. No credit will be given for an incorrect answer.
F	2	Full Credit: A line graph shows change over time. Time is not a variable in these data about different dog breeds' ideal weights. Sample answer: A line graph would be appropriate to display the weight of one dog over time, starting at birth. Partial Credit (1 Point) will be given for a correct explanation for not using a line graph OR a data set appropriate for a line graph. No credit will be given for an incorrect answer.
TOTAL	**11**	

Chapter 12 Performance Task

Part A

The data is not equally spread out over the range. It is not symmetrical and there are no peaks. There is a gap between 35 and 65 and more gaps at 20, 30, and 80. This means that there is no data on medium sized dogs.

Part B

Weight	Frequency
0-19	I
20-39	III
40-59	
60-79	IIII
80-99	II

Weights of Dogs

Frequency

Weights (lb)

Part C

The line plot has the advantage of showing the exact numbers which would allow you to determine the mode, mean, and median. The histogram allows you to easily see how many dogs fall into a specific weight range. The disadvantage of the line plot is that you can't quickly see a general picture. The disadvantage of the histogram is that you have no exact numbers. I think the better display is the line plot because you have the exact data if you need it and if you wanted, you could make a histogram from it.

Part D

15, 25, 25, 35, 65, 65, 70, 75, 85, 90

$Q_1 = 25$ $Q_3 = 75$

IQR: $75 - 25 = 50$

$50 \times 1.5 = 75$

$25 - 75 = -50$

$75 + 75 = 150$

No data is outside of this range, so no, there are no outliers.

Part E

Weights of Dogs (pounds)

The ideal weight of at least half the dogs is 65 because the line showing where the median is is at 65.

Part F

These are all different weights of dogs, and aren't connected to each other. Line graphs have data that are connected to each other because of time passing. Data about a dog that could be put on a line graph would be a dog's weight as it gets older.

Student Work Sample

Chapter 12 Performance Task

Part A

There is a wide spread of data with a gap in the middle.
This means there was no research done on medium sized dogs.

Part B

Weight (lb)	Number
0-20	1
20-40	3
40-60	0
60-80	4
80-100	2

Part C

Line Plot
pros: exact data
Cons: no easy overall picture

Histogram
pros: lets you get a general idea
con: no specific data

I would pick the histogram because you can see that the data has more medium large dogs than any other.

Part D

$IQR = 50$
$50(1.5) = 75$
Yes, because there is data greater than 75.

Part E

The ideal weight is at least 65 lbs.

Part F

It doesn't make sense to connect the points because it does not show change over time. You could graph height as a dog grows up on a line graph.

Chapter 12 Performance Task

Part A

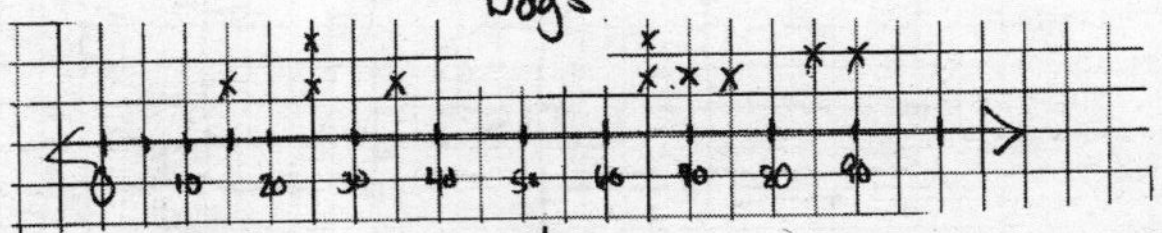

Dogs

The distribution tells us the dogs have differend weghts.

Part B

Weights	#
0-9	0
10-19	1
20-29	2
30-39	1
40-49	0
50-59	0
60-69	2
70-79	2
80-89	1
90-99	1

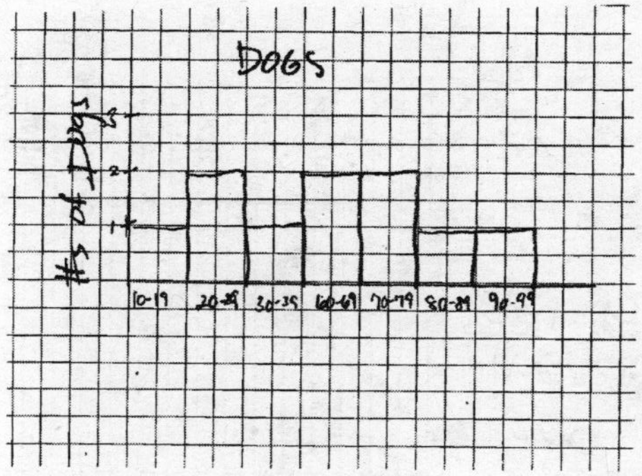

Dogs

Part C

I like the line plot more because you get to see a general overall picture of the data without worrying about the specifics.

Part D

15
25
25
35
65
65
70
75
85
90

There are no outliers because there is nothing too far away from the mean.

Part E

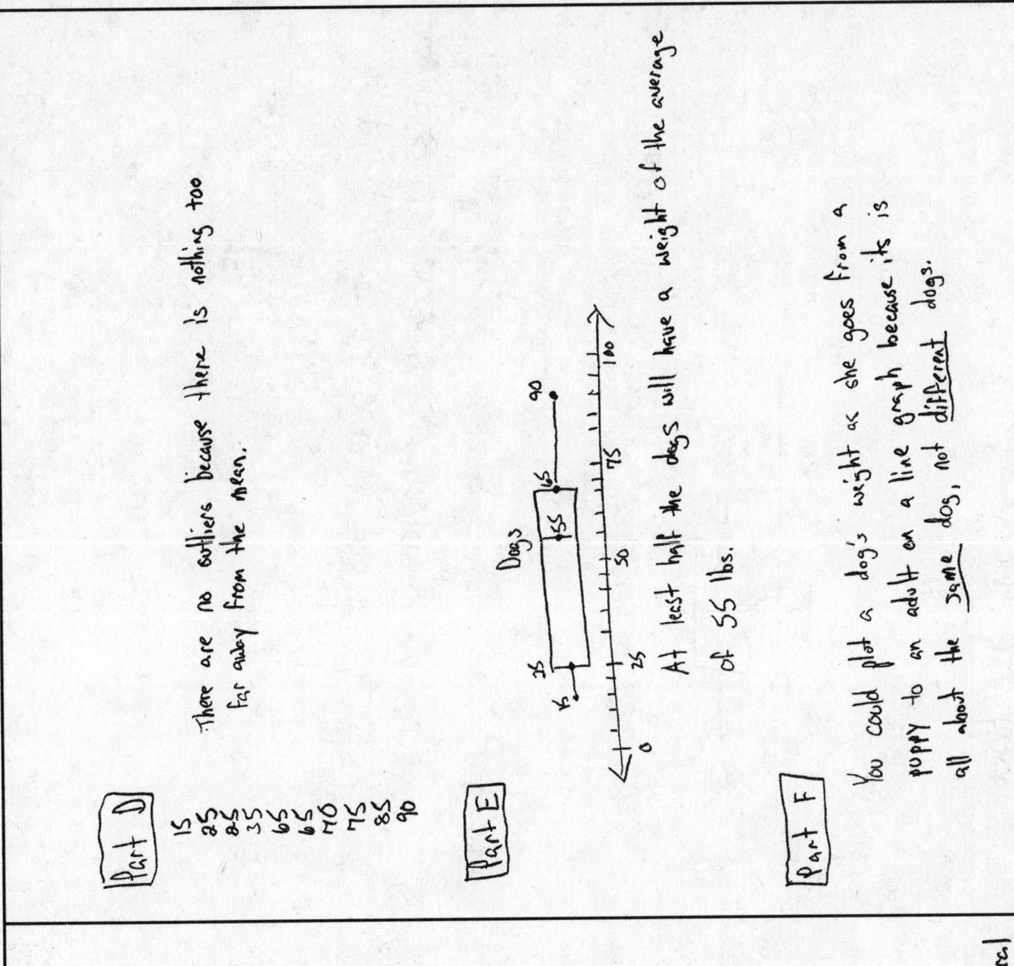

At least half the dogs will have a weight of the average of 55 lbs.

Part F

You could plot a dog's weight as she goes from a puppy to an adult on a line graph because its is all about the same dog, not different dogs.

Student Work Sample

Chapter 12 Performance Task

PART A

Poodle, Beagle, Cocker, Husky, Collie, Boxer, Golden, Setter, Doberman, German

0, 10, 20, 30, 40, 50, 60, 70, 80, 90, 100

e data
oes up as
the dogs
get bigger.

PART B

1, 2, 3, 4

0-25, 25-50, 50-75, 75-100

PART C
The second is better because it is
easier to display the data.

PART D

Yes. 90 and 15 are on the ends so
they are the outliers.

PART E

15, 52.5, 90

15, 52.5, 90

At least 1/2 dogs would weigh 52.5.

PART F

You could display dogs age on a line
graph because it has to do with time.

NAME ______________ DATE ________ PERIOD ______ SCORE ______

Benchmark Test, Chapters 1–4

1. Namid works for a florist and is making flower arrangements for the tables at a reception. He has 36 roses, 48 tulips, and 72 carnations. Each vase must contain the same number of each type of flower. How many vases will Namid need? How many of each type of flower will he put in one vase? 6.NS.4

Vases: 12

Flowers: 3 roses, 4 tulips, and 6 carnations

2. On a map, 3 centimeters represents 500 miles. 6.RP.3

Part A: Two cities are 9 centimeters apart on the map. How many miles apart are the two cities?

1,500 mi

Part B: Two national parks are 750 miles apart. How many centimeters apart are the two parks on the map?

4.5 cm

3. A restaurant sells an 8-oz drink for \$2.56 and a 12-oz drink for \$3.66. Which drink is the better buy? Justify your answer. 6.RP.2, 6.RP.3, 6.RP.3b

the 12-oz drink; The unit rate of the 12-oz drink is $3.66 \div 12 = \$0.305$ per ounce. The unit rate of the 8-oz drink is $2.56 \div 8 = \$0.32$ per ounce, and $0.305 < 0.32$.

4. Desta reads at a constant rate of 3 pages in 8 minutes. 6.RP.3, 6.RP.3a

Part A: Complete the ratio table for Desta's reading rate.

Number of Pages	3	6	9	12
Time (min)	8	16	24	32

Part B: Graph the ordered pairs that show the time it takes Desta to read 3, 6, 9, and 12 pages.

Time (min): 3, 6, 9, 12, 15, 18, 21, 24, 27, 30, 33, 36
Number of Pages: 1, 2, 3, 4, 5, 6, 7, 8, 9, 10, 11, 12

5. A train travels at a rate of 84 miles per hour. Select all of the rates that are equivalent to the train's speed. 6.RP.2, 6.NS.2

- ☐ 162 miles in 2 hours
- ■ 252 miles in 3 hours
- ■ 378 miles in 4.5 hours
- ☐ 489 miles in 6 hours
- ■ 621.6 miles in 7.4 hours

6. Sort the decimals into the appropriate bins by their percent values. 6.RP.3

1.3 | 0.9 | 89.2 | 0.398 | 1 | 0.095

Greater than 90%	Equal to 90%	Less than 90%
1.3 89.2 1	0.9	0.095 0.398

7. A student conducted a survey of other students to find the number of sports they play. The table shows the results of the survey. 6.RP.3

Number of Sports Played	0	1	2	3+
Portion of Responses	0.25	$\frac{1}{5}$	$\frac{3}{8}$	17.5%

Complete the table to order the responses from least to greatest percent of students.

	Number of Sports Played	Percent of Students
Least	3+	17.5
	1	20
	0	25
Greatest	2	37.5

8. Mr. Guerrero counted 60 students wearing a school shirt. Select all the expressions that represent this value. 6.RP.3, 6.RP.3c

- [x] 10% of 600 students
- [ ] 15% of 500 students
- [ ] 20% of 400 students
- [x] 25% of 240 students
- [x] 40% of 150 students

9. A sewing needle manufacturer states that an average of $\frac{1}{5}$% of the needles produced will be defective. Last week, 150,000 needles were produced. Predict the number of needles that were defective. 6.RP.3, 6.RP.3c

300 needles

10. In the first football game, the quarterback completed 18 out of the 24 passes he attempted. 6.RP.3, 6.RP.3c

Part A: What percent of the passes did the quarterback complete?

75%

Part B: In the next game, the quarterback completed 19 of the 26 passes he attempted. Explain the change in the quarterback's overall percentage of completion for the two games compared to his completion percentage from the first game.

The quarterback's overall percentage decreased. For the two games, he completed 18 + 19 = 37 passes out of 24 + 26 = 50 attempts, which is 74%. In the first game, he completed 75%, so his percentage decreased.

11. Amadahy wants to buy a card and two gifts for her friend. Cards cost $3.49 each and gifts cost $10.63 each. Amadahy has a $20 bill. Does she have enough money to buy these items? If so, how much change will she receive? If not, how much more money does she need? Explain. 6.NS.3

No, she does not have enough money. The items cost 2(10.63) + 3.49 = $24.75. So she needs 24.75 – 20 = $4.75 more.

12. Select all of the expressions that have a product with only two decimal places. 6.NS.3

- [x] 0.45 × 37
- [x] 6.7 × 5.3
- [ ] 2.17 × 3.48
- [ ] 6.148 × 6.32
- [ ] 5.02 × 8.04
- [x] 7.54 × 14.5

13. The rectangles have the same area. What is the length of the unknown side? 6.NS.3

1.8 m
9.36 m
?
3.6 m

4.68 m

14. The table shows Amiri's jogging workouts for four days. Complete the table to order the days from Amiri's slowest to fastest jogging rate. 6.RP.3, 6.RP.3b

Day	Distance (mi)	Time (h)
Monday	4.75	1.25
Wednesday	6.21	1.8
Friday	8.64	2.4
Sunday	9.13	2.2

	Day	Rate (mph)
Slowest	Wednesday	3.45
	Friday	3.6
	Monday	3.8
Fastest	Sunday	4.15

15. One machine at a manufacturer makes 81,600 paper clips in a day. 6.NS.2

Part A: The machine runs at a constant speed all day. How many paper clips are made each hour?

3,400 paper clips

Part B: One size box can hold 40 paper clips. How many boxes are filled each hour?

85 boxes

16. On a baseball diamond, the distance from home plate to first base is 90 feet. Sort the lengths into the appropriate bins by how each length compares to the baseball distance. 6.RP.3, 6.RP.3d

360 ft	30 yd	$\frac{1}{50}$ mi
900 in.	0.015 mi	1,090 in.

Less than 90 ft	Equal to 90 ft	Greater than 90 ft
900 in. 0.015 mi	30 yd	$\frac{1}{50}$ mi 360 ft 1,090 in.

17. Mrs. Harris took 6 oranges out of the refrigerator and cut them into wedges. Each wedge represents $\frac{1}{6}$ of the entire orange. Her children ate $\frac{3}{4}$ of the wedges. How many wedges are left? Justify your answer. 6.NS.1

9 wedges; Sample answer: $6 \div \frac{1}{6} = 36$ total wedges; $\frac{3}{4} \times 36 = 27$ wedges the children ate. Subtract $36 - 27 = 9$ wedges left.

18. A salami is $2\frac{3}{5}$ inches long. The salami is cut into $\frac{1}{8}$-inch thick slices. 6.NS.1

Part A: How many slices of salami were cut?

20 slices

Part B: Write the correct numbers to identify the length of the leftover piece of salami. You can write 1 or 2 numbers in each box to make either a 1-digit or a 2-digit number.

1 2 3 4 5
6 7 8 9 0

$\frac{1}{10}$ inch

19. Two numbers are multiplied and the product is $\frac{3}{8}$. 6.NS.1

Part A: Select whether each statement is true or false.

True	False	
☐	■	Both factors are less than $\frac{3}{8}$.
■	☐	One factor is less than $\frac{3}{8}$; the other factor is greater than $\frac{3}{8}$.
■	☐	Both factors are greater than $\frac{3}{8}$.

Part B: Give an example to support a true statement.

Sample answer: $\frac{3}{4} \times \frac{1}{2} = \frac{3}{8}$; both fractions are greater than $\frac{3}{8}$.

20. There are 75 boys in the sixth grade. The number of boys is $\frac{5}{12}$ of the students in the sixth grade. How many of the sixth-grade students are girls? 6.NS.1

105 girls

Page 156 • The Stock Market

Note to teacher: For this Performance Task, have students research stock data for three companies. Students should collect the price of the stock, the amount of increase or decrease from the previous day, the P/E ratio, a five-day history, and a five-year history. Have students share their findings.

Task Scenario Students will analyze, display, and represent real-world stock data by using rate and ratio reasoning and performing operations involving decimals, percents, and fractions.	
CCSS Content Standard(s)	6.RP.1, 6.RP.2, 6.RP.3, 6.RP.3a, 6.RP.3b, 6.RP.3c, 6.NS.3
Mathematical Practices	MP1, MP2, MP4, MP5, MP6, MP7
Depth of Knowledge	DOK2, DOK3

Part	Maximum Points	Scoring Rubric
A	2	Full Credit: The P/E is the ratio of the current price of stock per share to annual earnings per share. Sample data: Company A: 24.93; Company B: 2.26; Company C: 16.08 Company A: For every \$24.93 of the current price, the stock earns \$1.00 annually. Company B: For every \$2.26 of the current stock price, the stock earns \$1.00 annually. Company C: For every \$16.08 of the current stock price, the stock earns \$1.00 annually. Company B earns the most annually per share because a person receives more money when the stock price is lower. Company A earns the least annually per share. Partial Credit (1 point) will be given for correct ratio language describing the relationship between the two quantities OR the correct comparison of the ratios. No credit will be given for an incorrect answer.
B	1	Full Credit: Sample data: Company A: $\frac{\text{today's price (\$)}}{\text{yesterday's price (\$)}}: \frac{92.37}{89.14} \approx 1.0362 \approx 104\%$ Today's price is about 104% of yesterday's price. Company B: $\frac{\text{today's price (\$)}}{\text{yesterday's price (\$)}}: \frac{42.28}{46.59} \approx 0.9075 \approx 91\%$ Today's price is about 91% of yesterday's price. Company C: $\frac{\text{today's price (\$)}}{\text{yesterday's price (\$)}}: \frac{74.82}{65.92} \approx 1.1350 \approx 114\%$ Today's price is about 114% of yesterday's price. No credit will be given for an incorrect answer.

<table>
<tr><th>Part</th><th>Maximum Points</th><th>Scoring Rubric</th></tr>
<tr><td>C</td><td>4</td><td>Full Credit:
Sample data: Today's stock price: Company A: $92.37; Company B: $42.28; Company C: $74.82

Company A: Let x represent the number of shares and y represent the total value of the stock. So, $y = 92.37x$. The value of 15 shares is $1,385.55.

Company B: [graph: Total Value of Stock ($) (0, 50, 100, 150, 200) vs. Number of Shares (0, 2, 4, 6, 8, 10), axes x and y]

The value of 15 shares is 15 × 42.28 = $634.20.
Company C:

Shares: 0, 1, 2, 3, 4
Total Value ($): 0, 74.82, 149.64, 224.46, 299.28

The value of 15 shares is 15 × 74.82 = $1,122.30.

Partial Credit (1 point) will be given for the correct equation OR correct graph OR correct table OR correct prices for 15 shares.

No credit will be given for an incorrect answer.</td></tr>
<tr><td>D</td><td>2</td><td>Full Credit:
Sample data:

High Prices | Company A | Company B | Company C
Current | $92.37 | $42.28 | $74.82
5 years ago | $41.28 | $12.63 | $83.14

Company A: 92.37 – 41.28 = 51.09; Company A's stock has increased $51.09 per share since five years ago.

Company B: 42.28 – 12.63 = 29.65; Company B's stock has increased $29.65 per share since five years ago.

Company C: 83.14 – 74.82 = 8.32; Company C's stock has decreased $8.32 per share since five years ago.

Partial Credit (1 point) will be given for the correct differences OR sentences that accurately describe the difference in context.

No credit will be given for an incorrect answer.</td></tr>
<tr><td>TOTAL</td><td>9</td><td></td></tr>
</table>

NAME ______________ DATE ________ PERIOD ________ SCORE ________

Benchmark Test, Performance Task, Chapters 5–8

1. Mark owes Veronica \$19 for building a doghouse for his dog. Veronica has eight \$1 bills in her purse. Explain the meaning of 0 in this situation. 6.NS.5

The integer 0 represents neither owing money nor having money.

2. Last week, the town of Maineville was behind the average weekly rainfall by 3 inches. After today's rainfall, the town was ahead of the average weekly rainfall by 4 inches. Graph both points on the number line. 6.NS.6

–5 –4 –3 –2 –1 0 1 2 3 4 5

3. Circle all of the phrases that can be described by the same absolute value. 6.NS.7, 6.NS.7c

(a loss of 12°) (an increase in a room's temperature by 12°)

(12° above freezing) an increase in an oven's temperature by 10°

4. The table shows the melting points of five different elements to the nearest degree Celsius. Is the absolute value of the highest melting point greater than, less than, or equal to the absolute value of the lowest melting point? Justify your reasoning. 6.NS.7, 6.NS.7c

Element	Melting Point (°C)
Bromine	–7
Francium	27
Radon	–71
Rubidium	39
Mercury	–39

less than; Sample answer: Rubidium is the highest at 39°C. The lowest is radon at –71°C and |39| < |–71|.

5. A contractor needs bricks that are 8 inches long for a project. The table shows the difference between 8 inches and the actual length of four types of bricks. 6.NS.7, 6.NS.7a

Brick	Difference (in.)
A	$-0.\overline{6}$
B	$\frac{2}{3}$
C	$\frac{5}{6}$
D	–0.625

Part A: Which bricks are longer than what the contractor needs? Order the differences from least to greatest.

Bricks A and D

A < D < B < C

Part B: Between which two bricks is the brick size that the contractor needs? Justify your response.

Bricks D and B; Brick D is 8 – (–0.625) = 8.625, Brick B is $8 - \frac{2}{3} = 7\frac{1}{3}$ and $7\frac{1}{3} < 8 < 8.625$

6. The base of Ricardo's house is in the shape of a rectangle. The points *A*, *B*, and *C* represent three corners of the base of the house. 6.NS.6, 6.NS.6b, 6.NS.6c

Part A: Complete the table by identifying the ordered pair that names each point. Then identify the quadrant in which each point is located.

Point	Ordered Pair	Quadrant
A	(–4, 3)	II
B	(5, 3)	I
C	(5, –3)	IV

Part B: Identify the ordered pair for point *D*, the fourth corner of the base of the house.

(–4, –3)

7. Which expression is not equivalent to the other three? Justify your response. 6.EE.1, 6.NS.3

$0.3^2 + 8$ | $2^3 + 0.09$ | $2^3 + 0.03^2$ | $3^2 \div 10^2 + 2^3$

$2^3 + 0.03^2$; The other three expressions each have a value of 8.09, while $2^3 + 0.03^2 = 8 + 0.0009 = 8.0009$.

8. The table shows the pounds of corn picked by each of Shani's cousins at an All-You-Can-Pick corn farm. The cousins picked a total of 85 pounds of corn. 6.EE.2, 6.EE.6

Name	Corn Picked (lb)
Ann	x
Ben	23
Chris	35
David	15

Part A: Write the appropriate numbers, variables, and symbols in the expression to represent the total number of pounds of corn picked by the cousins.

+	–	×	÷	x
23	35	15	85	73

73 + x

Part B: How many pounds of corn did Ann pick?

12 lb

9. Each row in the table shows a pair of expressions.

Part A: Complete the second column in the table. Write whether the pairs of expressions in each row are equivalent.

Expressions	Equivalent? Yes or No	Property
7 – 3 and 3 – 7	No	
d × 1 and d	Yes	Identity Property of Mult.
(3 + y) + 2 and (y + 3) + 2	Yes	Commutative Property of Add.
(3 + y) + 2 and 3 + (y + 2)	Yes	Associative Property of Add.
0 × m and m	No	

Part B: Complete the third column in the table. Write the property that is applied for each pair of equivalent expressions. 6.EE.3

Associative Property of Add.	Associative Property of Mult.
Commutative Property of Add.	Commutative Property of Mult.
Identity Property of Add.	Identity Property of Mult.
Distributive Property	Addition Property of Equality

10. Marta and four friends went to a movie. The movie tickets were $7 each. Each person also paid y dollars for a snack and a drink. 6.EE.3, 6.NS.4

Part A: Write the appropriate numbers and variables in the expression to represent the amount they spent altogether.

4	5	7
12	28	y

5 × (7 + y)

Part B: Write the expression in simplified form.

35 + 5y

11. For a small-sized box, a shipping company charges x dollars to ship the package, y dollars to wrap the package, and $6 to insure the package. The expression $5x + 5y + 30 + x + y$ represents the total cost of shipping, packaging, and insuring 5 packages, and shipping and packaging 1 package without insurance. 6.EE.2, 6.EE.2b, 6.EE.4

List all the terms of the expression.

5x, 5y, 30, x, y

List the coefficients of the expression.

5, 5, 1, 1

List the constant(s) of the expression.

30

Write the expression in simplified form.

$6x + 6y + 30$

12. Select all of the equations that have a solution of 4. 6.EE.5

- ☐ $g - 3 = 7$
- ■ $\frac{20}{g} = 5$
- ■ $12 + g = 16$
- ☐ $\frac{g}{2} = 8$
- ■ $8g = 32$
- ■ $4(5 - g) = g$

13. Yang is y years old. His brother is 4.5 years younger than Yang. His brother is 9.5 years old. 6.EE.7

Part A: Write a subtraction equation to model the situation.

$y - 4.5 = 9.5$ OR $y - 9.5 = 4.5$

Part B: Solve the equation to find Yang's age.

14 years old

14. Mrs. Ruiz travels a distance of 144 miles to attend a business meeting. She drives for 3 hours at an average speed of r miles per hour. 6.EE.7, 6.RP.3

Part A: Write the appropriate numbers, symbols, and variables to represent the situation with an equation.

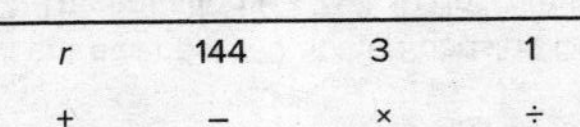

r	144	3	1
+	–	×	÷

144 = **r** **×** **3**

Part B: What is Mrs. Ruiz's average speed in miles per hour?

48 mph

15. Kathy rode her bike 8 miles today. This was $\frac{1}{4}$ of the miles she rode this month. How many miles m did Kathy ride her bike this month? Justify your answer using an equation. 6.EE.7

32 mi; Sample answer: $\frac{1}{4}m = 8$; multiply each side by 4 to get $m = 32$.

16. Todd's car consumes an average of 1 gallon of gas for every 25 miles he drives. Select all of the representations that model this function. 6.EE.9

■ 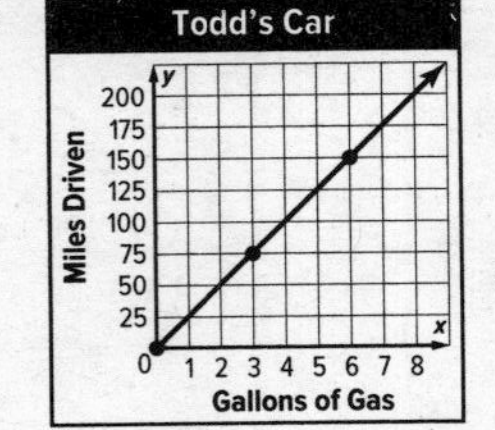

☐ $y = 20x + 5$, where y represents the total number of miles driven and x represents the number of gallons of gas

■

Miles Driven	250	300	480	600
Gallons of Gas	10	12	19.2	24

17. A recycling company uses the inequality $t \geq 3.5$, where t is the mass of paper recycled per month, to determine whether they recycle enough paper to make a profit that month. Sort the months into the appropriate bins based on whether the company made a profit that month recycling paper. 6.EE.5

Month	Mass of Paper, t
January	4.2
February	1.8
March	3.9
April	3.5
May	1.5
June	0.75

January February March

April May June

Made a Profit	Did Not Make a Profit
January March April	**February May June**

18. The construction crew has less than 7 days left to complete the road repairs. Let *d* represent the number of days left to complete the road repairs. 6.EE.6, 6.EE.8

Part A: Write an inequality to represent this situation.

$d < 7$

Part B: Graph the solution of the inequality on the number line.

0 1 2 3 4 5 6 7 8 9 10 11 12

19. Akeelah buys an $18 binder for her baseball cards. The baseball cards she purchases cost $12 per box. 6.EE.2, 6.EE.2c

Part A: Complete the table to find the cost when Akeelah buys 2, 3, 5, and 7 boxes of cards.

Number of Boxes, *x*	$12x + 18$	Cost ($), *y*
2	12(2) + 18	42
3	12(3) + 18	54
5	12(5) + 18	78
7	12(7) + 18	102

Part B: What is the cost of 10 boxes of baseball cards and a binder?

$138

20. All entrees cost $10 at the Roadside Diner. Each side dish is an additional $2. The equation $y = 2x + 10$ describes the total cost, *y*, for the number of side dishes, *x*. Graph the equation of the line. 6.EE.9

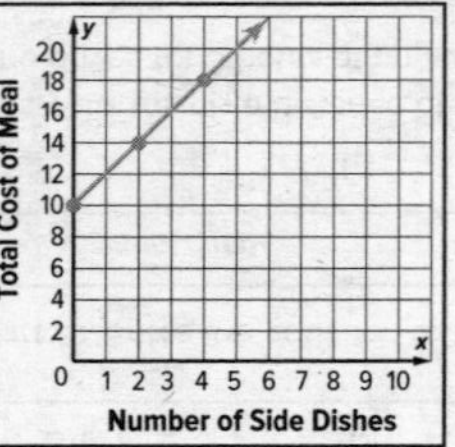

Page 164 • Big Foot

Note to teacher: For this Performance Task, have students measure the foot length of 10 other students. The measurements should be from the back of the heel to the top of the longest toe. Students should find the length of each foot to the nearest $\frac{1}{8}$ inch and to the nearest tenth of a centimeter. Have students share their findings.

Task Scenario	
Students will use, write, and graph rational numbers, expressions, equations, and functions to describe the relationship between the length of a foot in inches and its length in centimeters.	
CCSS Content Standard(s)	6.NS.8, 6.EE.2, 6.EE.2c, 6.EE.5, 6.EE.6, 6.EE.7, 6.EE.8, 6.EE.9
Mathematical Practices	MP1, MP2, MP4, MP5, MP6, MP7, MP8
Depth of Knowledge	DOK2, DOK3, DOK4

Part	Maximum Points	Scoring Rubric
A	2	Full Credit:

Sample data:

Length (in.)	$6\frac{5}{8}$	$7\frac{1}{4}$	$7\frac{3}{8}$	$7\frac{3}{4}$	$8\frac{1}{8}$
Length (cm)	16.8	18.4	18.7	19.7	20.6

Length (in.)	$8\frac{7}{8}$	9	$9\frac{3}{8}$	$9\frac{1}{2}$	$10\frac{1}{8}$
Length (cm)	22.5	22.9	23.8	24.1	25.7

Sample graph:

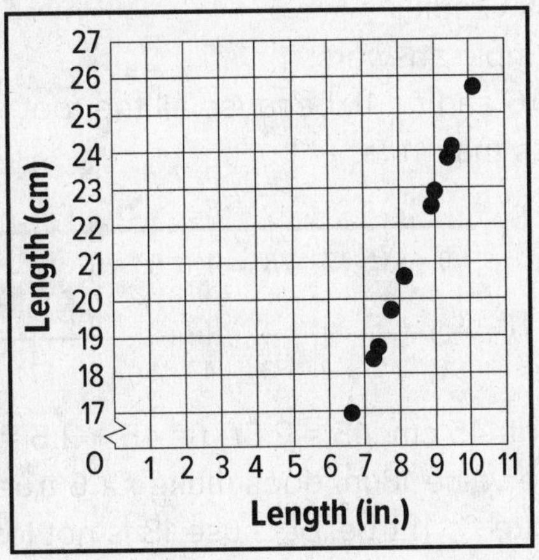

Partial Credit (1 point) will be given for a correct table OR a correct graph.

No credit will be given for an incorrect answer.

Part	Maximum Points	Scoring Rubric
B	2	Full Credit: Sample answer: The number of centimeters is about 2.5 times the number of inches. $2.5x$, where x represents the number of inches Caro's father's foot: 13 in. Substitute 13 for x in the expression: $2.5x = 2.5(13) = 32.5$ Caro's father's foot is about 32.5 cm long. Partial Credit (1 point) will be given for a description and expression OR the correct foot length in centimeters. No credit will be given for an incorrect answer.
C	3	Full Credit: Function: $y = 2.5x$ Negative integers would not make sense because length is always positive. Baily's foot: 23.125 cm; Substitute into the function. $23.125 = 2.5x$; Divide each side by 2.5 to get $9.25 = x$. Baily's foot is about 9.25 in. long. Partial Credit (2 points) will be given for 2 of these 3: the correct function OR an appropriate explanation of integers OR the correct foot length in inches. Partial Credit (1 point) will be given for 1 of the 3 above. No credit will be given for an incorrect answer.
D	3	Full Credit: Sample answers: $f \geq 6$ and $f < 11$, because all the foot lengths are at least 6 in. and less than 11 in. $f \geq 6$: 0 1 2 3 4 5 6 7 8 9 10 11 12 13 14 15 $f < 11$: 0 1 2 3 4 5 6 7 8 9 10 11 12 13 14 15 Foot: 45 cm: $45 = 2.5f$; $f = 45 \div 2.5 = 18$ in. The value 18 in. does make $f \geq 6$ true, because $18 \geq 6$. It does not make $f < 11$ true, because 18 is not less than 11. Partial Credit (2 points) will be given for 2 of these 3: two correct inequalities OR two correct graphs OR the correct answer and explanation. Partial Credit (1 point) will be given for 1 of the 3 above. No credit will be given for an incorrect answer.
TOTAL	**10**	

NAME ______________ DATE ________ PERIOD ______ SCORE ______

Benchmark Test A, Chapters 1–12

1. The Andersons drove 175 miles in $3\frac{1}{2}$ hours. 6.RP.2, 6.RP.3, 6.RP.3b, 6.RP.3d

Part A: What is their average driving rate, in miles per hour?

50 mph

Part B: At this rate, how many miles will the Andersons drive in $8\frac{1}{2}$ hours?

425 mi

Part C: What is the Andersons' driving rate in feet per second? Round to the nearest tenth.

73.3 ft/s

2. A bookstore advertises 4 paperback books for $18.00. Select all of the equivalent ratios. 6.RP.1, 6.RP.3, 6.RP.3a

- ☐ 1 book for $4.00
- ■ 3 books for $13.50
- ☐ 6 books for $25.00
- ■ 9 books for $40.50
- ■ 10 books for $45.00

3. Students at a middle school were surveyed to determine how they arrive at school each day. The table shows the results of the survey. Complete the table to order the responses from least to greatest percent of students. 6.RP.3

How Students Arrive at School	Portion of Students
Walk	29%
Bicycle	$\frac{1}{4}$
Dropped off	0.06
Bus	$\frac{2}{5}$

	How Students Arrive at School	Percent of Students
Least	Dropped off	6%
	Bicycle	25%
	Walk	29%
Greatest	Bus	40%

4. A principal estimated that 100 students attended the school's play. Select all of the statements that could represent this estimate. 6.RP.3, 6.RP.3c

- ■ 65% of 150 students
- ■ 24% of 394 students
- ☐ 52% of 140 students
- ☐ 78% of 211 students

5. A store reduces the price of a jacket by 40%. The sale price of the jacket is marked as $30.00. 6.RP.3, 6.RP.3c

Part A: What percent of the original price is the sale price?

60%

Part B: What was the original price of the jacket?

$50.00

6. Decide whether each product will have 3 decimal places. 6.NS.3

Yes	No	
☐	■	42.7 × 3.5
■	☐	6 × 1.732
■	☐	1.85 × 10.7
☐	■	20.34 × 5.02
☐	■	6.217 × 5.384

7. Sebastian ran 8.64 miles in 2.4 hours at a steady pace. 6.NS.2, 6.NS.3, 6.RP.3, 6.RP.3d

Part A: How many miles did Sebastian run in 1 hour?

3.6 mi

Part B: How many miles did Sebastian run in the last 24 minutes? Justify your answer.

1.44 mi; Sample answer: 24 min = 24 ÷ 60 = 0.4 h. After 2 hs, he ran 2 × 3.6 = 7.2 mi. During the last 0.4 h, he ran 8.64 – 7.2 = 1.44 mi.

8. Decide whether each product is less than 1, equal to 1, or greater than 1. Sort the products into the appropriate bins. 6.NS.1

$\frac{2}{3} \times \frac{3}{4}$ | $\frac{4}{5} \times 1\frac{1}{4}$ | $\frac{1}{6} \times 6\frac{1}{2}$ | $\frac{7}{10} \times 2\frac{1}{3}$ | $\frac{3}{5} \times \frac{9}{10}$

Greater than 1	Equal to 1	Less than 1
$\frac{1}{6} \times 6\frac{1}{2}$ $\frac{7}{10} \times 2\frac{1}{3}$	$\frac{4}{5} \times 1\frac{1}{4}$	$\frac{2}{3} \times \frac{3}{4}$ $\frac{3}{5} \times \frac{9}{10}$

9. A baker cuts pies into equal slices as shown in the diagram. Select all of the expressions the baker can use to find the total number of pie slices. 6.NS.1

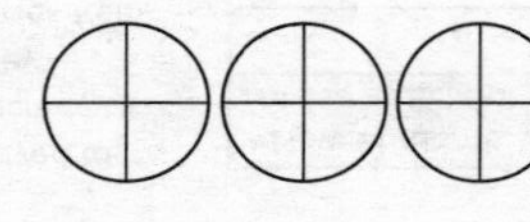
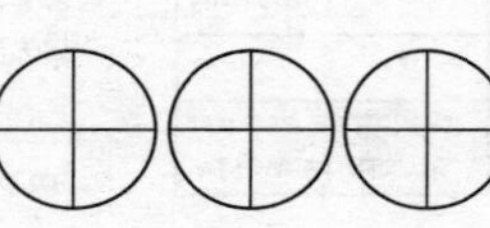
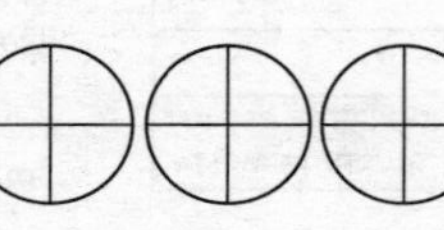
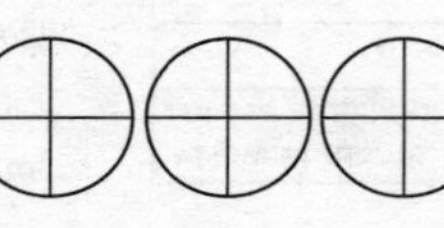
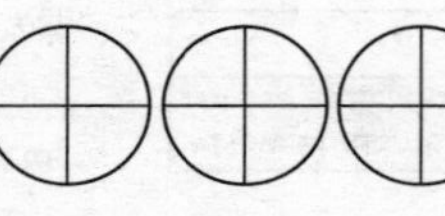

- ☐ $3 \div \frac{1}{4} = \frac{3}{4}$
- ■ $3 \div \frac{1}{4} = 12$
- ☐ $12 \div \frac{1}{3} = 4$
- ☐ $12 \div \frac{1}{4} = 3$

10. The length of Rosie's garden is $21\frac{1}{4}$ feet. Fencing comes in pieces $2\frac{1}{8}$ feet long. 6.NS.1

Part A: How many pieces of fencing will Rosie need along the length of her garden?

10 pieces

Part B: For each piece of fencing, 4 stakes are used to secure it in place. The stakes are equally spaced along the fencing piece, with one stake at each end. How far apart are the stakes on one piece of fencing?

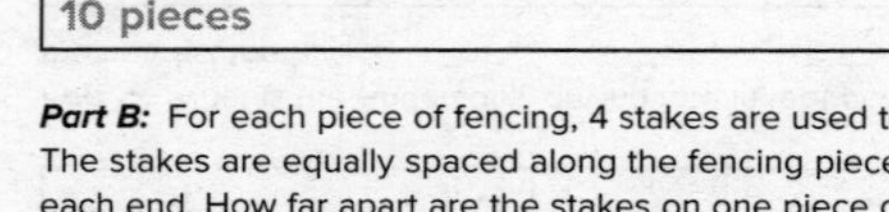

$\frac{17}{24}$ ft

11. The table shows the scores of five golfers at the end of a tournament. The integer 0 represents par. The greater the score, the more golf strokes a player makes. Complete the table to order the players from the fewest strokes to the most strokes. 6.NS.7, 6.NS.7b

Player	Golf Score
Isao	7
Vijay	–5
Phil	–12
Eldrick	2
Jack	0

	Score	Player
Fewest strokes	–12	Phil
	–5	Vijay
	0	Jack
	2	Eldrick
Most strokes	7	Isao

12. A student wants to compare these numbers. 6.NS.6, 6.NS.6c, 6.NS.7, 6.NS.7a

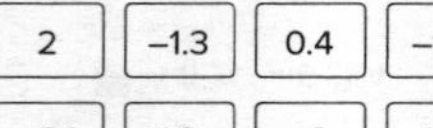

2 | –1.3 | 0.4 | $-1\frac{1}{2}$ | –3.1 | 1.3 | –2 | 4.0

Part A: Graph the points on the number line. Label the points.

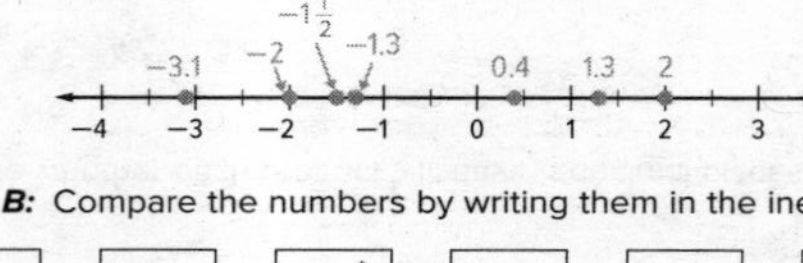

Part B: Compare the numbers by writing them in the inequality.

$-3.1 < -2 < -1\frac{1}{2} < -1.3 < 0.4 < 1.3 < 2 < 4.0$

13. Mr. Wong graphed points *A* and *B* on the coordinate plane and then connected them. 6.NS.6, 6.NS.6b, 6.NS.8

Part A: Reflect points *A* and *B* over the *y*-axis and then connect them.

Part B: How do the coordinates of the reflected points compare to the coordinates of the original points *A* and *B*?

The *x*-coordinates are opposites and the *y*-coordinates are the same.

14. Powers have a base and an exponent. Sort each power into the appropriate bin based on how the value compares to 16. 6.EE.1

4^2 5^3 3^5

2^4 3^2 8^2

Less than 16	Equal to 16	Greater than 16
3^2	4^2 2^4	5^3 3^5 8^2

15. Five friends went to an amusement park. The cost of admission per person is x dollars. Three friends paid $30 each for a front-of-line pass. The group had a $20 coupon off the total price. Circle all of the expressions that represent the total cost. 6.EE.2, 6.EE.2a, 6.EE.4

$5x + 30 - 20$ $3(30) + 2x - 20$ $5(x + 30) - 20$ $5x + 70$

$2x + 70$ $3(x + 30) + 2x - 20$ $3(x + 30 - 20) + 2x$ $5x + 10$

$3(x + 10) + 2x$ $3x + 30 + 2x - 20$ $3x + 90 + 2x - 20$ $5x + 30$

16. The rent for an apartment is $800 per month. The landlord charges one month's rent as a deposit plus a nonrefundable damage cost of $250. The expression $800(n + 1) + 250$ represents the cost of the renting the apartment for n months. 6.EE.2, 6.EE.2c, 6.EE.3

Simplify the expression.

$800n + 1{,}050$

How much does the apartment cost to rent for 2 years?

$20,250

17. A teacher said that the solution of an equation is $n = 6$. Select all of the equations that have 6 as the solution. 6.EE.5

- ■ $n + 8 = 14$
- ☐ $5n = 11$
- ☐ $\frac{n}{3} = 18$
- ■ $\frac{60}{n} = 10$
- ■ $15 - n = 9$

18. Nicole has run 2.75 miles so far in a race. The race is 10.5 miles. Write an addition equation and then solve to find out how much farther Nicole has to run. 6.EE.7

Addition equation:

$n + 2.75 = 10.5$

Miles Nicole has to run:

7.75 miles

19. A bus traveled 744 miles between two cities. The bus traveled at a speed of 48 miles per hour. Write a multiplication equation and then solve to find out how many hours it took for the bus to arrive at its destination. 6.EE.7

Multiplication equation:

$48n = 744$

Hours the bus takes to arrive:

15.5 hours

20. A health-club membership costs $30 to join and $40 per month. Select all of the representations of this function. 6.EE.9

■ 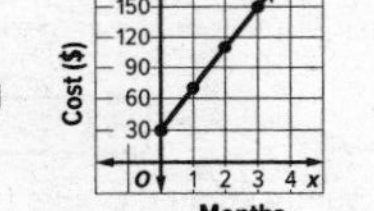

☐ $y = 40 + 30x$, where y represents the total cost and x represents the number of months

■

Number of Months	1	3	5	10
Cost ($)	70	150	230	430

Benchmark Tests

21. Jeremy has $20 to spend. He wants to buy some t-shirts that cost $6.25 each. 6.EE.6, 6.EE.8

Part A: Write an inequality to find out how many t-shirts Jeremy can buy. Identify any variables you include.

$6.25n \le 20$, where *n* represents the number of t-shirts

Part B: Solve the inequality. At most, how many t-shirts can Jeremy buy?

$n \le 3.2$; 3 t-shirts

22. Lakeesha says that the area of the parallelogram she is looking at is 24 square feet. Samantha says that the area of the triangle she is looking at is also 24 square feet. The girls exclaim, "How can this be?" Select whether each statement is true or false. 6.G.1

True	False	
☐	■	The heights are the same, and the base of the parallelogram is twice the base of the triangle.
☐	■	The base and the height of the parallelogram are both twice the base and height of the triangle.
■	☐	The bases are the same, and the height of the parallelogram is half the height of the triangle.
☐	■	The base and height of both figures are the same.

23. The figure shows the dimensions of a rectangular garden that Consuela originally planned to create. She realizes that a garden of this size will not be large enough for all of the vegetables and flowers that she wants to plant. Consuela considers tripling the length and width of the garden and thinks that the new garden size would be large enough for her plants. Select all of the statements that are true for Consuela's garden. 6.G.1

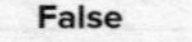

- ■ Consuela needs 3 times the length of fencing to enclose the larger garden than the smaller garden.
- ☐ Consuela needs 12 times the length of fencing to enclose the larger garden than the smaller garden.
- ☐ Consuela will have 3 times as much space for her plants with the larger garden than with the smaller garden.
- ■ Consuela will have 9 times as much space for her vegetables and flowers with the larger garden than with the smaller garden.

24. The diagram shows the outline of a school's playground. What is the area of the playground? 6.G.1

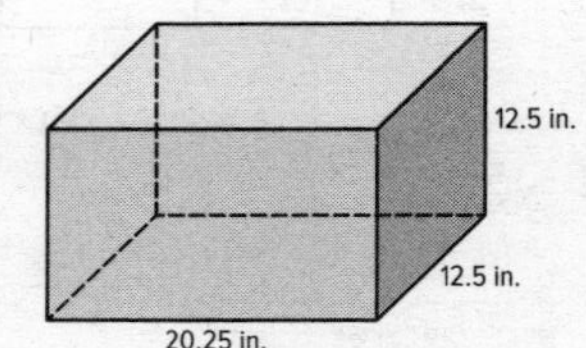

5,400 ft²

25. The diagram shows the dimensions of Paloma's fish tank. 6.G.2

Part A: What is the greatest volume of water that the fish tank can hold? Round to the nearest tenth.

3,164.1 in³

Part B: Paloma fills the fish tank with water to a height of 8 inches. How much more water can she put into the fish tank? Round to the nearest tenth.

1,139.1 in³

26. The points $A(-5, 3)$ and $B(3, -2)$ are the endpoints of the hypotenuse of a right triangle graphed on a coordinate plane. 6.G.3

Part A: What point can be graphed to make a right triangle whose hypotenuse is segment *AB*?

(−5, −2) OR (3, 3)

Use the coordinates of the point in Part A to find the lengths of the two sides that form the right angle in the triangle.

vertical side: 5; horizontal side: 8

Part B: Is there another point that can be graphed to make a different right triangle than the one described in Part A? Explain.

Yes; The point is on the other side of the hypotenuse. It can be either (−5, −2) or (3, 3).

27. Sheila purchases the gift box shown. What is the least amount of wrapping paper that Sheila needs to completely cover the box? 6.G.4

8 in. 6 in. 0.75 in.

117 in^2

28. The list shows a student's quiz scores. 6.SP.3, 6.SP.5, 6.SP.5a

6 10 5 6 6 10 8 9

Part A: Write the appropriate number for each data measure.

3.5	7.5
4	8
5	8.5
6	9.5
7	10

number of data values: 8

mean of quiz scores: 7.5

median of quiz scores: 7

mode of quiz scores: 6

range of quiz scores: 5

interquartile range of quiz scores: 3.5

Part B: What is the mean absolute deviation of the scores? Explain how you found your answer.

1.75; Sample answer: I found the absolute value of the difference between the mean 7.5 and each data value. I took the sum of those differences, 14, and divided by the number of data values, 8, to get 14 ÷ 8 = 1.75.

29. Jenna's bowling scores for five games are listed. Select whether each statement is true or false. 6.SP.3, 6.SP.5, 6.SP.5c

142 138 35 140 142

True	False	
☐	■	The mean is a better measure to represent the data than the median.
■	☐	The mean is less than the median.
■	☐	The range is affected by the lowest score.
☐	■	The mode is affected by the score that is an outlier.

30. The box-and-whisker plot represents the test scores in Ms. Alvarez's class. Select all of the statements that describe the data. 6.SP.4, 6.SP.5, 6.SP.5d

50 60 70 80 90 100

- ■ The median score is 75.
- ■ The range of the scores is 45.
- ☐ The box plot shows clusters and gaps in the data.
- ■ The same number of scores occurs between 55 and 60 as between 80 and 100.
- ☐ The shape of the data distribution is symmetric.
- ■ Half the scores are between 60 and 80.
- ☐ The most appropriate measures of center and spread to describe the data distribution are mean and mean absolute variation.

31. Students in one middle school class kept track of the books they read during summer vacation. The results are in the table. 6.SP.1, 6.SP.2, 6.SP.4

Books Read During Summer Vacation		
1	5	6
4	3	0
3	7	5
4	3	1
3	7	5
5	4	3

Part A: Complete the line plot by graphing points for the data values.

0 1 2 3 4 5 6 7

Number of Books Read

Part B: Is the question "How many books did the students read during summer vacation?" a statistical question?

Yes

Describe the shape of the data distribution.

Sample answer: The distribution is not symmetric. There is a peak at 3. There is a gap at 2. There is a cluster from 3–5.

Which two measures are the same? Explain.

mean and median; The mean is 69 ÷ 18 ≈ 3.83, which rounds to 4 books. The median is the average of the 9th and 10th values, which equals 4 books.

Page 175 • Boxes R Us

Task Scenario		
Students will design boxes given the volumes and will use proportional reasoning to explain why changing a dimension of the box changes its volume. They will analyze the sizes of boxes and make a suggestion as to how Isaiah can advertise his products.		
CCSS Content Standard(s)	6.NS.1, 6.EE.6, 6.EE.7, 6.EE.9, 6.G.1, 6.G.2, 6.G.4, 6.SP.3, 6.SP.5, 6.SP.5a, 6.SP.5c, 6.SP.5d	
Mathematical Practices	MP1, MP2, MP4, MP6, MP8	
Depth of Knowledge	DOK2, DOK3, DOK4	
Part	**Maximum Points**	**Scoring Rubric**
A	3	Full Credit: Sample answer: The lengths of the sides of the box are 3.5 inches, 4 inches, and 6 inches. 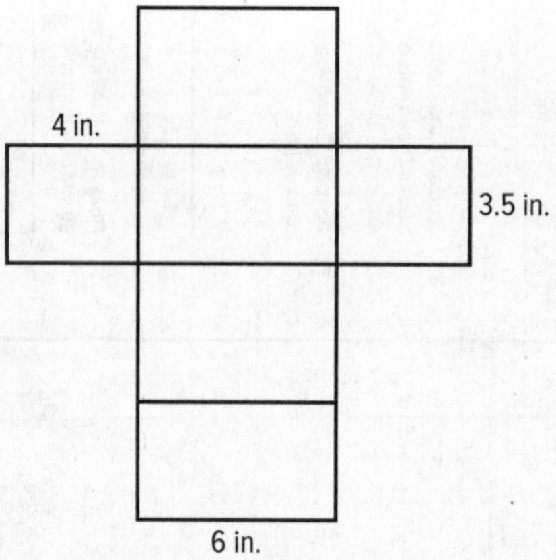 4 in. 3.5 in. 6 in. Partial Credit (1 point) will be given for the correct dimensions, including a fractional length OR correct net but without labels or with incorrect labels. No credit will be given for an incorrect answer.
B	2	Full Credit: Sample answer: Because the volume 336 is 4 times greater than 84, Isaiah can multiply one dimension of the base by 4 or two dimensions by 2 each. That will make the area of the base 4 times greater. Because the formula for the volume of a rectangular prism is $V = Bh$, or the area of the base times the height of the prism, multiplying the area of the base by 4 will also multiply the volume of the prism by 4. Partial Credit (1 point) will be given for correct ways to change the dimensions of the base OR correct analysis of volume formula. No credit will be given for an incorrect answer.

<table>
<tr><th>Part</th><th>Maximum Points</th><th>Scoring Rubric</th></tr>
<tr><td>C</td><td>2</td><td>Full Credit:
<table><tr><td>Side Length (in.)</td><td>1</td><td>2</td><td>3</td><td>4</td><td>5</td></tr><tr><td>Volume (in³)</td><td>1</td><td>8</td><td>27</td><td>64</td><td>125</td></tr></table>
<table><tr><td>Side Length (in.)</td><td>6</td><td>7</td><td>8</td><td>9</td><td>10</td></tr><tr><td>Volume (in³)</td><td>216</td><td>343</td><td>512</td><td>729</td><td>1,000</td></tr></table>
Compare volumes. For length 2, $V = 8$, and for length 4, $V = 64$. So, the equation is $V_2 = 8V_1$.
Partial Credit (1 point) will be given for the correct table OR the correct equation.
No credit will be given for an incorrect answer.</td></tr>
<tr><td>D</td><td>3</td><td>Full Credit:
48 boxes are in stock.
Mean = 33,900 ÷ 48 = 706.25 in^3
Median = 800 in^3
Mode = 800 in^3
Because there is no outlier and one number is not repeated many more times than all the others, the mean would best represent the data.
Partial Credit (2 points) will be given for correct answers in 2 of these 3 parts: number of boxes and accurate values for the measures of center OR the measure that best represents the data without an explanation OR correct explanation of choice of center.
Partial Credit (1 point) will be given for 1 correct answer in the 3 parts listed above.
No credit will be given for an incorrect answer.</td></tr>
<tr><td>E</td><td>1</td><td>Full Credit:
Sample answer: No. The warehouse does not contain large quantities for every size box. So Isaiah should either reword the ad or purchase more of the littlest boxes, the ones with volumes from 100–500 in^3.
Also, a box with volume 100 in^3 would be too big for a ring. Isiah should buy some boxes that are smaller than 100 cubic inches or choose an object other than a ring that has a volume closer to 100 cubic inches for the advertisement.
No credit will be given for an incorrect answer.</td></tr>
<tr><td>TOTAL</td><td>11</td><td></td></tr>
</table>

NAME ____________ DATE ________ PERIOD ______ SCORE ______

Benchmark Test B, Chapters 1–12

1. A bus driver drove 190 miles in $3\frac{4}{5}$ hours at a constant speed. Select whether each statement is true or false about the driver's rate of speed. 6.RP.3, 6.RP.3b, 6.RP.3d

True	False	
■	□	The average rate of speed was 50 miles per hour.
□	■	The average rate of speed was 60 miles per hour.
■	□	The bus driver drove 75 miles in $1\frac{1}{2}$ hours.
■	□	The bus traveled at a rate of 4,400 feet per minute.

2. A grocery store advertises 5 avocados for $6.25. Select all of the prices that are equivalent to the store's advertisement. 6.RP.1, 6.RP.3, 6.RP.3a

- ■ 1 avocado for $1.25
- □ 3 avocados for $2.75
- ■ 6 avocados for $7.50
- □ 8 avocados for $9.00
- ■ 10 avocados for $12.50

3. Children at a daycare center were surveyed to determine which activity is their favorite. The table shows the results of the survey. Complete the table by ordering the activities from the least to greatest percent of children. 6.RP.3

Activity	Portion of Children
Finger Paint	0.07
Outdoor Play	$\frac{2}{5}$
Read	23%
Build with Blocks	$\frac{3}{10}$

	Activity	Percent of Children
Least	Finger Paint	7%
	Read	23%
	Build with Blocks	30%
Greatest	Outdoor Play	40%

4. The manager of a retail store reported that on Friday, 100 shoppers used a coupon. 6.RP.3, 6.RP.3c

Part A: There were 400 shoppers on Friday. Is it likely that 25% of them used a coupon? Justify your answer.

yes; Sample answer: 0.25(400) = 100

Part B: There were 240 shoppers on Friday. Approximately what percent of the shoppers used a coupon? Explain your answer.

approximately 42%; $\frac{100}{240} = \frac{5}{12} = 0.41\overline{6}$, or $41.\overline{6}\% \approx 42\%$

5. A store discounts the price of a beanbag chair by 20%. The price of the beanbag chair is marked as $16. What was the original price of the beanbag chair? 6.RP.3, 6.RP.3c

$20

6. Select whether each product is less than both factors. 6.NS.3

Yes	No	
□	■	4.27 × 0.15
■	□	0.06 × 0.73
□	■	1.65 × 1.0007
■	□	0.0203 × 0.75
■	□	0.99 × 0.99

7. Arianna runs 3.5 miles in 1.25 hours. Select all of the rates that have the same constant rate of change as Arianna's rate. 6.NS.2, 6.NS.3, 6.RP.3, 6.RP.3d

- ■ 4.9 miles in 1.75 hours
- □ 6.5 miles in 2.5 hours
- ■ 0.84 mile in 18 minutes
- ■ 0.7 mile in 15 minutes

8. Sort the expressions into the appropriate bins by the value of their products. 6.NS.1

$1\frac{1}{8} \times 3\frac{3}{4}$ | $3\frac{3}{4} \times \frac{5}{4}$ | $\frac{2}{13} \times 6\frac{1}{2}$ | $\frac{9}{10} \times \frac{1}{3}$ | $\frac{2}{3} \times \frac{10}{15}$

Greater than 1	Equal to 1	Less than 1
$1\frac{1}{8} \times 3\frac{3}{4}$	$\frac{2}{13} \times 6\frac{1}{2}$	$\frac{9}{10} \times \frac{1}{3}$
$3\frac{3}{4} \times \frac{5}{4}$		$\frac{2}{3} \times \frac{10}{15}$

9. A carpenter has 8 boards of equal length. The diagram shows how he cuts each board into 6 pieces, each with a length of 2 feet. 6.NS.1

2 ft | 2 ft | 2 ft

Part A: Write the appropriate numbers to show how to find the total number of pieces of board that the carpenter will cut.

$8 \div \frac{1}{6} = 48$

1 | 2 | 6 | 8 | 14 | 48

Part B: The carpenter plans to cut one of the 2-foot boards into $\frac{2}{5}$-foot long pieces. What is the greatest number of pieces he can cut from one 2-foot board? Explain your answer.

5 pieces; $2 \div \frac{2}{5} = 2 \times \frac{5}{2} = 5$

10. The length of a parking lot is $76\frac{1}{2}$ feet. Cars are parked perpendicular to the edge of the lot in parking spots that are $8\frac{1}{2}$ feet wide. 6.NS.1

Part A: How many parking spots are along the length of the lot?

9 parking spots

Part B: There are 13 light poles equally spaced along the length of the lot, including one light pole at each end. Find the distance between light poles.

$6\frac{3}{8}$ ft

11. The table shows the location of each of four divers relative to sea level. The integer 0 represents sea level. 6.NS.6, 6.NS.6c, 6.NS.7, 6.NS.7b

Diver	A	B	C	D
Depth (ft)	2	−5	0	−3

Part A: Graph the points that show the locations of the divers.

B D C A
−5 −4 −3 −2 −1 0 1 2 3 4 5

Part B: Which diver is farther from sea level, Diver A or Diver D? Justify your answer.

Diver D; −3 is farther from 0 than 2, so Diver D is farther from sea level than Diver A.

12. Gordon correctly answered 12 out of 18 questions. Circle the values that are equivalent to the ratio of questions that Gordon got correct. 6.NS.6

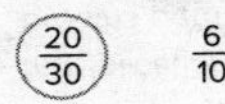

$\frac{20}{30}$ $\frac{6}{10}$ $\frac{3}{4}$ $\frac{4}{6}$ 0.1218 $\frac{22}{33}$

13. On a coordinate plane, a flagpole is represented by point (6, −2.5). A traffic light is represented by the point that is a reflection of (6, −2.5) across the *x*-axis. 6.NS.6, 6.NS.6b, 6.NS.8

Part A: Write the location of the traffic light as an ordered pair.

(6, 2.5)

Part B: What is the distance from the flagpole to the traffic light?

5 units

14. Sort the expressions into the appropriate bins based on how the values compare to 64. 6.EE.1

4^3 | 7^2 | 10^6 | 5^3 | 1^{64} | 2^6 | 8^2

Less than 64	Equal to 64	Greater than 64
7^2, 1^{64}	8^2, 4^3, 2^6	10^6, 5^3

15. The table shows the amount 6 friends spent at the fair. Together, they spent a total of $215. Select whether each statement is true or false. 6.EE.2, 6.EE.6, 6.EE.7

Name	Amount Spent ($)
Rafi	35
Esi	21
Ron	28
Julie	x
Charo	50
Mario	37

True	False	
■	□	The expression $(56 + x)$ represents the total amount Rafi, Esi, and Julie spent.
□	■	The total amount the 6 friends spent is $215x$.
■	□	Julie spent $44 at the fair.
□	■	Julie spent the least amount at the fair.

16. Jennifer and three of her friends bought the same pair of jeans and the same t-shirt. The table shows the cost of each item. 6.EE.3, 6.NS.4

Item	Cost ($)
T-shirt	15
Jeans	35

Part A: Write the appropriate numbers to represent the amount they spent altogether.

2 | 3 | 4 | 15 | 20 | 35

4 × (15 + 35)

Part B: Is the expression 20(3 + 7) equivalent to the total amount Jennifer and her friends spent? Explain your answer.

yes; Sample answer: 4(15 + 35) = (4)(5)(3 + 7) = 20(3 + 7)

17. The graph shows the number of magazine subscriptions sold. Write and solve an equation to find the difference d in the number of sports subscriptions and the number of craft subscriptions sold. 6.EE.5, 6.EE.7

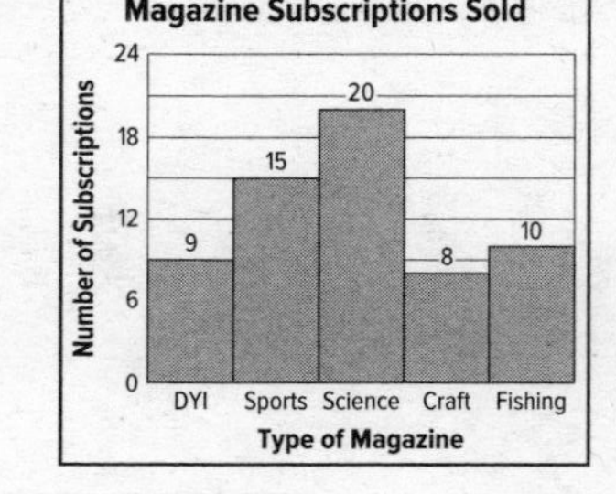

Sample answer: $d + 8 = 15$; $d = 7$, so 7 more sports subscriptions were sold than craft subscriptions.

18. Talutah has ridden her bike 3.25 miles so far. She plans to ride 7.75 miles in all. Let d represent how much farther she has to ride. Select whether each statement is true or false. 6.EE.7

True	False	
■	□	The equation $d + 3.25 = 7.75$ models the situation.
■	□	The equation $7.75 - 3.25 = d$ models the situation.
□	■	Talutah has 11 miles left to ride.
■	□	Talutah has 4.5 miles left to ride.

19. Danilo took 900 breaths in one hour. Write and solve a multiplication equation to find Danilo's average number of breaths per minute. 6.EE.7, 6.RP.3

Multiplication equation: $60n = 900$

Number of breaths per minute: 15

20. A cell phone company charges an initial fee of $50 plus $30 per month for unlimited minutes of phone usage. Complete the table to show the relationship for the total cost t of using a cell phone for m months. Then write an equation to represent the relationship between the total cost and the time in months. 6.EE.9

Number of Months, m	1	2	3	4
Total Cost ($), t	80	110	140	170

Equation: $t = 50 + 30m$

21. A bag can hold at most 45 kilograms of rice. Currently, there are 15 kilograms of rice in the bag. 6.EE.6, 6.EE.8

Part A: Write an inequality that represents how many more kilograms of rice k can be added to the bag.

$k + 15 \leq 45$

Part B: Then graph the solution of the inequality.

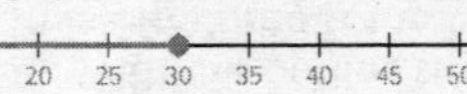

22. The diagram shows the top view of a wading pool. A fabric cover is used to cover the top of the pool. The cover is the same shape as the pool, but the base dimension is 1 foot longer, and the height is 2 feet longer than the pool. What is the area of the pool cover? 6.G.1

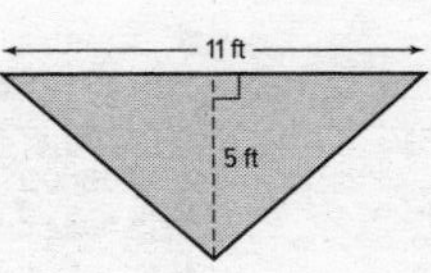

42 ft²

23. The dimensions of a child-sized, rectangular tabletop are $\frac{1}{3}$ the dimensions of an adult-sized tabletop. The adult-sized tabletop has an area of 2,268 square inches and a length of 63 inches. What are the dimensions of the child-sized tabletop? Justify your answer. 6.G.1

21 in. long by 12 in. wide; Sample answer: The width of the adult table is $w = \frac{A}{\ell} = \frac{2,268}{63} = 36$ in. The dimensions of the child-sized tabletop are $\frac{1}{3} \times 36 = 12$ and $\frac{1}{3} \times 63 = 21$.

24. The diagram shows the dimensions of an attic wall in David's house. Select all of the expressions that represent the area of the wall in square feet. 6.G.1

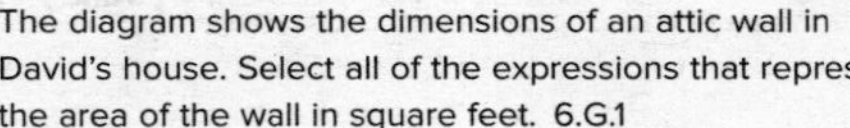

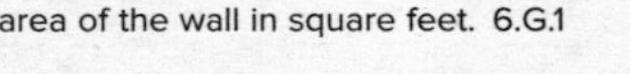

- ■ (5.5 × 5.6) + (4.5 × 8) + (0.5 × 2.4 × 5.5)
- ■ (10 × 8) – (0.5 × 2.4 × 5.5)
- ☐ (5.5 × 5.6) + (4.5 × 5.6) + (2.4 × 8) + (0.5 × 2.4 × 5.5)
- ☐ (10 × 5.6) + (4.5 × 8) + (0.5 × 2.4 × 5.5)

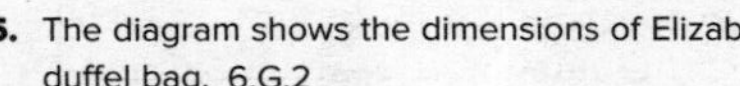

25. The diagram shows the dimensions of Elizabeth's rolling duffel bag. 6.G.2

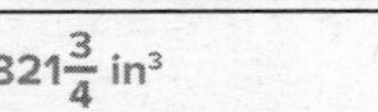

Part A: What is the volume of the duffel bag?

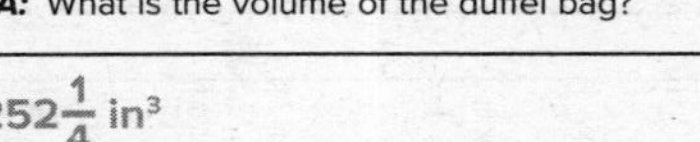

$2,252\frac{1}{4}$ in³

Part B: Elizabeth fills the bag to a height of 9 inches. How much space is left empty in her bag?

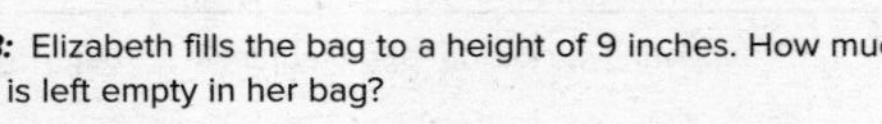

$321\frac{3}{4}$ in³

26. Three triangular prisms each have a height of 6.5 inches. The triangular base of prism A has an area of 6 square inches. The triangular base of prism B has a height of 4 inches and a base length of 2 inches. The triangular base of prism C has a height of 6 inches and a base length of 1 inch. Write the letters of the prisms in order from least to greatest volume. 6.G.3

A
B
C

	Prism
Least volume	C
	B
Greatest volume	A

27. The diagram shows the dimensions of a museum display case. All faces of the case are made of glass and are covered with a protective scratch-proof coating. Write the appropriate numbers to find the total amount of protective coating needed to cover each glass face. 6.G.4

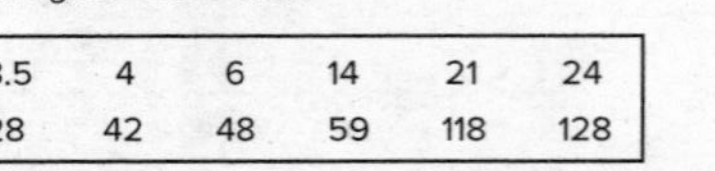

3.5	4	6	14	21	24
28	42	48	59	118	128

Surface area of front and back = 2 (4)(6) = 48

Surface area of top and bottom = 2 (3.5)(6) = 42

Surface area of the two sides = 2 (3.5)(4) = 28

Total amount of protective coating needed:

48 + 42 + 28, or 118 square meters

28. The list shows the number of students absent each day that school was in session in August: 8, 7, 9, 5, 5, 12, 2, 0. Select all of the statements that are valid based on the data. 6.SP.3, 6.SP.5, 6.SP.5c

- ☐ The range is 10.
- ■ The mean number of students absent is 6.
- ■ The median number of students absent is 6.
- ■ The mean absolute deviation of the data is 3.
- ☐ There is no mode.

29. The list shows the ages in years of seven sea turtles: 58, 62, 38, 60, 59, 63, 61. Identify the outlier in the data set. Explain which measure of center best describes the data with and without the outlier. 6.SP.3, 6.SP.5, 6.SP.5c, 6.SP.5d

38; median; With the outlier, the mean is 57.3, and the median is 60. Without the outlier, the mean is 60.5, and the median is 60.5. The outlier affects the mean more than the median, so the median best describes the data.

30. The list shows the number of books sold each hour a bookstore was open: 9, 12, 18, 10, 5, 10, 12, 2. 6.SP.4, 6.SP.5, 6.SP.5a

Part A: Complete the box-and-whisker plot to represent the data.

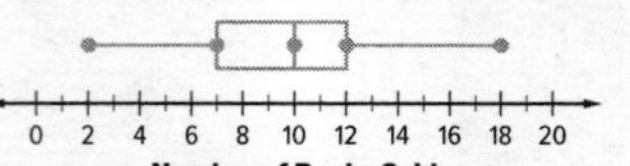

Part B: Between which two values are 50% of the data found?

between 2 and 10 or 7 and 12 or 10 and 18

31. The line plot shows the results of a survey question posed to fifth-grade students, "How many cavities did you have last year?" 6.SP.1, 6.SP.2, 6.SP.5, 6.SP.5d

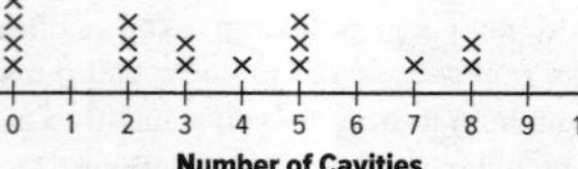

Part A: Why is the question a statistical question?

Sample answer: It anticipates a variety of answers, such as 0, 1, 2, 3, or more cavities.

Part B: Interpret what the mode represents in the data.

The mode is 0. More students said that they had no cavities than any other number of cavities.

Part C: Describe the shape of the data distribution.

Sample answer: not symmetric; There is a peak at 0, a gap at 1 and 6, and a cluster from 2 to 5.

Page 187 • The Fruit Stand

Task Scenario	
Students will analyze the prices at a fruit stand by calculating and comparing unit rates and by finding the mean. They will use expressions to represent the price of multiple bags of fruit and equations and inequalities to find how many bags are purchased. Students will also calculate the volume of the bags.	
CCSS Content Standard(s)	6.RP.2, 6.RP.3, 6.RP.3a, 6.RP.3b, 6.NS.1, 6.NS.4, 6.NS.5, 6.NS.6, 6.NS.6a, 6.NS.6c, 6.NS.7, 6.NS.7a, 6.NS.7b, 6.NS.7d, 6.EE.1, 6.EE.2, 6.EE.2b, 6.EE.2c, 6.EE.3, 6.EE.7, 6.EE.8, 6.G.2, 6.SP.3, 6.SP.5, 6.SP.5c
Mathematical Practices	MP2, MP4, MP5, MP6, MP7
Depth of Knowledge	DOK2, DOK3

Part	Maximum Points	Scoring Rubric
A	2	Full Credit: Unit Prices: 162 ÷ 3 = 54¢ per apple 64 ÷ 2 = 32¢ per banana 46¢ per orange (given) 144 ÷ 4 = 36¢ per kiwi mean unit price: $\frac{(54 + 32 + 46 + 36)}{4} = \frac{168}{4}$ = 42¢ per fruit Partial Credit (1 point) will be given for the 4 correct fruit unit prices OR the mean unit price for the entire fruit stand. No credit will be given for an incorrect answer.
B	2	Full Credit: Apple: 54 – 42 = +12 Banana: 32 – 42 = –10 Orange: 46 – 42 = +4 Kiwi: 36 – 42 = –6 A positive sign means that the fruit unit price is greater than the mean. A negative sign means it is less than the mean. 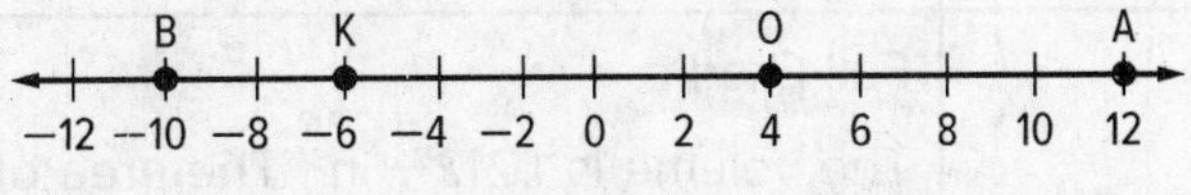 Partial Credit (1 point) will be given for the correct differences OR the correct explanation and graph. No credit will be given for an incorrect answer.

<table>
<tr><th>Part</th><th>Maximum Points</th><th>Scoring Rubric</th></tr>
<tr><td>C</td><td>2</td><td>Full Credit:
The difference for a banana was less than –7.
$-10 < -7$

Sample explanation: The unit price of a banana is more than 7¢ less than the average unit price for the entire stand.

Partial Credit (1 Point) will be given for identifying banana and writing a correct inequality OR a correct explanation of the price.

No credit will be given for an incorrect answer.</td></tr>
<tr><td>D</td><td>2</td><td>Full Credit:
(Students may use dollars as the unit, instead of cents.)
Bag 1: Sample expression: 2(54) + 3(36) + 32; cost: $2.48
Bag 2: Sample expression: 4(46) + 5(32); cost: $3.44

Partial Credit (1 Point) will be given for the correct expressions OR the correct total costs.

No credit will be given for an incorrect answer.</td></tr>
<tr><td>E</td><td>3</td><td>Full Credit:
Each bag has 6 bananas, 6 kiwis, and 6 apples.
Sample equivalent expression: $1.92b + 2.16b + 3.24b$

(Students may use cents as the unit, instead of dollars.)
$1.92b + 2.16b + 3.24b \leq 25$
$7.32b \leq 25$
$b \leq$ approximately 3.42

The restaurant could purchase 0, 1, 2, or 3 bags because 4 bags cost more than $25.

Partial Credit (1 Point) will be given for each of the 3 answers: identification of what is in each bag and an equivalent expression OR the correct inequality and its solution OR the correct number of bags that could be purchased.

No credit will be given for an incorrect answer.</td></tr>
<tr><td>F</td><td>1</td><td>Full Credit:
The volume is $1{,}212\frac{3}{4}$ in³. The area of the base is $67\frac{3}{8}$ in².
$V = Bh$
$1{,}212\frac{3}{4} = 67\frac{3}{8}h$
$18 = h$
The bag is 18 inches tall.

No credit will be given for an incorrect answer.</td></tr>
<tr><td>TOTAL</td><td>12</td><td></td></tr>
</table>